PLATE I

The Foucault pendulum experiment was performed in the Pantheon at Paris in 1851.
One explanation of its mystery is connected with modern limitations imposed upon
space and time. (From Hanotaux's "Histoire de la Nation Française," vol. xiv.)

# PHILOSOPHY

## *and*

# MODERN SCIENCE

*By*
PROFESSOR HAROLD T. DAVIS
Indiana University

THE PRINCIPIA PRESS
Bloomington    1931    Indiana

TO MY MOTHER

# CONTENTS

## CHAPTER IV.   DOES MATTER DRAG THE ETHER?

## CHAPTER V.   TIME, SPACE, AND THE FOURTH DIMENSION.

## CHAPTER VI.   WHAT IS GRAVITATION?

## CHAPTER X.   THE METAPHYSICS OF THE QUANTUM THEORY AND WAVE MECHANICS.

## CHAPTER XI.   THE DISCOVERY AND INTERPRETATION OF COSMIC RADIATION.

Horace to his friend Iccius:

"You, in the very midst of the contageous itch of gain, still have a taste far from mean, still set your thoughts on lofty themes: what causes hold the sea in check, what rules the year, whether stars roam at large of their own will or by law, what hides the moon's disk in darkness, what brings it into light, what is the meaning and what the effects of Nature's jarring harmony."

Epistle XII, book 1, lines 14-19.

# INTRODUCTION

The present book tells the romance of modern physical science. It attempts to humanize certain data and speculations which have emerged from a body of recent astonishing experiments. It begins with some problems first proposed by the Greeks and traces the story of their development during subsequent centuries. Particularly are the strange concepts of these recent days set forth as the logical culmination of past experience.

The author has long cherished the belief that we are witnessing in the present development of science the uniting of two great streams of speculative thought which have their sources in the high plateaus of Greek philosophy. They diverged during the course of the centuries, one stream flowing through the philosophies of Descartes, Berkeley, Kant, Poincaré, and Mach, the other through the experiences of Galileo, Newton, Fresnel, von Helmholtz, Faraday, Lord Kelvin, Maxwell, and Lorentz. In this modern era we have witnessed the merging of the two streams. It is difficult to say whether Einstein and his great colleagues in this golden age of science are subjective philosophers or investigators of physical nature. Their work is revolutionary, but it has produced not so much a factual as a conceptual renaissance. Relativity, the wave mechanics, cosmic radiation, and the mysteries of the new concepts of energy and the atom have caused us to turn a speculative eye upon the most cherished principles of the older physics. It is difficult to say for example whether the theory of gravitation is to be regarded as a development of geometry, or whether it is to be thought of as an explanation of objective experience.

The present volume attempts to set forth as simply as possible the basic postulates of physics and to trace their implications. Technical language has been avoided as far as the subject matter will permit. The philosophical aspect of the problems has been constantly

# INTRODUCTION

emphasized. It has been shown that the concept of the ether is found in the "extension" of Descartes. The history of man's attempt to endow this "necessity of reason" with material properties has been carefully developed down to the recent experiments at the basis of the wave mechanics, where it disappears in the mystical postulates of Schrödinger, Dirac, Heisenberg, and de Broglie.

The book was originally undertaken to prove to a friend that there is much that is poetical in the story of modern science. His contention was that "east is east; and west is west; and never the twain shall meet." But to one who will look past the long rows of figures in Leverrier's tables of the planets, or beyond the dreary pages of formulas in Maxwell's treatise on electricity and magnetism, there is a land of mystery and magic.

H. T. Davis.

Indiana University, 1931.

# CHAPTER I.

## SCIENCE—THE MODERN METAPHYSICS.

### 1. *Man and Mystery.*

WHEN we look into the processes of man's mind we find there an inherent love of mystery. It is beside the point to speculate upon the source of this attraction—perhaps it may be found in the dim recesses of the primeval forest from which man evolved—but there is no doubt that this love is real and universal. It is for this reason, perhaps, that natural philosophy appeals to those who have had the hardiness to revel in the new science of today, for mysterious and intriguing it has certainly become.

It is with the idea of giving insight into the new philosophy of nature and the metaphysics of modern science that these chapters are undertaken. The point of view is that of one who stands before the dial of a radio and marvels not that he can hear a station many miles away, but that here in the little space occupied by his instrument there is an invisible vibration in a *metaphysical* medium which we have called the ether.

In the last paragraph we have used the word metaphysical, and hence, after the manner of the scientific tradition, which we hope to follow, we must give it precise meaning. Unfortunately the term metaphysics has come into bad repute in recent times; it implies a vague groping after the nature of ultimate reality; it seeks to express in terms difficult to define, the nature of matter and mind and the processes by which we attain to knowledge. The metaphysician in his mystical vagaries has been likened to a man who is "groping within a dark room for a black cat that isn't there."

In the following pages where science lapses into metaphysics we shall mean merely that we are exploring the *concepts* upon which modern science seeks to found its theories; we shall be investigating the meaning of such terms as "the luminiferous ether, universal gravitation, action, entropy, wave electrons, etc." These concepts, however, will never be the frequently vague statements of traditional metaphysics, for without exception, however strange they may appear in words, they can be reduced to numerical calculation and the

I

formulas of mathematics.  There is no achievement in science higher than this.

A great many treatises on philosophy have been written in the past wherein the authors strive to look at nature from the revelation afforded by the science of that day.  The universal genius of Henri Poincaré made it possible for him to write a philosophy from the vantage point of his own fundamental contributions in nearly all the fields of physical, mathematical, and astronomical science.  His was a great achievement.  His treatise on the foundations of science treats philosophical problems as only a master of modern scientific discovery could treat them.[1]  They assume a new meaning and as we look back on the speculations of the Greeks and the imaginative theories of Descartes and Leibnitz we are amazed at the progress since made in the direction of understanding nature.

But even in the few years since the death of Poincaré there has been a great advance.  The theory of relativity has enlarged philosophic thought; the quantum theory of energy has progressed from experiment to experiment until it flowers into the wave mechanics, with its metaphysical postulates strongly substantiated by cold facts from the laboratory; the source of the sun's energy passes from the old combustion theory and the newer contraction hypothesis of Helmholtz into the modern idea of energy, which integrates matter and energy in a single concept.

In all of this there is need for the philosopher.  The men of science are too busy making new discoveries to give more than casual thought to the relationship between the mind of man and the reality of nature in its new revelation.  After all, the problem of philosophy is to find the relationship which exists between man's mind and objective nature.[2]  The history of philosophy is filled with the accounts of men who have sought to interpret nature in the light of man's experience.  The pendulum has swung and will probably continue to swing between the purely mechanistic view that all things belong to an external reality merely discovered by our minds and the subjective view that all things are entirely created by us.

---

[1] The Foundations of Science, containing Science and Hypothesis, The Value of Science, Science and Method.  Translated by G. B. Halsted with a special preface by Poincaré and an introduction by Josiah Royce.  Science Press (1913), xi + 553 pp.

[2] In a recent treatise entitled "The Revolt Against Dualism" (Open Court, 1930), A. O. Lovejoy has explored the attempts of modern philosophers to fuse together "nature and man's apprehension of nature into a monism free from logical contradictions." Lovejoy's conclusion is that this revolt against dualism has been a failure, but he does not indicate the nature of the dualism that presumably remains.  It is not the object of this book to enter into this ancient controversy.  We shall postulate an objective nature in the sense of the existence of a large body of scientific facts acquired from laboratory observations and we shall further postulate the existence of an observer of these facts. Whether these are separated or united concepts is a question which in spite of its long history and its great philosophical interest will not enter into our discussion.

## 2. *The Anthropomorphic Character of Scientific Concepts.*

It seems, indeed, a curious thing when one reflects about it that most of our discoveries in physical science should fit so neatly into purely rational concepts. In other words we are not constantly surprised by most of the things that we find out about nature. There seems to be a sort of anthropomorphic character to the behaviour of energy and matter; we can make equations about them and the marvel is that the equations which are derived purely from logical concepts are in such remarkable accord with the facts. It is little wonder that in building concepts about the Deity who according to our postulates has organized and ordered nature, we should have given him anthropomorphic character. Some satirist has remarked that if animals could have formulated conceptions of the world they would have pictured God in their images. This idea, ancient as man's thought, appears as follows in a fragment from Xenophanes of Colophon (570-480 B. C.)[3]:

But if cattle or lions had hands, so as to paint with their hands, and produce works of art as men do, they would paint their gods and give them bodies in form like their own—horses like horses, cattle like cattle.

With our characteristically human methods of arriving at abstract concepts through analogy it is not surprising that we have approached the problems of nature as if they were all subject to what we are pleased to call rational belief.

The age of science has been founded upon the postulate that nature is rational. By this word, which will appear frequently, we shall mean that nature obeys well ordered rules which are understandable by human intelligence and conform to models that man constructs upon the basis of his intuition. It is curious that the early intuitions of man led in the direction of the mystical and the supernatural. Man fled in terror before the thunder storm in the belief that it was evidence of an avenging Deity, instead of trying to give it a rational explanation. Mythology clings about the motions of the sun, the moon, and the stars. There did not seem to be even the slightest disposition among the vast majority of mankind and most of the poets to see in nature anything but caprice. The black plague was but an act of God before which man stood in stark

[3]See A. Fairbanks: The First Philosophers of Greece, Scribners (1898), p. 67. Also E. Hiller—W. T. Bergk: Anthologia Lyrica sive Lyricorum Graecorum Veterum praeter Pindar, Leipzig, (1901), p. 54 (17).

impotence. To be sure a great many things were lying within the reach of easy discovery which would have materially hastened the age of science, but there seemed to be a peculiar antipathy to the idea that nature was rational. The annals of mediaeval history are full of miracles and the credulity of that period would pass belief if it were not for similar material evidence in the present stage of civilization.

Why is it that man has always clung so tenaciously to the mystical view of nature? It was not primarily due to the fear felt by some that authority in religion was menaced although this had a powerful influence during the middle ages. It seems incredible that so beautiful a discovery as Galileo's that Jupiter was encircled by moons should have been met with a black and menacing prejudice. Why were not the minds of his day quickened by the discovery that nature can be investigated by instruments of precision? Why should the beautiful attempt of Copernicus to bring simplicity and order to the motion of the planets have met with sinister intolerance? We are able to study the same phenomenon in our own day in the antagonism that the proponents of evolution have encountered in propounding a rational rather than a mystical explanation of creation. Even though these ideas had not been in conflict with high authority we may reasonably doubt whether they would have been accepted with much less reluctance.

It is not the purpose of these chapters to discuss the curious problem why man prefers the mystical rather than the rational explanation of natural phenomena. It is far more instructive to start with the scientific reformation and to show how the postulate of a rational and intelligible nature has led to the magnificent discoveries of modern science and then has gone beyond to a new realm where rational intuition is no longer sufficient. In other words science which started out so auspiciously with the telescope of Galileo and with Newton's theory of the moon has through recent discoveries returned to a remarkable new metaphysics. Rational concepts again merge into mysticism, but with this difference, that the new mysticism is founded upon experiments carried out by instruments of the highest precision.

As we progress in our discoveries we are beginning to find a limit to the anthropomorphic analogy. The rational belief with which science regards nature and the actual behaviour of nature seem to be at least in partial accord. The attitude of science that all things can be explained in terms that do not conflict with the processes of our minds is certainly not in conflict with the major part of natural phenomena. However, there seems to be a limitation to this postulate. It is much the same as trying to fit a plane surface to a sphere. At every individual point the plane will fit, but if we progress to other points the divergence appears. For the so-called first-order phenomena, nature is in harmony with rational belief. Newton's laws of motion account for all the major movements of the planets but they fail to account for the tiny discrepancy in the motion of the perihelion of the planet Mercury.

In these pages we shall adopt the point of view that there exists an objective nature. If the views of Hume and Berkeley were altogether correct and nature merely an attribute of our subjective consciousness, then there would be no purpose in a discussion such as is projected here. In that event nature would surely conform to the character of its creator. Existing wholly within the mind it would necessarily be subjective; laboratory experiments could not reveal anything that was not in accord with mental processes and science would be merely an exploration of the behaviour of the mind. On such a hypothesis it would seem impossible to reach conclusions that would surprise us such as those which have recently led to the theory of wave mechanics.

Assuming that nature exists objectively our duty is to explore it from the point of view of what we may call rational belief. It is true that many of us differ in our postulates as to what constitutes rational belief, but I think that most of us differ only in inconsequential details. Let us consider, for example, that significant portion of modern physics which rests upon the postulates underlying the theory of probability. The foundation of this theory is certainly a rational belief. To put it in the simplest terms, the theory of probability rests upon the belief that if a coin be tossed sufficiently often the ratio of the number of times it falls tails to the total number of tosses can be made to equal ½ to within an error as small as one desires. This proposition can not be proved, but it is nevertheless so convincing that our minds seem willing to admit it without reservation.

Let us return to the postulate on penny tossing and reflect that nothing more radical than this was used as the fundamental postulate in studying the thermal behaviour of gases. It is no wonder that the theory of thermodynamics appears to rest upon an extraordinarily secure foundation. And yet it was the failure of the law of the equipartition of energy (see Chapter X) in this domain that led to

the perplexing difficulties of the quantum theory. Our anthropomorphic model failed as soon as investigations had been carried far
enough. This does not mean that an exception was found which
could be explained by introducing new terms into our equations or
by carrying them out to higher orders of approximation; the truth of
the matter is that our rational concepts break down and we are left
with a wholly irrational theory of radiant energy. These difficulties
will be more explicitly treated in subsequent chapters.

### 3. *Is Nature Rational?*

It is well in the beginning of our project to reach an understanding with one another. The reader has doubtless been taught and
now fully believes that man, the supreme animal, possesses within
himself a magnificent dominion over nature; that the code of mental
behaviour which we so proudly refer to as our rational processes
can always be used to formulate the laws of nature. Paradoxes and
exceptions, we affirm, merely indicate a lack of information. We
live in the happy faith that time and measurement will reveal a rational explanation for all discrepancies between conflicting data, and
between the theories of rival schools of natural philosophy.

But in this bewildering age of light quanta and ether waves, of
corpuscular matter and wave electrons, a small doubt regarding the
rationality postulate has appeared in certain eminent quarters. Are
we as sure today as we were a quarter of a century ago that nature
is wholly consonant with anthropomorphic reason? This is the
problem that will be considered in the following pages—not, however, for the purpose of advocating a postulate of irrationality in
nature, but rather of accentuating current doubts through a survey
of the philosophical situation as it pertains to the world of matter,
energy, and space-time.

This idea which we propose to develop is already to be found,
however hesitatingly advanced, in the growing literature of modern
natural philosophy. In the concluding paragraph of his "A, B, C of
Atoms," for example, Bertrand Russell makes the following significant remarks :[4]

It is *possible* that the desire for rational explanation may be
carried too far. This is suggested by some remarks, also by Eddington, in his book, "Space, Time, and Gravitation" (p. 200). The
theory of relativity has shown that most of traditional dynamics,

---

[4]The A, B, C of Atoms, New York (1923), pp. 157-158.

which was supposed to contain scientific laws, really consisted of conventions as to measurement, and was strictly analogous to the "great law" that there are always three feet to a yard. In particular, this applies to the conservation of energy. This makes it plausible to suppose that every apparent law of nature which strikes us as reasonable is not really a law of nature, but a concealed convention, plastered on to nature by our love of what we, in our arrogance, choose to consider rational. Eddington hints that a real law of nature is likely to stand out by the fact that it appears to us irrational, since in that case it is less likely that we have invented it to satisfy our intellectual taste. And from this point of view he inclines to the belief that the quantum-principle is the first real law of nature that has been discovered in physics.

This raises a somewhat important question: Is the world "rational," i. e., such as to conform to our intellectual habits? Or is it "irrational," i. e., not such as we should have made it if we had been in the position of the Creator? I do not propose to suggest an answer to this question.

The passage in the work of A. S. Eddington to which Russell refers is as follows:[5]

It is one thing for the human mind to extract from the phenomena of nature the exact laws over which it has no control. It is even possible that laws which have not their origin in the mind may be irrational, and we can never succeed in formulating them. This is, however, only a remote possibility; probably if they were really irrational it would not have been possible to make the limited progress that has been achieved. But if the laws of quanta do indeed differentiate the actual world from other worlds possible to the mind, we may expect the task of formulating them to be far harder than anything yet accomplished by physics.

The theory of relativity has passed in review the whole subject-matter of physics. It has unified the great laws, which by the precision of their formulation and the exactness of their application have won the proud place in human knowledge which physical science holds today. And yet, in regard to the nature of things, this knowledge is only an empty shell—a form of symbols. It is knowledge of structural form, and not knowledge of content. All through the physical world runs that unknown content, which must surely be the stuff of our consciousness. Here is a hint of aspects deep within the world of physics, and yet unattainable by the methods of physics. And, moreover, we have found that where science has progressed the farthest, the mind has but regained from nature that which the mind has put into nature.

We have found a strange foot-print on the shores of the unknown. We have devised profound theories, one after another, to

_____
[5]Space, Time, and Gravitation, Cambridge (1920), pp. 200-201.

account for its origin. At last, we have succeeded in reconstructing the creature that made the foot-print. And Lo! it is our own.

Shall we explore the lead suggested by these eminent philosophers? We can do no better than to begin with the story of the scientific reformation.

### 4. *The Scientific Reformation.*

Genuine scientific discovery started about the fifteenth century and commenced to flourish with Johannes Kepler, (1571-1630), and Galileo Galilei (1564-1642), in the sixteenth century. Perhaps many will feel that the assumption of a date so late in the history of mankind is doing scant credit to the contributions of Greek thought. All must do homage to those noble minds, but their excellence is not to be found in their investigations of natural phenomena. Except for Archimedes (287?-212 B. C.) and a few of the astronomers their thought was arbitrary and subjective. Even Aristotle (384-322 B. C.) was not at his best with those subjects where actual contact with objective nature was necessary to ascertain the truth, and his observations on these matters often seemed exact statements of current folklore and not founded upon even a casual examination of phenomena. The historic statement, the refutation of which came near to being the undoing of Galileo, that heavy bodies fall faster than light ones is but one of numerous errors in the work of this great scholar. This does not mean, of course, that the Greeks did not reach a very high level in scientific thought, for any people that could produce the "Elements" of Euclid (about 300 B. C.) has attained great eminence. Even in their mathematics the main impulse was to create a purely intellectual structure. The thought that it might have any application to natural phenomena was certainly not cherished even if it were not actually repugnant to the Greek ideal. In geometry we start not with atoms of matter but with abstract points without dimension, which are most certainly creatures of the imagination. Surely a people capable of creating the geometry of the Greeks could have developed also a calculus of computation provided they had seen the need. Without the urge of an objective science interested in testing theories with laboratory measurements, there was no reason why the science of calculation should have had even a small place in their thoughts.

As soon as Kepler had shown by computations based upon the tables of Tycho Brahe (1546-1601) that the orbits of the planets were essentially ellipses and had announced his other two famous laws of motion, the age of objective science was at hand. Galileo had founded the science of mechanics by comparing theory with experiment and had given to mankind his telescope which was certainly one of the most useful of laboratory instruments.

The next great advance came with the publication in 1687 of the "Philosophiae Naturalis Principia Mathematica" of Sir Isaac Newton. This great thinker was born on Christmas day, 1642 in the manor house of Woolthorpe about six miles south of Grantham in the county of Lincoln. Just as it was the good luck of Christopher Columbus to have been born at a time when the old world was on the verge of discovering the new so it was the fortune of Newton to have been born in a period when Kepler's magnificent discoveries were thrusting the idea of gravitation upon men's minds. But it is, perhaps, most fortunate of all for science that so great a genius should have appeared at this beginning of the scientific movement, for Newton by his powers united in a single work what might have been scattered in the writings of many less imposing books. This noble figure became the rallying post for those who saw the vision of the scientific revolution. If there is any value in selecting a group of heroes whose lives may be a guide and inspiration, Newton is preeminently the hero of the scientific revolution. Alas, even in this age, immensely enriched by the labors of those who followed the ideals of Newton small thought is ever given by the average man to the achievements of this great leader! Carlyle has written entertainingly of the hero as a priest, the hero as a god, the hero as a king, the hero as a man of letters, but where do we find evidence that the man of science is regarded as a hero? Even Yale university until recently memorialized with nothing more than a small tablet the place where Josiah Willard Gibbs made his historic discoveries about heat.

The work of Newton falls into two parts, the first having to do with gravitation, the second with the phenomenon of light. Countless generations of men have experienced with Matthew Arnold that sensation felt when one looks upon the restless action of the tides:[6]

> Listen! you hear the grating roar
> Of pebbles which the waves draw back, and fling,
> At their return, upon the high strand.
> Begin, and cease, and then again begin,

---

[6]Dover Beach.

With tremulous cadence slow, and bring
The eternal note of sadness in.
*    *    *    *    *
But now I only hear
Its melancholy, long, withdrawing roar,
Retreating, to the breath
Of the night wind, down the vast edges drear
And naked shingles of the world.

But to Newton there was in the ceaseless action of the tides a cosmic challenge. In them he saw more than a restless expanse of water deriving its activity from some hidden principle of nature. By a superb leap of the imagination he saw a connection between the distant moon and the puzzling activity of the tides. To him there had occurred the principle of *action at a distance* which at a single stroke united all the matter of the universe by a force which varied inversely as the square of the distance and directly as the mass. The genius of the discovery lay in the fact that Newton saw the possibilities latent in the postulate that two bodies, though separated by empty space, could still exert measurable influence upon one another. To be sure the ancient astrologers had maintained a similar postulate, but the difference between them and Newton was that he could foretell infallibly the effect of the gravitational influence, while their system failed in all crucial tests.

This significant fact should be borne in mind by any one who wishes to approach modern science in a philosophical attitude. The modern physicist seems willing to admit any concept however bizarre provided it is not in contradiction with known experimental evidence and can be so formulated as to lead to new investigations. It must merely satisfy the first test of consistency and the second test of pragmatic usefulness.

"Physics," explains the teacher of philosophy in Molière's "Le Bourgeois Gentilhomme," "is that which explains the principles of natural things and the properties of bodies; which discourses of the nature of the elements, the metals, the stones, plants and of animals, and teaches us the causes of all the meteors, the rainbow, will-o'-the-wisps, comets, lightning, thunder, forked lightning, the rain, snow, hail, the winds, and the whirlwinds."

A great deal for one word, truly, but it is like the Turkish language, also described in that delightful comedy, "which says much in few words." An explanation in these remarkable days need have no rational foundation provided it be sufficiently clothed in mathematics and not in contradiction with experimental evidence.

The second contribution made by Newton was his set of experiments on light and his subsequent formulation of a theory to account for what he had found. Here as in the case of gravitation he was faced with the necessity of making a postulate. In the light of modern knowledge we know that he might have offered either of the following hypotheses:

1. Light is a manifestation of energy transmitted from the bright object to the eye by means of tiny corpuscles.
2. Light is the manifestation of energy transmitted from the bright object to the eye by means of undulations in a tenuous medium which pervades all space.

Between these postulates one has at first on rational grounds little hesitation in choosing with Newton the first, yet its complete discomfiture during the nineteenth century shows that the second more metaphysical postulate was in better accord with the tests of a physical theory as stated above.

### 5. *Action at a Distance*.

The striking thing that we are to observe here is this. Newton introduced the age of reason into science. He stands preeminently as one who showed how the motions of the heavenly bodies can be reduced to exact calculation. He pointed the way of the scientific method by showing that one might have on the one hand a subjective theory and upon the other a set of experimental data to check against it. And yet was a rational theory ever built upon a more metaphysical foundation than his theory of gravitation? Was an idea ever introduced into rational thinking that is more repellant to reason than the concept of action at a distance?

During the winter of 1692-93 Sir Isaac Newton was called upon to answer several letters written to him by Rev. Richard Bentley, an eminent clergyman of that day, and in one of his replies he made this famous statement:[7]

. . . It is inconceivable, that inanimate brute matter should, without the mediation of something else, which is not material, operate upon and affect other matter without mutual contact, as it must be, if gravitation, in the sense of Epicurus, be essential and inherent in it. And this is one reason why I desire you would not

[7]From the works of Richard Bentley, in three volumes, London (1838), edited by Rev. Alexander Dyce. See Vol. 3, p. 212.

ascribe innate gravity to me.   That gravity should be innate, inherent, and essential to matter, so that one body may act upon another at a distance through a *vacuum,* without the mediation of any thing else, by and through which their action and force may be conveyed from one to another, is to me so great an absurdity, that I believe no man, who has in philosophical matters a competent faculty of thinking, can ever fall into it.   Gravity must be caused by an agent acting constantly according to certain laws; but whether this agent be material or immaterial, I have left to the consideration of my readers.

There seems to be a common illusion among those who so calmly enjoy the fruits of this modern world of discovery, that science progresses entirely by exact calculation and the slow drudgery of laboratory technique.   Nothing is further from the truth.   *Science progresses rather by sudden guesses about an almost mystical behaviour in nature, although, to be sure, these inspirations are derived from the slowly accumulated facts of the laboratory.*

If there exists a law of evolution why did it take so many years to formulate it?   Surely for the reason that first there had to arise in the mind of a man like Darwin the concept of some selective power in environmental conditions which would choose from the hurly-burly of life processes those factors which would lead to survival. There seems to be but little difference between the magnitude of one postulate which assumes the existence of a selective principle in nature and another which assumes that each particle of matter has an attraction for every particle across the empty space that separates them.

After Newton, the study of science was vigorously pursued by those who, forgetful of the metaphysical postulate upon which the Principia was built, saw only in the calculations an evidence of the rationality of nature.

### 6.   *The Principle of Least Action.*

It is difficult to isolate from the many principles discovered by those who labored under this assumption, a few which were the most important to development, but there is one that must not be neglected. This postulate goes under the name of the *principle of least action* and has the strange distinction of being perhaps the most fundamental and yet the most imperfectly understood law of physics.   Its basic character is seen in the fact that all the laws of mechanics are formulated in it, and its intriguing mystery resides in the numerous discomfitures of those who have tried to give it a rational existence.

The kernel of this principle may be summarized as follows:

When an event that requires energy is taking place in the physical universe, it must take place so that the mean value of the difference between the kinetic energy and potential energy involved, in the interval of time required for the event to take place, must be a minimum.

The layman to whom these ideas are novel can gain an appreciation of the meaning of the law by considering the path taken by a ball thrown into the air. What course will the ball take? There is no reason *a priori* to see why the ball should follow the course of that geometrical figure, called the parabola, the study of which is to be found in the works of antiquity. There are many arcs which the ball might travel. Why, then, does it pick out this particular one? In terms of our new principle the answer is that by pursuing this course the value of the difference between the gravitational pull of the earth and the kinetic energy possessed by the flying ball, averaged over the time when the ball left the hand of the thrower until it returned to earth again, is smaller than it would be for any other path.

Is there any sense to such an answer? Would it not be as rational to say that the ball takes the path of a parabola because that is the law of nature? The reply is that the law of least action which we have invoked appears to be valid not only for the path taken by the ball but for all the acts of the physical universe. It has become so fundamental a part of our system of mechanics that Einstein in creating his theory of relativity preferred to leave it alone and alter the nature of space and time instead.

But does it seem a part of rational belief to assume that events must take place in such a way that something is always a minimum? If the Creator of the universe were molded in the image of Browning's' "Caliban Upon Setebos,"

> Flat on his belly in the pit's much mire
> With elbows wide, fists clenched to prop his chin.
> And while he hides both feet in the cool slush,
> And feels about his spine small eft-things course,
> Run in and out each arm, and make him laugh,

one might easily formulate the laws of the universe in terms of a principle of *least energy*. But why should this nature within which man resides be so constructed that every material act takes place so as to conform to the strange principle of *least action?*

The law of least action was first announced, though imperfectly, by Pierre Louis Moreau de Maupertuis (1698-1759), who unfortunately is known more for the biting sarcasm of Voltaire's "A Dissertation by Doctor Akakia" than for his scientific achievements. Voltaire gives as a "judgment of the professors of the college of wisdom" the following appraisement of the least action principle:

The assertion that "the product of the space multiplied by the velocity is always a minimum," seems to be false; for this product is sometimes a maximum according to the opinion of Leibnitz and as may be easily proved. It would appear that the young author took only one-half of M. Leibnitz's ideas; and we, therefore, acquit him of the guilt of having ever comprehended one whole idea of M. Leibnitz.

Little did Voltaire realize that the law he so lightly lampooned along with Doctor Akakia's suggestions that a city should be founded in which Latin alone was to be spoken, that a hole should be dug to the center of the earth and that the brains of giants six feet high and of hairy men with tails should be dissected the better to discover the nature of the human mind, was destined to become, as Jacobi expresses it, "the mother of our analytical mechanics."

Maupertuis first stated his principle in a memoir entitled "Accord de differentes loix de la nature qui avoient jusqu' ici paru incompatibles," which he read to the French Academy on April 15th, 1744.[8]

The laws in question had to do with the reflection and refraction of light. As is well known, a ray of light when traveling in a homogeneous medium will pass from one point to another either directly or by reflection in the shortest time and by the shortest path. P. Fermat (1650-1665), the French contender for the honor of having invented the infinitesimal calculus, generalizing this observation, had assumed that the path of a refracted beam passing into a medium of greater or less density would also be determined by this minimum principle. But in his demonstration, Fermat had been obliged to differ with Descartes who assumed that the velocity of light increased with the density of the medium in which it was propagated. Maupertuis who belonged to the corpuscular faith and regarded light as a stream of particles, wanted to keep the beautiful minimum principle of Fermat, but also desired to reconcile it with the ideas of

[8]Historie de l'Académie de Paris (Published 1748), pp. 417-426. Oeuvres de Maupertius 1756, vol. 4, pp. 3-28.

Descartes. Hence Maupertuis' problem was to find out what minimum principle, if any, was involved and he came to the conclusion that light would travel by that path in which the *quantity of action* was least. The historic passage follows:[9]

I must now explain what I mean by the quantity of action. A certain action is necessary for the carrying of a body from one point to another: this action depends on the velocity which the body has and the space which it describes; but it is neither the velocity nor the space taken separately. The quantity of action varies directly as the velocity and the length of path described; it is proportional to the sum of the spaces, each being multiplied by the velocity with which the body describes it. It is this quantity of action which is here the true expenditure of nature, and which she economizes as much as possible in the motion of light.

Having arrived at this conclusion he ends with the following speculations:[10]

We cannot doubt that all things are regulated by a supreme Being, who, while he has imprinted on matter forces which show his power, has destined it to execute effects which mark his wisdom; . . .

and again,

Let us calculate the motion of bodies, but let us also consult the designs of the Intelligence which makes them move.

The same metaphysical cast appears in the thinking of Euler who gave form to the principle of Maupertuis and helped to place it in its present elevated position. He said:[11]

As the construction of the universe is the most perfect possible, being the handiwork of an all-wise Maker, nothing can be met with in the world in which some maximal or minimal property is not displayed. There is, consequently, no doubt but that all the effects of the world can be derived by the method of maxima and minima from their final causes as well as from their efficient ones.

We return again to the thesis of our discourse. In the light of the principle of least action, or of the more general dictum of Euler

[9]Historie de l'Académie de Paris (1748), p. 423, Oeuvres, vol. 4, p. 17. For an admirable account of the history of the principle of least action see an article by Phillip E. B. Jourdain: Maupertuis and the Principle of Least Action. The Monist, vol. 22 (1912), pp. 414-459.

[10]Historie, p. 423; Oeuvres, vol. 4, p. 17.

[11]Methodus inveniendi linear curvas maximi minimive proprietate gaudentes, Lausanne, 1744, p. 245. See also E. Mach: The Science of Mechanics, English translation by T. J. McCormack, Chicago, 2nd ed. (1902), p. 455.

that every act of nature is an example of some minimum property of things, does the science of mechanics rest upon a rational or a metaphysical foundation? It seems to be beyond the reach of our *a priori* intuitions to visualize the concept of action. Does action, therefore, belong to the realm of the subjective or is it a physical reality? According to Lord Kelvin (1824-1907) a thing has no physical validity unless it can be reduced to calculation.[12] Using this dictum as a criterion of epistemology, action certainly belongs to physical reality, since the quantity of action employed in simple systems, and by inference, the quantity of action employed in more complicated ones can always be calculated. But for all of this, is action any the less a metaphysical concept? Compare it, for example, with Newton's force of gravitation or the analogous force of electricity which Michael Faraday (1791-1867) so picturesquely and effectively thought of as tubes in the ether. These tubes of force, to be sure, have analogies with more material tubes experienced by our senses, and the power of the analogy is to be seen in the fact that Maxwell, and after him Hertz, actually thought of these tubes as being joined together into hoops and projected through space.[13] Who can say that it was not actually this analogy which conferred upon mankind the marvel of the radio? The mere fact that the analogy exists, however, and has power to guide us in the exploration of nature is not sufficient to confer objective reality upon the concept. Conversely the lack of this analogy scarcely seems sufficient reason to deny the objective reality of a thing such as action, for which we have little if any *a priori* feeling.

### 7.   *The Ether Postulate.*

Returning from such speculations to the progress of science we find that the next great concept of the materialists is that denied by Newton in favor of an atomic theory of light, i. e. the theory that the propagation of light consists of something analogous to vibration. But here again we are faced by a strange mystery. Newton, led to his theory of gravitation as the only possible logical explanation of the motions of the moon and the laws of Kepler, was under the categorical necessity of postulating the existence of a force which

---

[12]Life of Lord Kelvin, by S. P. Thompson (1910), vol. 2, p. 792; Also Popular Lectures and Addresses by Lord Kelvin, London (1889), vol. 1, p. 73. "I often say that when you can measure what you are speaking about, and express it in numbers, you know something about it; but when you cannot measure it, when you cannot express it in numbers, your knowledge is of a meagre and unsatisfactory kind."

[13]See H. Hertz, Electric Waves, English translation by D. E. Jones, London (1893), pp. 143-147.

acted between two bodies through the medium of a vacuum. In the case of light we have been driven to a similar necessity equally repugnant to the senses and yet just as categorical. We must postulate the existence of a vibration which will operate in a vacuum.

Let me pause a moment to recommend to those of you who would indulge in profound meditations without the necessity of thought, the perusal of two volumes which contain the kernel of many philosophical systems wrapped up in a delectable package. These books were written in the reign of Queen Victoria by the mathematician Charles Lutwidge Dodgson (1832-1898), better known under the name of Lewis Carroll and are entitled "Alice's Adventures in Wonderland" and "Through the Looking Glass." One way to approach the difficulties of modern physics seems to be through these books from which pertinent passages will be quoted from time to time.

You will remember in the first of these books that Alice made the acquaintance of a Cheshire cat who was noted for his knowledge and his grin. One day while walking in the forest Alice encountered the Cheshire cat who was seated upon the limb of a tree. After a polite conversation the cat disappeared and reappeared several times suddenly which disturbed the nerves of Alice who said:

"I wish you wouldn't keep appearing and vanishing so suddenly: you make one quite giddy!"

"All right," said the Cat; and this time it vanished quite slowly, beginning with the end of the tail, and ending with the grin, which remained some time after the rest of it had gone.

"Well! I've often seen a cat without a grin," thought Alice; "but a grin without a cat! It's the most curious thing I ever saw in all my life!"

It is almost as curious for us to think about waves without something in which they undulate as it is to think of a grin without a cat.

James Clerk Maxwell, (1831-1879), that profound speculator to whose genius we owe the electro-magnetic theory of radiation, says at the end of his second volume on electricity and magnetism in commenting upon the physical ideas of some of his contemporaries:[14]

There appears to be, in the minds of these eminent men, some prejudice, or *a priori* objection, against the hypothesis of a medium in which the phenomena of radiation of light and heat and the electric actions at a distance take place. It is true that at one time those who speculated as to the causes of physical phenomena were in the habit of accounting for each kind of action at a distance by

---

[14]A Treatise on Electricity and Magnetism, 3d edition (1904), vol. 2, p. 492.

means of a special aethereal fluid, whose function and property it
was to produce these actions. They filled all space three and four
times over with aethers of different kinds, the properties of which
were invented to "save appearances," so that more rational enquirers
were willing rather to accept not only Newton's definite law of
attraction at a distance, but even the dogma of Cotes (Preface to
Newton's Principia, 2nd edition), that action at a distance is one of
the primary properties of matter, and that no explanation can be
more intelligible than this fact. Hence the undulatory theory of
light has met with much opposition, directed not against its failure
to explain the phenomena, but against its assumption of the existence
of a medium in which light is propagated.

## 8.   *The Discovery of Entropy.*

Since our object at this time is to survey the concepts that have
guided laboratory experiment during the scientific revolution, we
can not now penetrate further into these speculations on the nature
of the ether but must proceed to another doctrine that has had
profound influence upon scientific progress. We refer to what is
commonly called the second law of thermodynamics, or the law of
entropy.

In the earliest histories of thought the physical universe was
classified under three heads, i. e. solids, liquids, and gases. A second
method of classification consisted in dividing things into cold bodies
and hot bodies, where a certain arbitrary temperature not far from
the center of the annual temperature range of the surface of the
earth was used as the dividing line of the classification. The question
might now be asked: Is there any connection between these two
classifications?

The study of thermodynamics started logically when data were
accumulated on the thermal properties of gases, and it was found
approximately at the same time by J. A. C. Charles (1746-1823),
and J. L. Gay-Lussac (1778-1850) in France that the pressure
exerted by a gas in a container of constant volume varies directly as
the temperature, provided this temperature be calculated so that its
zero is 460 degrees below the zero of our ordinary Fahrenheit
thermometer. It also became apparent that this temperature range
was essential to the classification of things into solids, liquids, and
gases, since the state of any particular kind of matter depends upon
the value of its temperature, measured from the absolute zero of the
gas thermometer. Iron, for example, is commonly regarded as a
solid and air a gas because most of us do not work either in a

Bessemer steel plant or in a factory devoted to the manufacture of liquid gases.

Proceeding from these elementary ideas now familiar to all of us, however obscure they may have been to the early workers in science, we now ask the question: Why should there exist a lower bound to temperature? Is it the result merely of our definition of temperature and therefore a limit put subjectively into nature or should we really be surprised at it as at a fact discovered about objective nature?

I believe that most people will agree that the existence of a lower bound to temperature is a startling fact. The human mind dislikes to think in terms of bounds. We regard the concept of boundless space as an inalienable right of the human imagination, and it is annoying to be told that the velocity of light is the ultimate velocity of material things since it is so easy to imagine a velocity double that of light. However finite the material world in which we live, we feel resentful at restriction and hold with Byron,[15]

> Eternal Spirit of the chainless Mind,
> Brightest in dungeons, Liberty.

Hence any fact wrested from the world of matter that imposes a bound to that which might conceivably be boundless is at first sight an important and somewhat disconcerting affair. Why should temperature be bounded and bounded at a level not so remotely distant from the very range of temperature within which we live?

To put the answer somewhat crudely, we may say that matter acts as a storehouse or container of a thing to which we have given the name of thermal energy and which is known to us through the myriad activities of living. Temperature is merely a gauge of the intrinsic energy content of matter, and when all energy has been pumped out of matter then the gauge sinks to zero. The mystery of the absolute zero is, in this sense, no more a mystery than the fact that your car stops when the gasoline tank is empty.

But in another way absolute temperature enters into one of the most mysterious concepts in physics, that of entropy. In order to gain some appreciation of this idea let us enquire into the nature of heat energy. Suppose that we have, for example, a piece of iron at the temperature of ice and apply a source of heat to it. Its molecules will gradually absorb the energy of the hot body; it will begin to

---

[15]The Prisoner of Chillon.

radiate heat; it will turn dark red, bright red, and finally attain the brightness of incandescence. At this stage let us remove the source of heat and apply a piece of ice until the iron has once more attained its first temperature. During the course of this experience, what has the iron gained and what has it lost again? According to R. J. E. Clausius (1822-1888), the father of thermodynamics, the iron has gained and lost a quantity of entropy which in the first case is by definition equal to the sum of each little increment of heat gained divided by the absolute temperature at which it was added, and in the second equal to the sum of each increment of heat lost divided by the absolute temperature at which the exchange took place. To put it otherwise, a mysterious entity has flowed through the iron, being first acquired at the expense of the hot body and then returned again to the ice. The iron has merely acted as a conveyor between the hot body and the cold, similar, for example, to the bed of a river along which the water of the mountain snows is conveyed to the water of the ocean. But the mystery remains. What is entropy and does it have objective existence? Is it something created in the mind of Clausius or is it a thing as real as Newton's force or Maxwell's ether or Maupertuis' action?

Mysterious though it may be and remote from all of our *a priori* feelings of reality as it is, a careful weighing of the evidence seems to force the idea of an objective entropy upon us as unescapably as the law of gravitation has led us to the concept of action at a distance.

The next question that we should like to ask is this: What has become of entropy once it has been absorbed into the substance of the ice? Is this not analogous to the question, where does all the water go that flows so ceaselessly toward the sea?

In the literature of social philosophy the most melancholy dictum that the writer knows is to be found in a passage of Emerson's essay on Self-reliance where he says:

Society never advances. It recedes as fast on one side as it gains on the other. Its progress is only apparent, like the workers of a treadmill. It undergoes continual change; it is barbarous, it is civilized, it is Christianized, it is rich, it is scientific; but the change is not amelioration. For everything that is given, something is taken.

In the literature of science there is no more melancholy thought than that of Clausius who said: "Heat cannot of itself pass from a colder to a hotter body," "the entropy of the universe tends to a maximum."

Water can not flow up hill; neither can entropy return to its first value unless it be put there by the expenditure of work. In the mind of Nicolas Leonard Sadi Carnot (1796-1832), a reflection of this kind led to the concept of an ideal system called the Carnot cycle. This ideal system was to act so that the heat that flowed down through the substance of the iron from the hot body to the cold was to be stored in the form of work and used again to pump the heat back from the cold body to the hot, or in terms of the richer concept, was to restore entropy to its former value. Unfortunately for those who seek in this a method for manufacturing a perpetual motion machine, the ideal engine of Carnot can not be attained in reality. There is always a certain amount of heat that can never be pumped back again. Entropy never quite attains its former level, but is always a little greater, since it is, in one sense, a measure of the difference between energy and the free energy that one can use in driving the machines of the world.

There is an elemental quality in this concept. Maupertuis had said that there was something which nature always strove to make a minimum. The dictum of Clausius sees in nature a quantity that always strives toward a maximum. I move my hand and that time is brought a little nearer when all the heat will have flowed down hill from the higher levels and free energy will have disappeared forever. Society never advances but recedes as rapidly on one side as it gains on the other. The energy upon which mankind depends for his existence is forever flowing down the temperature gradients that occur in all the activities of nature. Entropy forever increases to the fatal maximum. Was there ever pictured a more melancholy destiny for the universe and for the society of man?

Very naturally there has existed a speculative appeal in this concept of entropy, as a property of nature which when it changes always changes in one direction. A passage illustrating this point and bearing also upon the question of the objective validity of natural law is taken from the "Treatise on Thermodynamics" by Max Planck:[16]

The gist of the second law (of thermodynamics) has nothing to do with experiment; the law asserts briefly that *there exists in nature a quantity which changes always in the same sense in all natural*

---

[16]Vorlesungen über Thermodynamik, English trans, by A. Ogg, London (1903), p. 103.

*processes.* The proposition stated in this general form may be correct or incorrect; but whichever it may be, it will remain so, irrespective of whether thinking and measuring beings exist on the earth or not, and whether or not, assuming they do exist, they are able to measure the details of physical or chemical processes more accurately by one, two, or a hundred decimal places than we can. The limitations of the law, if any, must lie in the same province as its essential idea, in the observed Nature, and not in the Observer. That man's experience is called upon in the deduction of the law is of no consequence; for that is, in fact, our only way of arriving at a knowledge of natural law. But the law once discovered must receive recognition of its independence, at least in so far as Natural Law can be said to exist independent of Mind. Should any one deny this, he would have to deny the possibility of natural science.

The object of this discussion, introduced so early into our study of concepts that underlie modern physics, is not to give a full explanation of entropy, but to prepare the way for the later discussion of energy. It is well for us merely to see in as full view as possible this metaphysical character of the theory of heat which takes as one of its most fundamental concepts a thing which, though mathematically defined and so thoroughly measurable that its values are recorded in elaborate tables calculated to several places of decimals, is, nevertheless, quite beyond rational intuitions.

The savage as he sat at evening time on the banks of the Mississippi river must occasionally have reflected upon the source of the father of waters. Why did it flow forever toward the sea without finally emptying the source? If the dictum of Clausius be true why does not all the energy reach its final level? Why in the lapse of geologic time have not the stars all burned out, the motion of the planets ceased and all matter come to rest? Why does entropy which always seeks its maximum never arrive?

This thought has been expressed before by others and the answer seems to be that in the macroscopic universe the second law of thermodynamics may have an exception although none has ever been found in the microcosmic system such as we have within the limits of laboratory experiment.

The recent work of R. A. Millikan and others on the origin of cosmic radiation, which will be surveyed in more detail in a later chapter, gives strong evidence that the second law of thermodynamics is not true in the cosmic universe and that entropy is not necessarily approaching a maximum value. Heat may run uphill just as water does under the sucking action of the sun. These matters, however, are still dark and the truth is uncertain.

From another point of view the theory of heat has been fully developed upon the hypothesis that a hot body consists essentially of a large number of minute particles (molecules) whose mean kinetic energy, that is to say the mean energy of their velocities, determines the temperature. These molecules are distributed according to the laws of probability, some being rapidly moving ones and some being slow, according to the energies which they have acquired. In other words, the uniform temperature of a body is due to a statistical distribution of moving molecules and would be very different if it were determined by the energy of its most slowly moving molecule or by the energy of its most rapidly moving one. That part of the second law of thermodynamics which says that heat energy always flows from a hot body to a cold body can thus be picturesquely expressed by the statement that one can never separate the swift molecules from the slow, once they have been thoroughly mixed, just as one can never unscramble an egg.

This concept immediately suggests a question. What do we mean by statistical law? In another chapter the matter will be further explored. For our present need it will be sufficient to affirm that statistical law arises out of a complex of causes too intermingled for their separate influences to be apprehended and such that no single one dominates the situation. But does statistical law rule the activity of the universe or in isolated systems of activity do we find dominating influences guiding the destiny of events? The answer is obvious. Wherever intelligence enters the situation statistical laws are submerged in obedience to a more powerful factor. This, perhaps, is why satisfactory results are not always obtained when the statistical model is applied to biological or psychological problems where the mysterious attribute of intelligence may enter the material under investigation. We analyze the scores of a billiard player, for example, whose average ability is one billiard per inning. Consideration of a hundred games played by such an individual has shown that all save one are distributed within the limits of probability, an occasional game played on a day of low vitality sinking to a half billiard per inning, other games reaching the extreme limit of two. But one exceptional game is noted. One day when nervous energy was under greater control, when intelligence was at work to overthrow the statistical picture, when blind chance no longer dominated the average, the individual played at the rate of three and a third billiards per inning. An analysis of the problem by the methods employed in the blind tossing of pennies shows that this event is almost incalculably improbable. Another example may be cited. Let us consider the statistical problem presented by the dealing of four hands of cards. To make our experiment let us hand the deck to a child who knows nothing about cards and suggest that he distribute them into four piles. Let us regard his arrangement as a fortuitous event; let him, if you please, occupy the position of a card-dealing mechanism. The miracle is soon revealed. The small intelligence of the child is sufficient to bring us into the presence of the impossible. He will almost immediately separate the cards into the four suits. In a few moments he has accomplished what probably has never happened in the history of the world by chance.

We return to the problem which suggested this digression. How can we unscramble an egg or separate the molecules according to their velocities from the intricate mixture of a gas? The answer is that this miracle may be accomplished in theory by the proper introduction of intelligence. It is possible that in the distribution of molecules the swift ones might be separated from the slow provided a *sorting demon* of molecular size and with proper equipment were set to the task. This interesting idea is due to Clerk Maxwell who puts the matter in these words:[17]

One of the best established facts in thermodynamics is that it is impossible in a system enclosed in an envelope which permits neither change of volume nor passage of heat, and in which both the temperature and the pressure are everywhere the same, to produce any inequality of temperature or of pressure without the expenditure of work. This is the second law of thermodynamics, and it is undoubtedly true so long as we deal with bodies only in mass and have no power of perceiving or handling the separate molecules of which they are made up. But if we conceive a being whose faculties are so sharpened that he can follow every molecule in its course, such a being, whose attributes are still as essentially finite as our own, would be able to do what is at present impossible to us. For we have seen that the molecules in a vessel full of air at uniform temperature are moving with velocities by no means uniform though the mean velocity of any great number of them, arbitrarily selected, is almost exactly uniform. Now let us suppose that such a vessel is divided into two portions A and B, by a division in which there is a small hole, and that a being, who can see the individual molecules, opens and closes this hole, so as to allow only the swifter molecules to pass from A to B, and only the slower ones to pass from B to A. He will thus,

_____

[17]Theory of Heat, p. 328.

without expenditure of work, raise the temperature of B and lower that of A, in contradiction to the second law of thermodynamics.[18]

## 9.  *Science—The New Metaphysics.*

With this remark we have reached the goal set by the present chapter.  We have surveyed some of the great concepts upon which the founders of modern physics have built their structure.  They are concepts with which the giants of the nineteenth century struggled and turned over as unsolved puzzles to their successors of the twentieth.  The vast amounts of laboratory data that have been accumulated in attempting to explore their consequences, the volumes of formulas to which they have led, and the machines that have been created from them, form one of the richest heritages ever passed on by one century to another.

But the object of this volume is to show the philosophical foundation upon which physical science rests and how the nature of reality becomes more perplexing and mysterious as we proceed.  Science is not and can not be wholly material and rational so long as action at a distance, the ether of radiation, the action of Maupertuis, and the entropy of Clausius remain as the foundations of its structure. Great progress in investigation has been made during the first part of the present century until, in the enthusiastic estimate of some critics, the total scientific knowledge of the world has been doubled since 1900.  But progress toward the mystery of reality has merely led to newer mysteries. The perplexing puzzle today presents a greater challenge to those who would pick up pebbles with Newton on the beach where "the immense ocean of truth extends itself unexplored."

---

[18]Even this seemingly impregnable argument of Maxwell has been assailed in this agnostic age by attributing a kind of entropy to the demon himself.  See an article by L. Szilard in the Zeitschrift für Physik, vol. 53 (1929), p. 840.  P. Clausing later, however, controverts the position of Szilard.  *Ibid.*, vol. 56 (1929), p. 671.

# CHAPTER II.

## THE PHILOSOPHICAL BACKGROUND OF MODERN PHYSICS.

### 1. *The Value of Abstract Speculation.*

SOME philosopher has aptly said: "Every science begins as philosophy and ends as art; it arises in hypothesis and flows into achievement." After science has attained its strength and the vague language of its early concepts has been crystallized into the language of laboratory instruments and mathematical symbols, it looks with a measure of distrust upon its origin. Science advances while philosophy seems to recede. But there is nothing ignoble in philosophy, and he shows little comprehension of the real foundations of his science who is either ignorant or scornful of the great philosophical systems of the past. Particularly is this true of the physicists who, even in so commanding a figure as that of Lord Kelvin, have been wont to point the finger of disdain at the philosopher with his uncertain and often mystical approach to the nature of reality.

The physicist has in this age become the mystic and the metaphysician. Within a short time sober and intelligent experimenters in the laboratory of the preeminently practical American Telegraph and Telephone company have declared, upon the basis of their investigations, that matter may be regarded as having the nature of a wave, while light, that elusive mystery of modern physics, has assumed material properties. If we are to remain materialists we must now join the ranks of those who think in terms of immaterial entities, which are more elusive to the rational thinker than the monads of Leibnitz. In fact the affair has gone so far that an eminent physicist in a lecture reviewing the progress of science during the past quarter of a century put the matter thus: "Mathematicians are happy in their logic; chemists are happy in their common sense; but physicists are happy because they have neither logic nor common sense."

Perhaps the cause of this attitude toward abstract speculation is to be found in the pragmatic values that have come in such startling profusion from science. The Greeks, knowing no better and not realizing the material benefits to be derived from collections of data,

were willing to spend their days in meditation on the trisection of
the angle and the duplication of the cube.   To most people it will be a
surprise to know that men of profound learning have spent in this
recent day many fruitless hours trying to discover whether *any* map,
no matter how complicated its structure, can be colored with only
four colors, that is to say, so that no two adjoining countries will be
represented by the same hue.   If in the readjustment of the map of
Europe following the late war it had only happened that the new
distribution of countries had required the use of five instead of four
colors to distinguish them from one another, then this ancient problem would have been settled and the war surely not have been fought
in vain.   As it is, however, one can show without difficulty that three
colors are not enough, and that five are sufficient.   The middle case
of four colors still presents a problem of baffling difficulty.   This
digression is made merely to point out the fact that where questions
can be asked, whether the answer is of the slightest material use or
not, there will always be a yearning to explore the cause.   It is out
of this hidden want in the nature of man that philosophy still finds
sustenance.

In approaching philosophical speculation it is well to start as
far back as possible with the first questions of the race and then to
trace the answers through the writings of the learned of different
ages.   There is a tremendous human as well as philosophical appeal
in the naive cosmology which we find in the writings of Mark Twain.
You will remember how in his Odyssey of the Mississippi River
Huck and Tom and Jim were lying on a raft floating down the
channel at night.   Above them stretched the great canopy of the sky;
the eerie spell of the river was upon them and they fell into
speculation.

We had the sky up there all speckled with stars, and we used to
lay on our backs and look up at them, and discuss about whether
they was made or only just happened.   Jim he allowed they was
made, but I allowed they happened; I judged it would have took too
long to make so many.   Jim said the moon could 'a' laid them; well
that looked kind of reasonable, so I didn't say nothing against it,
because I've seen a frog lay most as many, so of course it could be
done.   We used to watch the stars that fell, too, and see them streak
down.   Jim allowed they'd got spoiled and was hove out of the nest.

In these words we have a perfect phrasing of the first great
problem of metaphysics, namely, that which concerns itself with the
origin and nature of things.   To this problem the human spirit must

attach considerable importance or it would not have been the cause of so much bitterness and strife in the dark ages of scientific thought.

Some of you in early school days when you first became aware of the existence of the stars must have propounded to yourselves or to your teacher the question as to the goal toward which a cannon ball would proceed if it were fired off the earth in such a direction as never to hit a star. To you it may have seemed inconceivable that it should float forever without a goal. The fleet of Magellan, by going always in one direction, finally arrived at home. Is it not difficult to think that the material iron of the cannon ball would not arrive if it continued to go? The question has been poetically put in a lecture on the size of the universe by Professor Archibald Henderson, who asks:[1]

If a voyager of the skies travel deep into the interstellar spaces, past the great blue helium stars of Orion, past Betelgeuse and Antares, beyond the white variable Cepheids, the gaseous red and yellow giant-stars, the faintest of the super-nebulæ, "lying like silver snails in the garden of the stars" but whirling in fiery spirals in the dim void of remoter space—will he ever reach any limit to the universe?

With these words we set ourselves the second great problem of metaphysics: what is the nature of space and time and what is man's relationship to these twin entities? Since it is one of the purposes of this book to show how far the foundations of modern physical science rest upon the concepts of metaphysics and how far we have progressed toward a solution of some of the problems involving space, time and matter it will be the part of wisdom to review a few of the pertinent philosophical systems of the past.

## 2. Zeno's Paradoxes.

What were some of the striking features of Greek thought where it touched upon matters of metaphysics? We find, for example, Anaximenes of Miletus (450 B. C.) asserting that air is the first principle of nature, from which we get by condensation and rarefaction, fire, wind, clouds, water, and earth.

Heraclitus (530-470 B. C.), an early Greek philosopher who lived at Ephesus, said that the fundamental form of existence was fire and that all things were in eternal flux. Matter continuously trans-

---

[1] Is the Universe Finite? American Mathematical Monthly, vol. 32 (1925), pp. 213-223, in particular p. 215.

forms into fire and fire back again into matter. The law of the world is change; nothing is quiet and that which seems at peace is still subject to unseen movements. His concept of the universe is one of ceaseless energy.

In direct contrast to the philosophy of Heraclitus is that of Zeno of Elea (450 B. C.) who has left us some of the most perplexing paradoxes of philosophy. As late as 1915 Professor Florian Cajori (1859-1930) published a long series of articles on the Zeno problem, and explanations of the difficulty still not infrequently appear in the public press.[2] We shall have occasion in a later chapter to discuss the theory of point sets and the problem of atoms versus the continuum. Hence it is worth recording here that these puzzles are direct descendants of the Zeno problem. Perhaps it was his reflections concerning the flux and movement of the world of Heraclitus which led Zeno to the pregnant idea that the supposition of the real existence of things manifold and changing leads to contradictions. His philosophy was thus made to assume that nothing moves, and he defended his position with the following arguments:

1. Motion can not begin, because a body in motion can not arrive at another place until it has passed through an unlimited number of intermediate places.

2. Achilles can not overtake the tortoise, because as often as he reaches the place occupied by the tortoise at a previous moment, the latter has already left it.

3. The flying arrow is at rest.; for it is at every moment only in one place.

These arguments can be put a little more picturesquely, perhaps, as follows. Drop an elastic ball upon a smooth table and watch it bounce. Let us suppose that at each impact with the table top it rebounds through half of the distance through which it falls. The question is: Will the ball ever come to rest? At first thought we might be inclined to say no, because, on the assumption of a rebound every time, the ball must bounce an infinite number of times. To be sure these bounces will soon approach molecular size and then submolecular size, but nevertheless there will be an infinite number of them. As a matter of fact we know either from experience or from calculation based on the law of falling bodies, that the ball will come to rest in a very few seconds. For example, it is not a difficult mathematical exercise to show that if the fall is through a distance

[2]History of Zeno's Arguments on Motion, American Mathematical Monthly, vol. 22 (1915).

of sixteen feet, the ball will come to rest in less than six seconds. This problem will seem more real if one will verify this statement by making the calculation oneself.

The point of Zeno's paradox that we wish especially to stress is the connection which it effects between space and time through the concept of velocity. Let us think of the space through which the ball bounces as being infinitely divisible. We must similarly regard an interval of time as being capable of unlimited divisibility. It is in the subtle connection between the space concept and that of time and the limiting values of the two sequences involved in the motion of the ball that the paradox resides. What is velocity? How is the progress of matter through space connected with the partitioning of time?

Have the paradoxes of Zeno been answered? Professor Cajori at the end of his notable papers, to which we have already alluded, makes the following interesting observation:[3]

As now we pause and look backward, we see that a full and logically correct explanation of Zeno's arguments on motion has been given by the philosophers of mathematics. Looking about us, we see that the question is still regarded as being in an unsettled condition. Philosophers whose intellectual interests are remote from mathematics are taking little interest in the linear continuum as created by the school of Georg Cantor. Nor do they offer a satisfactory substitute. The main difficulty is not primarily one of logic; it is one of postulates or assumptions. What assumptions are reasonable and useful? On this point there is disagreement. Cantor and his followers are willing to assume a continuum which transcends sensuous intuition. Others are not willing to do so. Hence the divergence. In the Koran there is a story that, after the creation of Adam, the angels were commanded to make due reverence. But the chief of the angels refused, saying: "Far be it from me a pure spirit to worship a creature of clay." For this refusal he was shut out from Paradise. The doom of that chief, so far as the mathematical paradise is concerned, awaits those who refuse to examine with proper care the massive creation by our great mathematicians without which the tiniest quiver of a leaf on a tree remains incomprehensible.

### 3.   *The Atomists.*

Very closely associated with the Zeno problem, which focuses our attention upon the infinitesimal, is the concept of the atomic nature of the universe. Leucippus (445 B. C.) and Democritus (460-360 B. C.) among the Greeks and Lucretius (98-55 B. C.) among the

---
[3]Pp. 296-297.

Romans were exponents of the atomistic philosophy. According to them nature was formed from the "full" and the "void": The full consisted of indivisible, primary particles of matter, or atoms, which are distinguishable from one another only in form, position and arrangement. For example, the atoms of fire and of the soul are round; pleasant tastes are caused by smooth, and bitter tastes by jagged atoms.

The philosophy of the atomists reaches full flower in the poem of Lucretius, "De Rerum Natura," where the poet lets his bold imagination range over most of the problems of man's relation to the universe. This poem is remarkable not only for the fact that it anticipates many of the concepts important to modern scientific thought, such as, for example, the atomic structure of matter, Darwin's theory of evolution, conservation of matter and energy, etc., but also in its exploration of the concept of infinity.

Professor C. J. Keyser has pointed out the very modern point[4] of view which Lucretius seems to have had with regard to the concept that lies at the basis of mathematical philosophy. Atoms in the view of Lucretius must lie between an upper and a lower bound and finite sums of them are always finite. But since the matter of the universe is infinite the number of atoms of which matter is composed is also infinite. The following striking passage is characteristic of the arguments of the poet:[5]

Again unless there shall be a least, the very smallest bodies will consist of infinite parts, inasmuch as the half of the half will always have a half and nothing will set bounds to the division. Therefore between the sum of things and the least of things what difference will there be? There will be no distinction at all; for how absolutely infinite soever the whole sum is, yet the things which are smallest will equally consist of infinite parts. Now since on this head true reason protests and denies that the mind can believe it, you must yield and admit that there exist such things as are possessed of no parts and are of a least nature. And since these exist, those first bodies also you must admit to be solid and everlasting.

We see in this passage a mind struggling with the great concept of infinity. Does matter consist of ultimate particles which can not be further sub-divided and a finite sum of which makes up the structure of any given piece of matter; or can matter be infinitely divided and is the object in your hand merely the materialization of

[4]The Rôle of the Concept of Infinity in the Work of Lucretius, Bulletin of the American Mathematical Society, vol. 24 (1917-18).
[5]From the translation by H. A. J. Munro (1910), p. 15.

the limit of an infinite sum of the infinitesimal quantity with which the science of mathematics plays? A careful study of the words of Lucretius which we have quoted will yield the conclusion that the poet, in that dark age of science, was quite unaware of the existence of the latter possibility and that his gem of thought is clouded. We shall return to these questions in a later chapter.

Turning from a study of the ultimate structure of matter Lucretius next gives thought to the extension of space and the possibility of conceiving that the universe has a bound. This passage has more than historical interest for us because it focuses the common concept of the boundlessness of space into a passage of rare beauty and force. Since the discoveries of modern astronomy, particularly as they apply to the great recessive velocities of the spiral nebulæ, and modern speculations as to the cause of the inertia of matter will lead us to a consideration of this problem of metaphysics, it seems worth while to set forth the arguments by which Lucretius decided that space was without a bound:

Well then the existing universe is bounded in none of its dimensions; for then it must have had an outside. Again it is seen that there can not be an outside of nothing, unless there be something beyond to bound it. . . . And it matters not in which of its regions you take your stand; so invariably, whatever position any one has taken up, he leaves the universe just as infinite as before in all directions. Again if for the moment all existing space be held to be bounded, supposing a man runs forward to its outside borders and stands on the utmost verge and then throws a winged javelin, do you choose that when hurled with vigorous force it shall advance to the point to which it has been sent and fly to a distance, or do you decide that something can get in its way and stop it? For you must admit and adopt one of the two suppositions; either of which shuts you out from all escape and compels you to grant that the universe stretches without end. For whether there is something to get in its way and prevent its coming whither it was sent and placing itself in the point intended, or whether it is carried forward, in either case it has not started from the end. In this way I will go on and, wherever you have placed the outside borders, I will ask what then becomes of the javelin. The result will be that an end can no where be fixed, and that the room given for flight will still prolong the power of flight. Lastly, one thing is seen by the eyes to end another thing; air bounds off hills, and mountains air, earth limits sea and sea again all lands; the universe, however, there is nothing outside to end.[6]

---

[6]Munro's translation, p. 23.

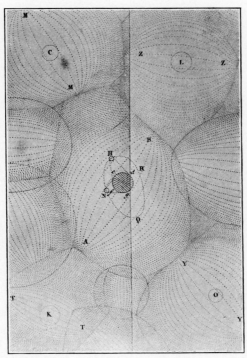

PLATE II

Descartes' picture of the celestial vortices. The disk
in the center represents the sun

Our estimate of "De Rerum Natura" must be that of others who have been struck by the power and imagination of the poet. Alas, Lucretius lived in an age when speculation could not be checked by the cold facts of laboratory experiment; when the tool invented by Newton and Leibnitz and sharpened by their followers, when the telescope of Galileo and instruments of precision were not available to turn dreams into theories and speculations into formulas. The poem contains a statement of most of the problems of natural philosophy and proceeds to their solution only in so far as the unaided mind can go.

## 4. *The Philosophy of Descartes.*

In passing over the philosophical system of Plato, Aristotle and the other Greeks we do not mean to slight this noble heritage, but a philosophy of natural phenomena developed without competent objective data must necessarily have had small influence upon the real progress of scientific thought. We pass, therefore, to the system of René Descartes (1596-1650) whose theory of vortices played a conspicuous part in the pre-Newtonian period of science.

In this ambitious theory Descartes assumed that there was no such thing as empty space and that matter was spread not as atoms, but continuously throughout the whole universe. Naturally in the motion of this all pervading matter, whirlpools or vortices would be set up as whirlpools are set up in flowing water. As the particles rub against one another some are worn round like stones in a stream and the part that is worn off becomes a sort of cosmic dust. This dust tends to accumulate at the center of the vortices where it forms suns and stars. The globular particles are thrown like cream in a separator to the outside and form the atmosphere of the sun. By exercising his imagination with these hypotheses Descartes was able to build up a theory which accounted for many of the phenomena of nature. He, however, like Lucretius lacked in considerable measure though not completely the experimental observations with which Newton was later able to convince the intelligence of his contemporaries and win belief for his theory of light and gravitation.

It will be illuminating to record the precise thoughts of Descartes on the questions with which we shall later be most concerned, namely those which have to do with definitions of space, time, and the fluid that fills the "void."

Thus we find in the eleventh principle of the second book of his

"Principles of Philosophy" a discussion of the meaning to be attached to the statement "that space is not different from corporeal substance":

And it will be easy for us to recognize that the same extension which constitutes the nature of body likewise constitutes the nature of space, nor do the two mutually differ, excepting as the nature of the genus or species differs from the nature of the individual, provided that, in order better to see what is the true idea that we have of body, we take a stone and reject from it all that does not belong to the nature of body. Let us then first reject hardness, because, if one should reduce this stone to powder, it would no longer have hardness, and yet would remain a body; let us reject color, because we have seen occasionally some stones so transparent that they have not had color; let us reject weight, because we have seen fire, which, although it is very light, still possesses body; let us reject cold, heat, and all of the other qualities of this kind, because we do not think that they are in the stone, or rather that the stone does not seem to change its nature because it is either hot or cold. After we have thus examined this stone we find that the real idea which forces us to think that it is a body, consists in this alone, that we perceive distinctly that it is a substance extended in length, breadth, and depth; and this is comprised in our idea of space, not only of that which is full of body, but that which is called empty.

Having thus arrived at the concept of extension Descartes proceeds to analyze the meaning of empty space. Is it possible to conceive of a perfect vacuum or must all extension be endowed with corporeal properties? The keynote of the philosophy of the French thinker is to be found in his answer to this question. With him there is no vacuum. Space is filled with an ethereal fluid whose mutual reaction with matter comprises the totality of phenomena. We who reflect upon the revelation of modern science are not yet sufficiently satisfied about the nature of radiation and the method by which heat reaches us from the surface of the sun to be wholly scornful of the following passages which are the sixteenth and seventeenth principles in the second part of Descartes' philosophy:

With regard to a vacuum, in the philosophical sense of the word, where we mean a place in which there is no substance, it is evident that there is no such place in the universe, because the extension of space or of internal place is no different from the extension of body. And since from the fact that a body is extended with regard to length, breadth and depth, we have reason to conclude that it is a substance, because it is quite inconceivable that that which is nothing has extension, we must therefore conclude the same thing of space which one supposes to be empty, that is to say, since it has extension it must necessarily also have substance.

But when we take this word according to ordinary usage, and we say that a place is empty, it is an established fact that we do not wish to say that there is nothing at all in this place or in this space, but merely that there is nothing of that which we presumed ought to be there. Thus because a pitcher is made to hold water, we say that it is empty when it contains only air; and if there is no fish in a fish-pond we say that it is empty, although it be full of water; thus we say that a vessel is empty, when in place of the merchandise which it is designed to carry, it is loaded only with sand, in order that it might be able to resist the impetuous violence of the wind: it is in this same sense that we say that space is empty when it contains nothing that affects our senses, even though it contains created matter and an extended substance. For we consider ordinarily only those bodies which are near to us in so far as they create in the organs of our senses, impressions so strong that we are able to perceive them. And if, in place of our knowing what we ought to understand by the words vacuum or nothing, we conceive hereafter of a space where our senses perceive nothing as containing nothing created, we shall fall into an error as great as if, because one ordinarily says that a pitcher is empty in which there is only air, we therefore judge that the air which it contains is not a substantive thing.

Those who have followed the warfare between the corpuscular theory of light and the theory of propagation of waves in a continuous medium, and the struggle of the concepts of the continuum in mathematics, will see here that Descartes arrays himself upon the side of the continuists. In another passage he very definitely indicates his break with the atomists, when he shows the difference between the postulate of an ethereal fluid throughout empty space and the postulate of Democritus that the material world was constructed out of atoms which were separated from one another by complete emptiness (Principle 202, part 4). In order to finish the story that we are tracing we must examine the attitude of Descartes toward the extent of this primary substance. This, he says, is infinite for the reasons quoted below. Would you say that he has made an advance over the arguments of Lucretius?

"We also know that this world, or the material extent which composes the universe, has no limit," says Descartes in the twenty-first principle of part two, "because whatever limit we wish to imagine, we are still able not only to imagine some indefinitely extended spaces beyond, but such spaces as we have conceived them to be; namely, that they contain a body of indefinite extent. For the idea of extent which we conceive in any space whatever is the same idea which we ought to have of body."

It is not our purpose to pass judgment upon the character of these concepts of Descartes. We are merely interested in tracing the philosophical background from which modern science arose; but we can easily see how the minds of scientists that followed were prepared by such doctrine for the concept of an ether filling the vacuum of empty space and extending without limit in all directions.

At the basis of Descartes' idea of the primary nature of "extent," which is the basic property of matter and hence of space, there is merely a postulate as to the nature of reality. Let us, for example, consider the concept represented by the modern word "ether." We first proceed to endow it with a set of properties; we conceive of it as space-filling, tenuous beyond the limits of measurement of our material instruments, perfectly elastic, fluid, etc. We bring to bear upon the concept the machinery of mathematics and translate such of these properties as we can into the language of symbols. We deduce certain consequences of our definitions and then seek to verify them by instruments of precision. Should the concept break down because experimental data fail to confirm the mathematical conclusion, it is discarded. One by one the properties are thus tested and rejected until only the primary one of extension remains. Is the ether thus denied existence? Without doubt its sensory existence is severely jeopardized, but is this sufficient to deny it objective reality? In other words, how many and what properties are necessary to objective existence?

We turn finally to the brief consideration which Descartes gave of time. Time to him was subjective and resided in the mind rather than in the object.

Thus he said in the 57th principle of part I the following:

Of these qualities or attributes, there are some which are in the things themselves, and others which are only in our thought; thus, for example, time which we distinguish from duration considered in general, and which we call the measure of movement, is only a certain way of regarding duration, for we do not think that the duration of things which are changing is different from that of things which are not: for it is evident that if two bodies move during an hour, the one rapidly and the other slowly, we do not consider more time to exist for one than for the other, although we suppose more movement to have taken place in one than in the other. But finally in order to comprehend the duration of all things under the same measure, we usually avail ourselves of the duration of certain regular movements which make days and years, and this we call time. Hence this adds nothing to the notion of duration, generally considered but a mode of thinking.

### 5. *Are there Postulations of Normal Intuition?*

We must now pause for a slight digression in the historical account of the philosophical speculations which preceded the age of science and ask this question. Is it possible to formulate a set of postulates of normal intuition? That is to say, are there certain primary statements of belief which can be set down without fear of reasonable differences arising among rational people? We have seen how Lucretius and Descartes held as a fundamental tenet that space was limitless, although they differed completely in their opinion as to the ultimate divisibility of matter. Is this limitlessness of space, admitting that it is beyond the possibility of experimental proof, a fundamental postulate of all reasonable people? Is it more rational to believe that space is boundless rather than that it is bounded or is the question wholly without meaning? It is of considerable interest to note that in a debate on the theory of relativity so able a mathematician and astronomer as W. D. MacMillan of the University of Chicago attempted to formulate a creed of rational belief. It will be entertaining to many to survey these postulates of normal intuitions thoughtfully and to analyze their own reactions toward them. Professor MacMillan says:[7]

1. The physical universe is continuous in time.
2. The physical universe is not bounded in space.
3. There exist physical units, which for finite intervals of time preserve their identities and exhibit characteristic properties. These are, for example, electrons, atoms, molecules, stars, galaxies etc.
4. The sequence of physical units is infinite both ways. That is to say, there is no largest physical unit and there is no smallest one.
5. The phenomena of nature occur always in such a way that certain relations remain invariant.
6. The energy within a region of space does not increase or decrease unless there is a corresponding decrease or increase in some other region of space.
7. The universe does not change always in any one direction.
8. The geometry of the physical universe is Euclidean.
9. The time of the physical universe is Newtonian.

One of the objects contemplated by this volume is to exhibit the struggle of modern physics with these tenets. Guided by the re-

---

[7] A Debate on Relativity, Open Court (1927), pp. 42-43.

searches of Einstein, Millikan, Michelson, Shapley and many others science has now accumulated experimental evidence from the laboratory and the sky which bears directly upon these philosophical problems. That the evidence is conclusive is doubtful; that it is stimulating to the imagination and encouraging to bold speculation is to be preeminently admitted.

### 6.  Newton's Absolute Space and Time.

We proceed now to consider the philosophy of Newton which finds its place in the postulates of rational intuition cited above. Velocity, said Newton, is equal to an increment of space divided by an increment of time; acceleration is an increment of velocity divided by an increment of time; force is mass times acceleration.  Construed in less technical language these definitions are the abstract formulation of the common observation that a stone falling under the influence of gravitation moves with a constantly increasing velocity. These ideas seem simple enough until we reflect that in them there is found a basic relationship between space and time as it seems to apply to the objects of the material universe.  In them time appears as an implicit variable, a quantity which can not be dissevered from the velocity or acceleration to which it pertains.

It is important for subsequent chapters to have a clear concept of what Newton thought regarding time and space.  In the first part of the Principia, that brightest record of human reason, he makes these celebrated remarks :[8]

I do not define time, space, place, or motion, as being well known to all.  Only I must observe that the vulgar conceive those quantities under no other notions but from the relation they bear to sensible objects.  And thence arise certain prejudices, for the removing of which, it will be convenient to distinguish them into absolute and relative, true and apparent, mathematical and common.

1.  Absolute, true, and mathematical time, of itself, and from its own nature flows equably without regard to anything external, and by another name is called duration; relative, apparent, and common time is some sensible and external (whether accurate or unequable) measure of duration by means of motion. . . .

2.  Absolute space, in its own nature, without regard to anything external, remains always similar and immovable.  Relative space is some movable dimension or measure of the absolute space.

3.  Place is a part of space which a body takes up, and is according to the space, either absolute or relative.

---

[8]This is a resumé of a scholium appended to his initial definitions, pp. 6-7 of the Glasgow edition (1871).

4. Absolute motion is the translation of a body from one absolute place into another; and relative motion, the translation from one relative place into another.

It will be clear from a study of these definitions that Newton regarded space and time as being real entities, things of an absolute physical character which existed exterior to our mental perception of them. To him there was an absolute space and an absolute time and if all material objects were removed it is conceivable, although the point is not explicitly made, that the framework of absolute time and space would still exist.

P. W. Bridgman has recently brought an interesting point of view to bear upon these concepts of philosophy, by means of which he would eliminate many questions as meaningless.[9] His idea is that every concept of physics or of mathematics must be measured in terms of the actual operations necessary to define it. Are there such things as absolute space and absolute time or is the question without meaning? To explore these possibilities one must investigate the operations by which time and space are measured and he will see that these are all relative. Hence, employing the criterion that "the concept is synonymous with the corresponding set of operations," we see that it is meaningless to speak of absolute time and space. Other questions to which Bridgman suggests that this criterion of reality should be applied are: "May time have a beginning or an end?," "Why does time flow?," "May space be bounded?," "May space or time be discontinuous?," "Why does nature obey laws?," etc. Perhaps this is the solution of the problem of philosophy, but while man sees or thinks he sees the possible synthesis of natural law in such abstract concepts as entropy and action he will not wish to dismiss thus lightly from his speculations any abstractions which might lead to deeper insight. It is but a step from the vacuum of Descartes to the ether of Maxwell.

## 7. The Contributions of Locke and Leibnitz.

It is difficult to estimate the relation of "An Essay Concerning Human Understanding," the principal work of John Locke (1632-1704), to the scientific revolution, but there is no doubt that it exerted a powerful influence upon the speculative thought of that formative period. Locke was much influenced by the arguments of Descartes with regard to extension and duration, but he was un-

---

[9]The Logic of Modern Physics, Macmillan, 1927, pp. 28-32.

willing to believe that a vacuum necessarily possessed attributes of a body. "Our own clear and distinct ideas plainly satisfy us, that there is no necessary connection between space and solidity, since we can conceive the one without the other."[10]    The following naive argument shows that his belief in space was similar to that of Newton as something having an objective validity:

For if they (plain men) had not the idea of space without body, they could not make a question about its existence; and if their idea of body did not include in it something more than the bare idea of space, they could have no idea about the plenitude of the world; and it would be as absurd to demand whether there were space without body, as whether there were space without space, or body without body, since these were but different names of the same idea.[11]

Lock's concept of duration adds nothing to that of Descartes and is concerned mainly with the distinction between duration "considered as going in one constant, equal, uniform course"[12] and the means taken to measure it.    He devotes a chapter to the mutual relationship which exists between time and space, and reaches the conclusion that "expansion and duration do mutually embrace and comprehend each other; every part of space being in every part of duration, and every part of duration in every part of expansion."[13] That this mutual embrace could be reduced to formulas and applied in tracing the movements of the planets, the motion of the tides and other phenomena of the material world was certainly very far from his immediate thoughts.

The philosophy of Gottfried Wilhelm Leibnitz (1646-1716), the contemporary of Newton who shares with him the honor of discovering the principles of the calculus, centers about a mystical theory of monads.    Monads are to be thought of as primary entities like atoms, but atoms in which there is a spark of intelligence.    They differ from the atoms of Democritus and Lucretius in the assumption that they have no measurable dimensions, but are points and are endowed with active forces which consist of ideas.    Had Leibnitz been able to show that collections of his monads violated some of the laws of abstract probability by reason of their intelligence, such as might be expected from a group of Maxwell's demons mixed up in a collection of material atoms, then his idea would have had far more ob-

---

[10]Book 2, Chap. 13, § 22.
[11]Book 2, Chap. 13, § 24.
[12]Book 2, Chap. 14, § 21.
[13]Book 2, Chap. 15, § 12.

jective reality. As it is, monadology is but an interesting historical incident in the struggle of man toward the light.

The philosophy of Descartes exerted a strong influence upon Leibnitz and he has recorded in various places his opinions concerning the principles of the French thinker. That one which has for us perhaps the most significance is his question whether the essence of a body consists merely in extension.

If the essence of body consists in extension, this extension alone ought to be sufficient to account for all the properties of body. But this is not so. We notice in matter a quality, called by some *natural inertia*, by which body resists in some way motion; so that it is necessary to employ some force to set it in motion (even making abstraction of the weight), and a large body is moved with more difficulty than a small body.[14]

We shall see later how this idea of Leibnitz persisted through speculation, gained an entire new meaning in the behaviour of the Foucault pendulum and the motion of the gyrocompass, and led to the attempt of Mach to find its explanation in the other material of the universe. "All this shows," says Leibnitz, "that there is in matter something other than what is purely geometrical; that is, than extension and its changes pure and simple."[15]

## 8.  *Immanuel Kant and the Subjective View.*[16]

A new point of view, new in the sense that ideas expressed in the writings of his predecessors here appear systematically stated and logically developed, was injected into philosophy with the work of Immanuel Kant (1724-1804), who in 1781 published his celebrated "Critique of Pure Reason." Those who hesitate to include this name in a history of the development of physical ideas would do well to recall that Kant's early thought was dominated by the work of Newton and he shares with Laplace the credit for having first stated with systematic arguments the nebular hypothesis of the origin of the earth. That his speculations finally led him to advance the possibility of the subjective existence of nature comes more impressively from him than from one who had struggled in vain with the ideas of Newton.

---

[14]Letter on the Question, Whether the Essence of Body Consists in Extension (1691). Translated by G. M. Duncan: The Philosophical Works of Leibintz, 2nd ed. New Haven (1908) p. 42.

[15]*Ibid.*, p. 44.

[16]To those to whom an apology is due for the use of this term, we refer to the transcendental idealistic point of view.

These pages are tracing the growth of speculative thought and one must not imagine that the ideas of Kant are without ancestry. Great theories which we encounter for the first time in our study often seem like isolated bursts of imagination; we marvel at their complexity, their applications, the far reaching vistas that they open. They seem like the great buttes, isolated on the high plateaus of western landscapes, gigantic masses towering in striking relief against the sky, the "monuments more enduring than bronze" of which the poet Horace wrote. But isolation is rarely the case in speculative thought, which resembles, rather, the growth of mountain ranges rising from foot hills to mesas and from mesas to the great peaks. The work of Kant was but the logical culmination of the idealistic view of George Berkeley (1685-1753), Bishop of Cloyne, and David Hume (1711-1776), who sought to undermine the materialism of their age by denying the reality of the world. Matter to them was but a complex of ideas. This was the inheritance of Kant.

In his book on the critique of reason, Kant turns away from the objective space and time of Newton and argues that space and time do not exist of and by themselves or as properties of matter, but they are what he calls *a priori* concepts of the human mind. Without the human mind there would be neither space nor time just as there would not be sound without a human ear to hear it. In other words he wishes to make the whole question a subjective one and would deny that we could ever arrive at any concept of either that could not be derived from pure reason alone. Time and space in his philosophy lose their objective significance; they are not entities which we can study by means of the instruments of science. The geometry of space resides in the mind and one can make any set of postulates with regard to it that he may desire, provided they satisfy the canons of logic and are consistent. There can never be any question as to whether the geometry of Euclid, or that of Riemann or of Lobatchevski is the true geometry of space, because the mind through pure reason can not differentiate between them.

One is reminded when he reflects upon the consequences of this full subjective philosophy of the conversation between Alice and the twin brothers Tweedledee and Tweedledum. Tweedledee exclaimed:

". . . if he (the Red King) left off dreaming about you (Alice) where do you suppose you'd be?"

"Where I am now, of course," said Alice.

"Not you!" Tweedledee retorted contemptuously. "You'd be nowhere. Why, you're only a sort of thing in his dream!"

"If that there King was to wake," added Tweedledum, "you'd go out—bang!—just like a candle!"

"I shouldn't!" Alice exclaimed indignantly. "Besides, if I'm only a sort of thing in his dream, what are *you*, I should like to know?"

"Ditto," said Tweedledum . . . ; "you know very well that you're not real."

"I *am* real!" said Alice, and began to cry.

Kant's metaphysics with regard to space and time are summarized below in his own words and can be compared with the views previously stated by Newton:[17]

1.   Space does not represent any property of objects as things in themselves, nor does it represent them in their relations to each other; in other words, space does not represent to us any determination of objects such as attaches to the objects themselves and would remain, even though all subjective conditions of the intuition were abstracted.

2.   Space is nothing else than the form of all phenomena of the external sense, that is, the subjective condition of the sensibility, under which alone external intuition is possible.

3.   Time is not an empirical conception, that is, one derived from experience.

4.   Time is necessary representation, lying at the foundation of all our intuitions.

5.   Time has only one dimension; different times are not coexistent but successive.

6.   Time is not a discursive or, as it is called, general conception, but a pure form of the sensuous intuition.

7.   The infinity of time signifies nothing more than that every determined quantity of time is possible only through limitations of one time lying at the foundation.

To put this in simpler language, the mind of man is so constructed that he is born with an inherent knowledge or feeling for three dimensional space and a consciousness of the sequence of events. He is thus able without confusion to locate objects about him. If he is to have a cup of tea at half past three at the house of a friend he will not find, as sometimes happens in dreams, that the house and the hour keep changing as he tries to find them.

### 9.   *The Antinomies of Reason.*

Before we can hope to appreciate the real revolution which modern discoveries in physics have effected and to appraise their

---

[17]Sections 1 and 2 of Part I.

philosophical importance it is necessary for us to understand the meaning of the word *antinomy* as it appears in Kant's philosophy.

After he had defined the catagories of pure reason, Kant turned to the interesting problem of why certain concepts always implied their opposites and why attempts to ascertain *the truth* of one or the other always failed. He was led to the conclusion that there exist fundamental antinomies, or contradictions, in reason, which appear whenever we try to pass from human experience to the absolute. Of these antinomies the following four occupy a central place in the Kantian dialectic:[18]

I.  *Thesis*: The World has a beginning in time, and is also limited as regards space.

*Antithesis*: The World has no beginning and no limits in space; it is infinite regards both time and space.

II.  *Thesis*: Every composite substance in the world is made up of simpler parts and nothing anywhere exists save the simple or what is composed of the simple.

*Antithesis*: No composite thing in the world is made up of simple parts, and there nowhere exists in the world anything simple.

III.  *Thesis*: Causality in accordance with laws of nature is not the only causality from which the appearances of the world can one and all be derived. To explain these appearances it is necessary to assume that there is also another causality, that of freedom.

*Antithesis*: There is no freedom; everything in the world takes place solely in accordance with laws of nature.

IV.  *Thesis*: There belongs to the world, either as its part or as its cause, a being that is absolutely necessary.

*Antithesis*: An absolutely necessary being nowhere exists in the world, nor does it exist outside the world as its cause.

It is rather an amazing contemplation to reflect that there exist propositions about the absolute in nature which, though mutually contradictory, may both be assumed as postulates from the application of which we may expect no contradictions. The present situation in physics, as will be revealed in the ensuing pages, presents other antinomies from laboratory experiments which have the same contradictory nature. The tenets of the modern theory of wave mechanics, for example, assume that light is for one purpose a corpuscular phenomenon and for another a continuous undulation.

The antinomies of Kant struck fire in the thought of Georg W. F. Hegel (1770-1831) and led him to his difficult philosophy of

---

[18]Critique of Pure Reason. Transcendental Dialectic, book 2, chap. 2, sec. 2.

the Absolute Idea. This system may be characterized by the term *dialectic* by which Hegel meant the process of exhibiting the incomplete character of any concept except the all inclusive concept of the Absolute Idea. Because of the fundamental antinomies in reason any concept is incomplete, but through its implications we may establish a kind of successive approximation through an infinite sequence of stages to the forever unattainable absolute.

### 10. *Psychological Duration.*

Is this subjective concept of time to be confused with duration, which Henri Bergson so picturesequely says "is the continuous progress of the past that gnaws into the future and which swells as it advances"?[19] I do not feel that the philosophical picture which we have tried so briefly to trace would be complete without pushing the subjective view to the limit. It is true that here we must leave philosophy and pass over into psychology, where the subjective and the objective are so strangely mingled that one can not trace the threads; but the peculiar mystery of matter immersed in a three dimensional continuum of space and a one dimensional continuum of time which is perceived and studied by a living scientist most certainly has a subjective as well as an objective side. One can scarcely be accused of mysticism in any approach that he might make to this puzzling problem with which the great speculative genius of the past has so often struggled. Therefore, without further apology, let us consider what we might term the psychological aspect of time and space.

The matter has been very vividly put by Thomas De Quincey in his "Confessions of an English Opium Eater" in which he describes some of the bizarre dreams that came to him after prolonged use of the terrifying drug. These words are poetry rather than science.

The sense of space, and in the end the sense of time, were both powerfully affected. Building, landscapes etc. were exhibited in proportions so vast as the bodily eye is not fitted to receive. Space swelled, and was amplified to an extent of unutterable infinity. This, however, did not disturb me so much as the vast expansion of time. I sometimes seemed to have lived for seventy or one hundred years in one night; nay, sometimes had feelings representative of a millenium, passed in that time, or, however, of a duration far beyond the limits of any human experience.

---

[19]*L'évolution créatrice*, 6th. ed. Paris (1910), p. 5; English trans. by A. Mitchell, New York (1911), p. 4.

Again in the sequel: "Suspiria de Profundis" we have a vivid picture of subjective time:

In the Opium Confessions I touched a little upon the extraordinary power connected with opium (after long use) of amplifying the dimensions of time. Space, also, it amplifies by degrees that are sometimes terrific. But time it is upon which the exalting and multiplying power of opium chiefly spends its operation. Time becomes infinitely elastic, stretching out to such immeasurable and vanishing termini, that it seems ridiculous to compute the sense of it, on waking, by expressions commensurate to human life. As in starry fields one computes by diameters of the earth's orbit or of Jupiter's, so, in valuing the virtual time lived during some dreams, the measurement by generations is ridiculous—by millenia is ridiculous; by aeons, I should say, if aeons were more determinate, would be also ridiculous. On this single occasion, however, in my life, the very inverse phenomenon occurred. . . . Instead of a short interval expanding into a vast one, upon this occasion a long one had contracted into a minute.

Are these but dreams and have they nothing to do with reality? This subjective character of existence as it relates to man in his environment has, of course, been the subject of extensive study. It is at the basis of the Bergsonian philosophy. William James (1842-1910), whose clear vision laid the foundation of rational insight into what was personal and what was nature, considers psychological time in various places in his "Principles of Psychology," from which the following statement is quoted:[20]

Thus it appears indubitable that all space relations except those of magnitude are nothing more or less than pure sensational objects. But magnitude appears to outstep this narrow sphere. . . . Suppose no feeling but that of a single point ever to be awakened. Could there possibly be the feeling of any special whereness or thereness? Certainly not. Only when a second point is felt to arise can the first one acquire a determination of up, down, right or left, and these determinations are all relative to that second point.

In another place he calls attention to the subjective character of time by citing the phenomenon that time *appears* to flow so much more rapidly in old age than in youth.[21] In fact this may be roughly stated by the formula that a year at age x appears to represent approximately $1/x$ of one's life. For example, in childhood a year seems like $1/10$th of one's life; at 50 a year in passing appears but as $1/50$th of the whole span.

---

[20]Vol. 2 (1890), pp. 151 and 154.
[21]Principles, vol. 1 (1890), p. 625.

Lamartine, the mystic French poet, has expressed this well in "La Lac," one of the most beautiful of poems:

O time suspend your flight, and you, glad hours,
    Suspend your rapid course,
Let us delight in swiftly passing joys,
    These days without remorse.

Enough of wretched ones implore thy flight,
    Speed, speed away for them,
Take with their days their cares and weary pain,
    Forget the happy ones.

But I demand in vain some moments more,
    The time slips by and flees;
I say to night: Yet tarry here! and dawn
    Comes glowing through the trees.

Love then, love then, and from the rushing hours
    Let's hasten while we live,
Man has no port; time has no shore or bound;
    It flees, we pass away.

### 11. *Poincaré and the Foundations of Geometry.*

We are now upon the threshold of the modern world and we might expect the philosophy of those who are the heirs of Newton and Kant and the immediate predecessors of Einstein to indicate real progress in exact thinking about the concepts of time and space. In order to exhibit the best of pre-Einsteinian thought we can profitably examine the ideas of two, a mathematician and a physicist, whose thought has played a conspicuous part in the new science. The men to whom we refer are Henri Poincaré (1854-1912) and Ernst Mach (1838-1916). Henri Poincaré, as we have already remarked in the first chapter was mathematician, physicist, astronomer, and philosopher. During the course of his thirty-three years of active scientific work he produced more than 1,500 memoirs in addition to numerous books. For the fifteen years before his death he was by common consent the dominant figure in those scientific groups with which he was associated. His mind ranged over most of the speculative problems of these four branches of science and his philosophical ideas have been condensed in a series of essays first published under three heads: Science and Hypothesis, The Value of Science, and

Science and Method, and later collected in one volume called "The Foundations of Science." These essays are particularly noted for their brilliant style, and many quotations from them have found their way into scientific literature.

Because of the scope of the philosophy of Poincaré it is difficult if not impossible to condense it into a single system. His aim is to give careful scrutiny to the foundations of the physical sciences, particularly where they are mathematical in character. He focuses his attention upon the concepts of space and time as they appear in geometry and in the equations of dynamics; he keeps forever before him the mystery of probability "so strongly does this vague instinct which lets us discern probability defy analysis";[22] what, he asks, are the basic concepts of mathematics and wherein is the secret of their application to the world of matter?

It would be impossible in the scope of a few paragraphs to systematize his philosophy, since it is so interwoven with the specific phenomena of physics; this, perhaps, is the main reason why his ideas have made so little progress among laymen, who would find many of his observations without meaning because of their ignorance of the physical situations which occasion them. Hence his speculations will be introduced from time to time in this book at those places where the special phenomenon is being discussed. His essays form a volume to be read slowly at intervals of time. It is a book to which one may turn for moments of meditation.

Perhaps the keynote of Poincaré's attitude toward science is contained in the following statement.[23]

The scientist does not study nature because it is useful; he studies it because he delights in it, and he delights in it because it is beautiful. If nature were not beautiful, it would not be worth knowing, and if nature were not worth knowing, life would not be worth living. Of course I do not here speak of that beauty which strikes the senses, the beauty of qualities and of appearance; not that I undervalue such beauty, far from it, but it has nothing to do with science; I mean that profounder beauty which comes from the harmonious order of the parts and which a pure intelligence can grasp. This it is which gives body, a structure so to speak, to the iridescent appearances which flatter our senses and without this support the beauty of these fugitive dreams would be only imperfect, because it would be vague and always fleeting. On the contrary, intellectual beauty is sufficient unto itself, and it is for its sake, more

[22]Foundations of Science, p. 30.
[23]Foundations of Science, pp. 366-367.

perhaps than for the future good of humanity, that the scientist devotes himself to long and difficult labors.

His approach to the problem of space is through the mathematical concept of geometry. Geometrical space to Poincaré has five fundamental properties: "(1) It is continuous; (2) it is infinite; (3) it has three dimensions; (4) it is homogeneous, that is to say, all its points are identical one with another; (5) it is isotropic; that is to say, all the straight lines which pass through the same point are identical one with another."[24] Geometrical space is to be compared with *perceptual space,* "the frame of our representations and our sensations."

In this geometrical space we have set up three geometries by purely logical processes. These geometries differ from one another on the basis of the postulate with regard to the number of straight lines that can be drawn through a single point parallel to a given straight line.

Since this idea, in spite of its long history, is still novel to many people, it is perhaps well to make a brief digression for the purpose of explaining it. To Euclid, "parallel straight lines are straight lines which, being in the same plane and being produced indefinitely in both directions, do not meet one another in either direction." One is immediately struck by the fact that this definition is essentially negative since parallel lines are characterized by what they do not do.

Euclid in order to proceed with his deductions soon found it necessary to introduce into his geometry a postulate regarding the nature of parallel lines. This postulate can be stated in various ways, but for our purposes it will be convenient to express it in the affirmation that through a given point there is not more than one parallel to a given straight line.

The real nature of this postulate did not become apparent until a long succession of geometers had tried in vain to prove it. Then the idea seemed to occur simultaneously in various parts of the mathematical world, to Carl Friedrich Gauss (1777-1855) in Germany, to Nicholaus Lobatchevski (1793-1856) in Russia, and to Wolfgang Bolyai (1775-1856) in Transylvania, that the postulate of Euclid could not be proved, in other words, that a systematic geometry could be constructed without it.

The new Non-Euclidean geometry which resulted, began with the definition: "In relation to a line, all the lines of a plane can be

---

[24]Foundations of Science, pp. 66-67.

divided into *intersecting* and *non-intersecting* lines. The latter will be called parallel, if in the pencil of lines proceeding from a point they form the limit between the two classes; or in other words, the boundary between the one and the other." Hence from this positive, in contrast to Euclid's negative, definition of parallel lines we derive the postulate that more than one line can be drawn through a point so as to be parallel to another line. This definition also introduced the idea of an *angle of parallelism,* that is to say, the angle between the parallel and the perpendicular from the given line to a point, P, on the parallel. This angle of parallelism changes with the distance of the point P from the given line.

Later the great German mathematician Georg F. B. Riemann (1826-1866) pointed out that a third possibility existed and that another geometry, now commonly referred to as Riemannian, could be constructed on the postulate that no line could be drawn through the given point parallel to a given line.

One striking feature of these three geometries is exhibited in the theorem which concerns the sum of the angles in a triangle. According to Euclid, the sum of the angles in any triangle equals two right angles; with Lobatchevski this is no longer true and the sum of the angles of a triangle is always less than two right angles; Riemann on the contrary shows that the sum is always greater than two right angles.

Bewildered by this strange situation, mathematicians asked which was the true geometry. An answer was sought for by the astronomers. If Lobatchevski is correct then the parallax of every star, (see the definition on page 95) no matter how far away it may be, is always positive; if Riemann's geometry is the geometry of space then the parallaxes are all negative; if Euclid has defined the true behaviour of parallels, then the parallaxes are all positive but have the limit zero as the distances of the measured stars increase. But parallax is a very difficult thing to measure because of its extreme smallness and the numerous errors of observation that tend to mask it. Some negative parallaxes have been found; the largest positive parallax is $3/4''$; most of them are zero. No answer seems possible from this source until instruments of greater precision are invented.

But has the question any meaning? In a celebrated passage Poincaré makes the following statement:[25]

[25]Foundations of Science, p. 65.

The *axioms of geometry therefore are neither synthetic a priori judgments nor experimental facts.*

They are *conventions;* our choice among all possible conventions is *guided* by experimental facts; but it remains *free* and is limited only by the necessity of avoiding all contradiction. Thus it is that the postulates can remain *rigorously* true even though the experimental laws which have determined their adoption are only approximative.

In other words, *the axioms of geometry* (I do not speak of those of arithmetic) *are merely disguised definitions.*

Then what are we to think of that question: Is the Euclidean geometry true?

It has no meaning.

As well ask whether the metric system is true and the old measures false; whether Cartesian coordinates are true and polar coordinates false. One geometry can not be more true than another; it can only be *more convenient.*

In considering the concept of time Poincaré fixes his attention upon the idea of simultaneity. "When we say that two conscious facts are simultaneous, we mean that they profoundly interpenetrate, so that analysis can not separate them without mutilating them."[26] He considers time in connection with the individual who is studying phenomena and asks the questions: "Can we transform psychologic time, which is qualitative, into a quantitative time? Can we reduce to one and the same measure facts which transpire in different worlds?"

His answer to the first question is put in the following words:[27]

. . . *We have not a direct intuition of the equality of two intervals of time.* The persons who believe they possess this intuition are dupes of an illusion. When I say, from noon to one the same time passes as from two to three, what meaning has this affirmation?

The last reflection shows that by itself it has none at all. It will only have that which I choose to give it, by a definition which will certainly possess a certain degree of arbitrariness. Psychologists could have done without this definition; physicists and astronomers could not. . . .

As to the definition of simultaneity of distant events, Poincaré affirms that this is wholly a matter of convenience.[28]

This simultaneity of two events, or the order of their succession, the equality of two durations, are to be so defined that the enunciation of the natural laws may be as simple as possible. In other words, all these rules, all these definitions are only the fruit of an unconscious opportunism.

---

[26]Foundations of Science, p. 223.
[27]Foundations of Science, p. 224.
[28]Foundations of Science, p. 224.

He cites, for example, the appearance of the new star in 1572, whose description is vividly given in the works of Tycho Brahe. That tremendous cosmic upheaval took place in a very distant part of the sky, perhaps two hundred light years from the earth. The conflagration of which Tycho had just become aware was thus, in point of fact, an event that took place before the discovery of America; but is there any meaning to be attached to the statement that the phenomenon occurred after the "formation of the visual image of the isle of Espanola in the consciousness of Christopher Columbus"? The answer made by Poincaré is that this statement has meaning only as the result of a convention in accordance with the dictum stated above.

The laws of probability also played an important part in the thoughts of Poincaré and he has devoted two chapters to his reflections upon this subject. "Has probability been defined? Can it even be defined? And if it can not, how dare we reason about it?" Since these questions will be the subject of a subsequent chapter we shall be satisfied at this point merely to state them and shall postpone our consideration of their answers until a more systematic development of basic ideas is possible.

Can we estimate the importance of the philosophy of Poincaré? It is too early, perhaps, to reach a just appraisement, and to trace the force of his arguments through so many phases of speculation. The least that can be said is that he focused the attention of his contemporaries upon the speculative relationship between abstract ideas and the specialized collections which comprise the various branches of modern science.

### 12.  *Ernst Mach—Relativity and Inertia.*

When Poincaré died in Paris on July 17th, 1912, the whole scientific world felt the shock of this great loss. His passing left the feeling that a light of truth had gone out. Eulogies were written in most of the languages of the world, and there was universal expression among astronomers, mathematicians, and physicists that the race would wait long before the appearance of another such universal genius.

Contrast this with the passing of Ernst Mach who died on February 19, 1916, near Munich. At that time there was little expression throughout scientific journals of the value of his contributions to knowledge. He died neglected as he had feared. But whose duty was it to appraise his works? Was he psychologist, philosopher, or physicist? To the psychologists he seemed an enigma; to the philosophers his points of view upon the problems of mechanics appeared to lack significance because the genius of an Einstein was required to appreciate their consequences and formulate them in such language that they could be tested by objective experimentation; with the physicists Mach himself indicated his complete schism in a communication directed to Max Planck, wherein he said:[29]

We can see that the physicists are on the surest road to becoming a church, and are already appropriating all the customary means to this end. To this I simply answer: If belief in the reality of atoms is so essential to you I hereby abandon the physicist manner of thought, I will be no regular physicist. I will renounce all scientific recognition; in short the communion of the faithful I will decline with best thanks. For dearer to me is freedom of thought.

Ernst Mach was born in 1838 at Turas, Moravia, and was educated at Vienna. He was professor of mathematics at Graz in 1864 and in 1867 became professor of physics at Prague where he was rector magnificus in 1879-80. He held the chair of philosophy at the University of Vienna (1895-1901) when he retired. His early youth and first teaching experience were spent in comparative poverty, against which he struggled with rare patience and resolution.

The essence of the philosophy of Mach is to be found in his acceptance of sensations as the essential realities. These he calls the elements of the world and the quotation already cited shows how strongly he differed from those who believed that atoms are the realities. The book upon which his greatest reputation rests is "The Science of Mechanics," published in 1883, which is a critical and historical account of the development of this fundamental subject.

The greatness of Mach's philosophy now appears to be his anticipation of the theory of relativity. He strongly differed with Newton's concept of an absolute time and an absolute space, which he characterized as mediaeval. In an attempt to replace it with a better point of view he found himself called upon to consider the mutual relationship of things, not in a small isolated system, but

---

[29]See Paul Carus: Mach and his Work, Monist, vol. 21 (1911), pp. 19-42, in particular p. 33. The present tendency seems to be to agree with Mach. We thus find A. E. Ruark and H. C. Urey beginning their treatise on "Atoms, Molecules and Quanta" (1930), with the remark: "Once, when the famous Boltzmann had concluded a lecture on atoms and molecules, the equally famous Mach arose and said, in effect, You do not know that molecules exist. Boltzmann replied, I *know* that there are molecules. Mach answered, You *do not*, and so the debate ended. Today, the most ardent lover of modern atomic theory would side with Mach. . ."

in the actual complicated and vast system of universal nature. The following statements are now recognized as legitimate anticipations of the theory of relativity :[30]

No one is competent to predicate the things about absolute space and absolute motion; they are pure things of thought, pure mental constructs, that cannot be produced in experience. All our principles of mechanics are, as we have shown in detail, experimental knowledge concerning the relative positions and motions of bodies. Even in the provinces in which they are now recognized as valid, they could not, and were not, admitted without previously being subjected to experimental tests. No one is warranted in extending these principles beyond the boundaries of experience. In fact, such an extension is meaningless, as no one possesses the requisite knowledge to make use of it.

Let us look at the matter in detail. When we say that a body K alters its direction and velocity solely through the influence of another body K', we have asserted a conception that it is impossible to come at unless other bodies A, B, C, . . . are present with reference to which the motion of the body K has been estimated. In reality, therefore, we are simply cognizant of a relation of the body K to A, B, C, . . . If now we suddenly neglect A, B, C, . . . and attempt to speak of the deportment of the body K in absolute space, we implicate ourselves in twofold error. In the first place we cannot know how K would act in the absence of A, B, C, . . .; and in the second place, every means would be wanting of forming a judgment of the behaviour of K and of putting to the test what we have predicated,—which latter therefore would be bereft of all scientific significance.

You have seen earlier in the chapter how Leibnitz made the inertia of matter a property as fundamental to its definition as the property of extension. Newton in his Principia merely incorporated the objective fact of inertia but did not inquire into its cause. With Mach this speculation takes a leading rôle and he now asks the question: "Why is the inertia of matter?" Is it, as Leibnitz believed, inherent in the nature of matter itself, or is there an outside cause? Can it be that inertia is a reflection of the existence of the other matter in the universe? To put the question picturesquely, suppose that we consider all the material in the universe except a single stone to be blotted out of existence. Would this stone now resist motion as it does in the actual world? Would it move in a straight line? Or is such a question meaningless without the presence of other matter to create a frame of reference? All matter, excepting the

---

[30]The Science of Mechanics, Trans. by T. J. McCormack, Chicago, 2nd. ed. (1902), pp. 229-230.

sun, the planets, their satellites, the asteroids, and a small amount of cosmic dust, is so tremendously remote from our little earth that the influence of its gravitational pull is too infinitesimal to be measured by the most refined of instruments. How, then, are the stars, the nebulae, the great dark masses of the sky connected, if at all, with the behaviour of bodies on our earth? To be sure they form a sort of statistical reference frame which we can consult by means of telescopes in order to exhibit our annual motion about the sun, our daily rotation and the drift of the solar system, but have they, perhaps, a more fundamental connection with the intrinsic properties of matter? Can we find in them the source of material inertia? As you swing a pail of water about your head, is the fact that the water clings to the pail and does not spill a cosmic phenomenon whose explanation ultimately goes back to the total quantity of matter in the universe?

You can see that Mach was dealing with a great idea and that merely to have asked the question created a fruitful field for speculation. This point of view is a genuine advance over the rather sterile philosophy of Descartes, who merely saw in matter the one fundamental property of extension.

The following is a significant passage and is representative of the idea which Mach enlarges in a magnificent way, to his immortalization.[31] Surely Einstein had a rich inheritance.

Let us now examine the point on which Newton, apparently with sound reasons, rests his distinction of absolute and relative motion. If the earth is affected with an *absolute* rotation about its axis, centrifugal forces are set up in the earth: it assumes an oblate form, the acceleration of gravity is diminished at the equator, the plane of Foucault's pendulum rotates, and so on. All these phenomena disappear if the earth is at rest and the other heavenly bodies are affected with absolute motion round it, such that the same *relative* rotation is produced. This is, indeed, the case, if we start *ab initio* from the idea of absolute space. But if we take our stand on the basis of facts, we shall find we have knowledge only of *relative* spaces and motions. *Relatively,* not considering the unknown and neglected medium of space, the motions of the universe are the same whether we adopt the Ptolemaic or the Copernican mode of view. Both views are, indeed, equally *correct;* only the latter is more simple and more *practical.* The universe is not *twice* given, with an earth at rest and an earth in motion; but only *once,* with its relative motions, alone determinable. It is, accordingly, not permitted us to say how things would be if the earth did not rotate. We may interpret the

[31]The Science of Mechanics, pp. 231-232.

one case that is given us, in different ways. If, however, we so interpret it that we come into conflict with experience, our interpretation is simply wrong. The principles of mechanics can, indeed, be so conceived, that even for relative rotations centrifugal forces arise.

This is a remarkable statement when we reflect that it was written prior to the historical papers of Einstein. Mach had surely gone far beyond the absolutism of Newton, the subjectivity of Kant, and had seen in the problem of the inertia of matter a connection between man and the cosmic structure. What rich speculation is awakened as we read: "When, accordingly, we say that a body preserves unchanged its direction and velocity *in space,* our assertion is nothing more or less than an abbreviated reference to *the entire universe.*"[32] There are no isolated systems and no isolated experiments. In every action we have a direct connection with the remainder of the universe no matter whether its separate particles be miles or millions of light years from us. Certainly there exists in all philosophy no richer speculation than this, and the triumph of it is to be found in the pages of the special and general theories of relativity.

### 13.  *The Intellectual Evolution.*

One who reads the history of science must be struck by the frequency of the coincidence of discovery. There is great emotional appeal in the following story, related in the biography of Lord Kelvin. Lord Kelvin, then William Thomson, at the beginning of his studies, had gone to Paris, fired with a devotion to the mathematical ideas of Joseph Fourier and George Green. The latter had privately published his investigations in a work entitled "An Essay on the Application of Mathematical Analysis to the Theories of Electricity and Magnetism," but its contents were little known in England and completely unknown in France.

One night about three weeks after the arrival of William Thomson, eager footsteps were heard before the door of his lodging and with a hasty knock Jacques Charles Sturm burst into the room. The visitor was in a state of high excitement and asked permission to see the manuscript of Green which Thomson had with him. Turning the pages rapidly, Sturm scanned the contents of the essay. As his eye fell upon the formulas with which Green anticipated his theorem on the equivalent distribution,[33] he suddenly jumped from his chair crying: "Ah, voilà mon affaire."

---

[32]The Science of Mechanics, p. 233.

This is stark tragedy, but it is a tragedy that has been and will be enacted many times. Ideas are not the product of individuals but rather the product of movements, to which each individual has added his increment of thought. Logarithms were invented by Baron John Napier, say the text books, but they were certainly independently found by the Swiss, Joost Burgi. Newton discovered the law of gravitation, but very probably the law would soon have appeared in the writings of another. Certainly the idea of the inverse square law is to be found in the conjectures of Newton's contemporaries Robert Hooke, E. Halley, C. Wren, and C. Huygens. The unfortunate quarrel between the followers of Leibnitz and those of Newton over the priority of the discovering of the calculus is too well known to need telling here. We have already commented upon the discovery of non-Euclidean geometry, and similar coincidences could be multiplied without end.[34]

Ideas are the product of an intellectual evolution in which individuals are but incidents. In the dark tangle of modern quantum mechanics and the theory of radiation there is a bright truth to be discovered. We shall greatly reward, as we should, the individual who first has the vision, but the solution will really be the solution of the race. Struggle as he may, the individual can only see as far as the data of the instruments of his period and the intellectual vision of his predecessors permit. Newton himself admitted that he stood upon the shoulders of giants; it was his great individual glory that he was the first to interpret what he saw.

Swiftly and imperfectly we have traced the golden thread of a single thought from the magnificent Greeks to the beginning of the present age. Has the race made real progress in examining this philosophical problem of the nature of space and time and the relation of matter to its framework? Did Descartes make a contribution in his vacuum that was not empty? Did Leibnitz hit upon a fundamental aspect of the problem in the attention which he gave to inertia? Has Newton helped us by systematizing the arguments which would show that space and time formed an eternal, unchanging, absolute framework of reality? What shall we say to the catagorical imperative of Kant and the psychical duration of William James? Does Mach see the furthest of all when he insists that there is not a single isolated system in the universe, but that every part of matter is related to the cosmic structure by the effects of inertia and all phenomena are but relative?

[33]Life of Lord Kelvin, by Silvanus P. Thompson (1910), vol. 1, p. 119.
[34]For a list of similar coincidences see W. F. Ogburn; Social Change, New York (1922), pp. 90-102.

# CHAPTER III.

## IS THERE AN ETHER?

### 1. *Galileo and Inertia.*

IN THE last chapter it was shown that there were several ways of looking at space and time. Sir Isaac Newton advanced the theory that we were to regard these entities as absolute and unchangeable factors independent of matter for their existence. They are, perhaps, what is meant by the trite expression "eternal verities." The idea might be regarded as a sort of absolutism. Space and time in the philosophy of Newton together make up the unchanging framework of the world, a four-dimensional manifold into which the phenomena of nature fit and where they may be thought of as residing.

Immanuel Kant, perplexed by the attempts of others to give reality to space and time, and under the influence of the idealism of Berkeley and Hume, adopted the full subjective view. Time and space are the eternal verities, not objectively, but subjectively. They are *a priori* intuitions of the human mind. Destroy the mind and you have destroyed all.

Ernst Mach, reflecting upon the point of view of Leibnitz that matter has inertia as well as extension, had a new revelation according to which time and space were aspects of a cosmic relativity. Space and time in his opinion are not entities with an independent existence, fixed and unchangeable, but are to be thought of as attributes of matter. Create but a single electron and you have started to manufacture space and time. Create two electrons and with them space and time appear, although their existence is limited to the neighborhood of the newly created matter. In other words space and time grow with the growth of matter, just as in a certain sense there is more red in two red apples than in one. With the creation of matter inertia appears and may be regarded as a phenomenon related to the totality of matter in the universe.

In this chapter we shall survey the history and arguments relating to the creation of the metaphysical space-filling medium which we are accustomed to call the ether, or in more recent times, the luminiferous ether. Before embarking upon the hazardous journey thus projected, it might be well to state a text which can be very properly chosen from the pages of Lewis Carroll's treatise on the life and habits of the people of the country which lies beyond the looking glass.

Alice in her adventures encountered the White Queen who appeared to be in a somewhat distraught frame of mind. During their conversation, the matter of ages came up for discussion and the queen remarked:

"Now I'll give *you* something to believe. I'm just one hundred and one, five months and a day."

"I can't believe that!" said Alice.

"Can't you?" the Queen said in a pitying tone. "Try again: draw a long breath, and shut your eyes."

Alice laughed. "There's no use trying," she said: "one can't believe impossible things."

"I daresay you haven't had much practice," said the Queen. "When I was your age, I always did it for half-an-hour a day. Why, sometimes I've believed as many as six impossible things before breakfast. . . ."

In the last chapter we mentioned several times the word inertia. This word appears not infrequently in common language and for most purposes may be defined as that property of matter which enables it to resist a change of motion. The meaning of this seems simple enough; it is in keeping with the nature of things to experience a resistance, different from friction, when one moves a marble across a table top.

But let us take our view from another vantage point and push our speculations to some entertaining conclusions. We ask you to regard a historical incident. A few years before the birth of Sir Isaac Newton, a famous Italian astronomer by the name of Galileo Galilei (1564-1642) found himself in serious difficulty with the clergy of his day. He had made the heretical statement that the earth and not the sun was in motion.

That was, alas, an age in which only a timid few held the view that one could learn anything from experiment. In fact it was not only difficult but dangerous to differ with authority provided the authority was sufficiently seasoned with years; to try to prove oneself correct by appealing to the evidence of phenomena was to flirt with death. While Galileo sojourned at Padua in the year 1600 a public spectacle was held which was calculated to make anyone pause who too earnestly wanted to look about him and tell others what he saw. Filippo Giordano Bruno (1548-1600) was burned at the stake in order to expiate the crime of holding to the Copernican view that the earth and not the other heavenly bodies was in motion. Galileo had already experienced an unpleasant difficulty in his teaching experience at Pisa where he had dared to differ from the Aristoteleans who argued, because the statement was found in the writings of the master, that a heavy weight always fell more rapidly than a light one. Galileo, not satisfied with this authority, offered to prove that Aristotle's statement was wrong and climbed the celebrated leaning tower with a heavy shot and a light one. The two were observed to fall together making one sound as they struck the ground, but this evidence was regarded with unfriendly eyes. It only succeeded in discrediting the young experimenter and making him an object of suspicion.

Galileo, however, was a man of courage and persisted in his dangerous pursuits. Among other things he invented an instrument by means of which distant objects could be brought to nearer view and with it he was able to discern the moons of Jupiter. Did the world welcome these new discoveries? Was not the imagination of his contemporaries stirred by this remarkable new information? It would be bewildering to us of this modern age to interpret the black suspicion of those days if there were not evidence today of the same distrust in spite of the many benefactions conferred by objective discovery. This attitude of man toward the discoveries of truth is a perplexing mystery.

How characteristic of the bigotry of the day is the attitude which inspired the following letter written by Galileo to Kepler:

Oh, my dear Kepler, how I wish we could have one hearty laugh together! Here, at Padua, is the principal professor of philosophy whom I have repeatedly and urgently requested to look at the moons and planets through my glass, which he pertinaciously refuses to do. Why are you not here? What shouts of laughter we should have at this glorious folly! And to hear the professor of philosophy at Pisa laboring before the grand duke with logical arguments, as if with magical incantations, to charm the new planets out of the sky.[1]

We return to the main theme of our story which was the dangerous predicament in which Galileo found himself as the result of his heresy of statement that the earth moved. Bruno had dared to spread such malicious doctrine and had met death by public torture; Galileo, however, had gained some prestige among a few, whose imaginations had been fired by his discovery of the moons of Jupiter and the

[1]See Sir Oliver Lodge: Pioneers of Science, London (1919), p. 106.

PLATE III

Galileo "with a sincere heart and unfeigned faith" denying his belief in the motion of the earth. From the painting by J. V. Robert Henry.

possibilities of the telescope, and some protection was to be expected from high authority. However he trod upon dangerous ground.

Unfortunately Galileo had little if any experimental evidence for his assertion. The size of the sun and the nature of the stars were practically unknown. It did not seem strange to the people of that day that the firmament with the sun, the planets, and all of the stars should revolve around the earth once in twenty-four hours. Our own pity of their ignorance is largely derived from the fact that we know the stars to be huge suns, larger than our own, which are at such immense distances from us that we have to use the distance that light travels in a year as a yard-stick to be able to talk about them. If any one tried to tell us that the earth stood still and the stars revolved around it we could effectively answer him by computing the incredible velocity with which Polaris, the pole star, for example, would have to move in order to make the circuit of the earth in a single day. Polaris to accomplish this journey would have to move with more celerity than the man who was so swift that he could turn off an electric light and be in bed before the room was dark.

Let us change the facts of history and let us imagine that Galileo performed the following experiment: that he had asked permission to suspend a heavy weight by a long cord from the dome of a cathedral and had set it in motion above a circle drawn on the floor. Imagine the picture, the dim light from the tinted windows falling upon the dark circle of the clergy and the heretic. And what would they have seen in that breathless hour? The pendulum, as though plucked by some cosmic hand, would have been seen to change gradually its plane of oscillation, and whereas it was swinging in a North and South direction at twelve o'clock, it would have been found to oscillate in a different plane at six. How could the accusers of Galileo have answered or explained away this strange phenomenon? As he arose from his knees after repenting the abjuration of his heresy would he then, as the apocryphal legend affirms he did, have had to mutter under his breath those immortal words, "e pur si muove" (and yet it moves)?

It is amazing that this simple phenomenon was not observed until the middle of the nineteenth century. If weather maps had been available as we now know them it would have immediately struck the attention of any one who studied them that the great weather cyclones (or "lows") of the northern hemisphere always whirl in one direction, namely counterclockwise, while in the southern hemisphere the spiral motion is clockwise. The great currents of the ocean which so profoundly modify our weather are examples of the same phenomenon.  I wonder if those who witnessed the sufferings of Bruno and those who heard poor, aged Galileo say: "with a sincere heart and unfeigned faith I abjure, curse, and detest the said errors and heresies," would have seen the implication of this tendency of natural currents.

## 2.  Foucault's Pendulum Experiment.

And what is the explanation of the motion of the pendulum and the direction of the vortical motions of the earth?  Most of you will say at once that these phenomena prove the rotation of the earth. The motion of the pendulum is not due to any transcendental or mysterious force from without, but is due simply to the fact that the earth turns under the swinging weight.  And yet perhaps the explanation is not so simple since the experiment was performed for the first time in 1851 by Jean Foucault (1819-1868).  Simple facts have not usually remained undiscovered for so many years.

Foucault performed his experiment in the Pantheon at Paris, from the dome of which he hung a heavy iron ball about a foot in diameter by a wire more than 200 feet in length.  A circular rail about twelve feet in diameter was built on the floor of the Pantheon and a little ridge of sand constructed upon it in such a way that at each vibration the ball would record a mark to indicate its point of passage. The ball was then displaced from the vertical by a small thread and left for a few hours until it had come absolutely to rest.  The thread was then burned and the ball set in motion across the ridge of sand. And what did those who witnessed it behold?  Slowly, hour after hour, the ball changed its plane of vibration.  The floor of the Pantheon was in visible motion.  The principle for which Bruno died and for which Galileo suffered was vindicated.  The earth moved! Those who visit Washington may see a Foucault pendulum swinging in the building of the National Academy of Sciences.

And yet let us consider a simple question.  With respect to what is the earth in motion?  This is a legitimate question from the point of view of Mach, to whom all motion is relative.  The point can be put more strikingly by making the assumption that the sun and all the stars and the nebulae and all the matter of the universe except the earth are completely destroyed.  If this step seems a little difficult to take, let us suppose merely that the earth is far enough removed from all visible matter to be essentially in complete isolation;

that is to say, let the sky be completely devoid of light from any source. Then, since we should have no outside point of reference in the solitudes of space, should we be able to say whether the earth revolved or not? Under these strange circumstances would the Foucault pendulum change its plane from hour to hour, and would the weather cyclones, if any existed, persist in revolving in a single direction? Now let but a single point of light break through our darkness from a single star on the edge of a huge, but very distant, universe. If this single point of light appeared to change its position in the sky from hour to hour could we hold this as evidence that we were in rotation?

There are several explanations that have been advanced to account for the fact, truly surprising when we review it thus speculatively, that we are able to detect the rotation of the earth without reference to outside bodies.

The first of these hypotheses is strangely a denial of the reality of the rotation of the earth. We may assume that the earth is actually non-rotating and that the stars really have the tremendous velocities which would result from such an assumption. A. S. Eddington, whose interpretation of the theory of relativity and whose theory of the source of stellar energies are monuments of scholarship and imagination, comments upon this proposition in his delightful book, "Space, Time and Gravitation"[2] in the following words:

If the earth is non-rotating, the stars must be going around it with terrific speed. May they not in virtue of their high velocities produce gravitationally a sensible field of force on the earth, which we recognize as the centrifugal field? This would be a genuine elimination of absolute rotation, attributing all effects indifferently to the rotation of the earth, the stars being at rest, or to the revolution of the stars, the earth being at rest; nothing matters except the relative rotations. I doubt whether anyone will persuade himself that the stars have anything to do with the phenomenon. We do not believe that if the heavenly bodies were all annihilated it would upset the gyrocompass. In any case, precise calculation shows that the centrifugal force could not be produced by the motion of the stars, so far as they are known.

A second hypothesis, which we shall consider later in connection with Einstein's theory of space-time, postulates a vast quantity of unobserved world-matter. Beyond the fixed stars and the spiral nebulae

---

[2]Space, Time and Gravitation (1921), p. 153.

there may be quantities of matter which we have never beheld, whose unseen influence penetrates to the laboratory of our little earth in the form of a modification of our customary ideas of space and time. This is obviously not the place to explore this mystical postulate.

A third alternative is that the earth actually has an absolute rotation independent of the other matter of the universe, and that this rotation takes place with respect to a great ocean of ether which pervades all space and permeates all matter. The ether we shall find to be the seat of the kinetic energy of the earth, which is very great. One does not realize what a tremendous storehouse of energy is involved in this speculation. Assuming an average specific gravity of 5.5 for the earth, we may calculate by a simple formula that the total kinetic energy of rotation of the earth is approximately $2 \times 10^{29}$ foot-pounds. To put this statement into more understandable terms, this amount of energy would keep eleven billion horse power engines running for about a billion years.

### 3.  A Discursion on Energy.

Let us pause to ask a question about this energy. The general formula for kinetic energy seems to tell us that kinetic energy is not absolute but relative, since it can be calculated only by comparing the velocity of one body with another. Thus in the above calculation the angular velocity which appeared in the formula used was calculated from the time that elapses between one sunrise and another. Is it not possible, therefore, that this great store of energy is merely a mathematical fiction, and if the sun and stars were blotted from our vision by clouds, might it not cease to exist and in an instant that whole sum total of energy vanish like the ghost of Banquo? As Macbeth mused,

> Can such things be,
> And overcome us like a summer's cloud,
> Without our special wonder?

The Foucault pendulum seems to deny this possibility, but take away the concept of the ether and the energy explanation becomes one of great difficulty. Potential energy, from its definition, is the energy of position; kinetic energy is the energy derived from change of position. But the fundamental question is, position with regard to what?

Consider for a moment the properties of a piece of matter. A stone a few feet from the top of the table is certainly a different thing from a stone resting upon the table's surface. The first possesses an attribute which we call potential energy. If we let it drop, this potential energy at once transforms into kinetic energy which, by definition is equal to half of the product of the mass by the square of the velocity. The stone strikes the table and comes to rest. In a moment the kinetic energy is gone and with it the potential energy which it once possessed. We now know, though the knowledge only became the general property of the human race in 1843 through the work of James P. Joule (1818-1889), that this useful energy has disappeared in heat and in the internal energy of the atoms which have been disturbed by collision with the table top.

In the foregoing statement of the history of the falling stone have we used only words? Did we get at the reality behind the exchanges of energy from the energy of position to the energy of heat? What was the source of the original energy? Where was it stored? Did it reside in the stone or in the medium surrounding the stone?

In this connection there is much to think about in a simple experiment first performed by Benjamin Franklin. A Leyden jar is merely a glass jar coated inside and out to within a short distance of the top with metal foil, the inner coat being connected with a conducting knob. This device possesses the valuable property of acting as a reservoir, in which a charge of electricity can be stored. Let us perform the experiment of first charging the jar and then removing from it all of the metal foil. Take the glass from one place to another, use it in other capacities, finally reconvert it into a Leyden jar again by replacing the metal foil, and connect the conducting knob with the outer coat. The resulting spark is evidence that the energy has not been dissipated by the removal of the foil. But where during the history of the glass jar was the energy of the electricity stored? Was it in an elastic strain set up within the glass material by the electrical energy, or did it reside in the surrounding medium?[3]

It is a fact worthy of much reflection that the total amount of kinetic and potential energy in an isolated system which does not store up internal energy, is always constant. An example of this is found in the journey of the earth around the sun. Why does the earth never slow down, but continue in its path year after year in

---

[3]This experiment has recently been repeated with a Leyden jar made out of paraffin and the electrical charge was found to be removed with the metal coverings. A similar result was obtained for glass which had been thoroughly dried, but the mystery of where the energy resides is by no means elucidated by this discovery. See C. L. Addenbrooke, Philosophical Magazine, vol. 43, 6th series, (1922), pp. 489-493.

remarkable opposition to those who deny the possibility of perpetual motion? This, we say, is because the sum of the kinetic and potential energies is a constant, and if we draw too near the sun, thus losing part of our potential energy, we immediately hasten our footsteps and draw away again. A pendulum at the bottom of its swing has converted its entire supply of potential energy into kinetic energy and would continue to oscillate indefinitely were not a certain amount of the total constantly dissipated in friction both with the air and at its point of support.

There is a remarkable theorem in the theory of electrical radiation which was discovered in 1884 by John Henry Poynting (1852-1914). This theorem had to do with the transfer of energy in an electromagnetic field. You are all familiar with what happens when the terminals of a battery are connected with a motor or a heater or some other electrical device to which energy is to be conveyed. The electricity flows along the wire in a current and energy disappears from the battery to reappear at the motor. But how is this transport made? It had been the common custom before Poynting's time, to think that the energy was carried from the battery along the wire by the current itself much in the same way as the energy of a stream of water is conveyed through a pipe. But in the electro-magnetic theory of Clerk Maxwell, the storehouse and vehicle of energy is the medium surrounding the wire, and it was Poynting's achievement to show that *the energy does not flow along the wire but into it at right angles to the current.*[4]

In this connection we shall quote a significant passage from the great book of H. A. Lorentz (1853-1928), "The Theory of Electrons," in which the father of relativity reflects upon the meaning to be attached to the phrase: "A flow of energy":[5]

. . . the flow of energy can, in my opinion, never have quite the same distinct meaning as a flow of material particles, which by our imagination at least, we can distinguish from each other and follow in their motion. It might even be questioned whether, in electromagnetic phenomena, the transfer of energy really takes place in the way indicated by Poynting's law, whether, for example, the heat developed in the wire of an incandescent lamp is really due to energy which it receives from the surrounding medium, as the theorem teaches us, and not to a flow of energy along the wire itself. In fact, all depends upon the hypothesis which we make concerning the

---

[4]See J. H. Poynting: On the transfer of energy in the electromagnetic field. Trans. of the London Phil. Soc. vol. 175 (1884), pp. 343-361. See also H. A. Lorentz: Theory of Electrons, (1909), p. 23.
[5]P. 25.

internal forces in the system, and it may very well be, that a change
in these hypotheses would materially alter our ideas about the path
along which the energy is carried from one part of the system to
another. It must be observed however that there is no longer room
for any doubt, so soon as we admit that the phenomena going on in
some part of the ether are *entirely* determined by the electric and
magnetic force existing in that part. No one will deny that there
is a flow of energy in a beam of light; therefore, if all depends on the
electric and magnetic force, there must also be one near the surface
of the wire carrying a current, because, here, as well as in the beam
of light, the two forces exist at the same time and are perpendicular
to each other.

### 4. The "Elastic Solid" Ether.

The mystery of energy and the mystery of inertia are but phases
of a greater problem: Is there an ether? The fundamental property
of matter is extension, said Descartes, and this extension is characteristic also of a vacuum which is thus not to be regarded as entirely
empty. But according to Leibnitz, Descartes is not wholly right,
because matter also possesses the inherent property of inertia. Were
these savants, perhaps, after all, talking about aspects of the same
thing, and is the problem of inertia the problem of the ether?

Is there an ether and if so, how can we define it? When we are
thus required to represent an idea by a word and to reduce some
profound and perplexing experiences of the race to language, we are
reminded of a conversation that took place between Alice and Humpty
Dumpty.

"I don't know what you mean by 'glory,'" Alice said.

Humpty Dumpty smiled contemptuously. "Of course you don't—
till I tell you. I meant 'there's a nice knock-down argument for
you!'"

"But 'glory' doesn't mean 'a nice knock-down argument,'" Alice
objected.

"When I use a word," Humpty Dumpty said, in rather a scornful tone, "it means just what I choose it to mean—neither more nor
less."

"The question is," said Alice, "whether you *can* make words
mean so many different things."

"The question is," said Humpty Dumpty, "which is to be the
master—that's all."

What meaning shall we give to the word ether that will remove
it from the realm of metaphysical speculation and introduce it into

the world of real experience? It is obvious that one rational way to proceed is to set down a few postulates and then to subject them to the test of experimental evidence.

We shall begin with the concepts of the so-called "elastic solid" theory which was thoroughly explored in a long series of brilliant papers by the physicists of the nineteenth century. This intricate subject can, perhaps, be best reviewed by setting forth a few tentative postulates and investigating their consequences and contradictions.

Are we not reminded in this adventure of the quest of the Holy Grail? Surely those who pondered over their equations during the romantic middle years of the last century might well have sung with Sir Galahad,

> Sometimes on lonely mountain-meres
> I find a magic bark;
> I leap on board: no helmsman steers:
> I float till all is dark.

We shall begin by making the following assumption.

1. The ether is an *isotropic elastic medium* of unlimited extension.

By this proposition we commit ourselves to an analogy with ordinary matter. The ether is to be regarded as an elastic substance which differs from the material of sensuous experience only in degree and is possessed of the two fundamental properties of elasticity and density. The word *isotropic* very much simplifies the mathematical problem, because by it we assume that the ether is equally elastic in all directions. What this means mathematically is that instead of having to deal with the twenty-one coefficients which appear in the general theory of elastic bodies we shall be concerned with only two. The first of these, the *modulus of compression,* is a measure of the elastic behaviour of the material under tension and compression; the second, the *coefficient of rigidity,* describes the elastic properties under shearing forces which cause distortion. The material is then defined, as far as its ability to transmit energy by elastic vibrations is concerned, as soon as we know its density in addition to the two constants just described. The entire history of the theory of the "elastic solid" ether is an account of the efforts of mathematical physicists to adjust these three constants in a set of equations in such a way that all the phenomena of light propagation, its reflections and refractions, both in empty space and in crystalline matter, could be systematically accounted for.

We proceed to the second postulate which may be stated as follows:

2. The constants measuring elasticity, rigidity, and density must be so chosen that no longitudinal vibrations will take place in the ether.

The great quest started with a hunt for an equation. In what way, asked these Sir Galahads, may the vibrations of an isotropic medium be described? It was the good fortune of Claud Navier (1785-1836) first to formulate the correct equation governing the displacement of elastic particles, although in his work only the constants of rigidity and density appear.[6] His researches happily fell into the hands of the great analyist Augustine Louis Cauchy (1789-1857), who added to the equation of Navier the modulus of compression and put before the world the problem of adjusting these constants in such a way that all the phenomena of light might be properly described.[7]

Let us first ask ourselves the question: Can the ether be thought of as a very tenuous gas, resembling air, and are the waves in it similar to the waves of sound? In an ether of this sort as was shown by the mathematician Simeon Denis Poisson (1781-1840) the vibrations would be both longitudinal and transverse in character, that is to say the energy would be transported both by expansions and compressions in the ether, and also by deformations perpendicular to the direction of motion.[8] Each wave would have its own velocity of propagation, and if the rigidity and density were small, the important wave would be the longitudinal one.

That the luminiferous ether can not possibly be of this character is proved by a number of experiments which show that light vibrations are not longitudinal in character at all, but consist wholly of transverse motions of the medium. This transverse motion of light is beautifully illustrated by a very simple experiment performed with two crystals of tourmaline (see fig. I). Let a beam of light fall upon a plate of tourmaline which has been cut parallel to the axis of the crystal and examine the structure of the light which has been transmitted. In order to do this, place a second plate of tourmaline in front of the transmitted beam with its axis parallel to the first and

---

[6]Mémoire de l'Académie de France, vol. 7 (1827), p. 375.
[7]Exerçices de mathématiques, vol. 3 (1828). Oeuvres, vol. 8, ser. 2, pp. 195-226.
[8]Mémoire de l'Académie de France, vol. 8 (1828), p. 623.

then gradually turn it through an angle of ninety degrees. What a mystery we see! As the second plate is rotated the light gradually fades until at the maximum position when the two crystals are at right angles to one another it has been completely extinguished. The mystery is explained by saying that the vibrations which make up the beam of light are transverse and not longitudinal, for such an experiment would not affect vibrations of the latter sort. The beam of light that has passed through the tourmaline and thus acquired a two-sidedness is said to be *plane-polarized*. The phenomenon of polarization has been the greatest foe to the elastic solid theory.

At the very outset, therefore, we see that we must choose the three constants at our disposal in such a way that longitudinal vibra-

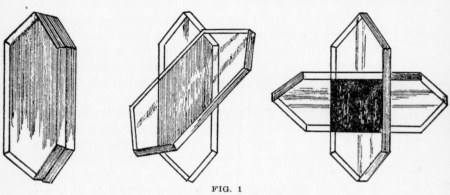

FIG. 1

Tourmaline crystals illustrating
the polarization of light.

tions are excluded from the ether. To the skillful analyst, of course, this would not offer great difficulty, however much the method might displease the practical physicist, who thinks that he must always deal with reality in the form of mechanical models. Cauchy calmly settled the difficulty of longitudinal waves by equating to zero the expression in his equation which gave rise to the longitudinal disturbance. To be sure the modulus of compression became a negative number, but in this assumption the *contractile* or *labile* theory of the ether was created. At first it seemed that the possibility of inventing a mechanical model was jeopardized by this assumption, but Lord Kelvin, who devoted considerable attention to this ether, was able to overcome most if not all of the mechanical difficulties of the theory in so far as it pertained to propagation through a uniform continuous medium.

A second possibility was suggested by James MacCullah (1809-1847) in a paper presented to the Royal Irish Academy in 1839.[9] This paper presented the possibility of an ether in which the potential energy depended only upon the rotation of the volume elements of the medium, and not, as in the case of ordinary elastic bodies, upon the change of the size and shape of the elements, that is to say, upon their compression and distortion. This idea was, in fact, a truly notable contribution, but its significance did not become evident until G. F. Fitz Gerald (1851-1901) called attention to it, nearly forty years later when Maxwell's theory had superseded the older elastic solid concepts. The fact is that MacCullah actually hit upon the truth, that is, in so far as Maxwell's ideas may be regarded as the truth in these bewildering days, but he was unable to give any plausibility to an ether in which the coefficients of density and rigidity no longer had their ordinary dynamical significance.

It might be of interest at this point to mention calculations made by Lord Kelvin upon the value of the density of the ether. Lord Kelvin published his speculations in 1854 under the poetical title: "Note on the possible density of the luminiferous medium and on the mechanical value of a cubic mile of sunlight."[10] His conclusion was that the ether in a cubic mile at the surface of the earth contained not less than the billionth of a pound of matter. This statement, however, does not carry a high probability of belief because it can not be experimentally verified, and in fact rests upon the purely tentative estimate that the ratio of the velocity of vibration of the ether to the velocity of light does not exceed one-fiftieth. Making the further speculative assumption that the ratio of the amplitude of the energy in a ray of light to the wave length of the light is one one-hundredth, J. Larmour calculates the elastic modulus to be many times smaller than that of glass.[11] We might thus conclude that the ether is a very tenuous material with slight elasticity.

In another instance Lord Kelvin regarded the ether as a highly rarefied though very rigid entity and discussed the question of how the planets can then move through it without their motion being visibly affected. His answer was to call attention to the fact that Trinidad pitch is a brittle solid and yet is permeable, although slowly, to a solid body placed upon it. Thus he assumed that the ether may

[9]Trans. Royal Irish Academy, vol. 21. Collected Works, p. 145.

[10]Trans. of Royal Soc. of Edinburgh, vol. 21, pp. 57-61; Comptes Rendus, vol. 39, pp. 529-534; Phil. Mag., vol. 9, pp. 36-40; Collected papers, vol. 2, art. 67, pp. 28-33.

[11]Encyclopaedia Britannica, Article on Aether, 11th ed., p. 292.

resemble this model and its rate of permeability to matter be merely greater than that of pitch.

Luminiferous ether must be a body of almost extreme simplicity. It may perhaps be soft. We might imagine it to be a body whose ultimate property is to be incompressible; to have a definite rigidity for vibrations in times less than a certain limit, and yet to have the absolute yielding character that we recognize in wax-like bodies when the force is continued for a sufficient time. It seems to me that we must know a great deal more of the luminiferous ether than we do. But instead of beginning with saying that we know nothing about it, I say that we know more about it than we do about air or water, glass or iron—it is far simpler; there is less to know. That is to say, the natural history of the luminiferous ether is an infinitely simpler subject than the natural history of any other body.[12]

By these and other assumptions the concept of an elastic solid ether can be made to fit experimental evidence, but the troubles grow when we try to press the matter further by exploring the optical properties of solid substances in terms of the density and rigidity concepts. We come to another postulate, upon which lie the wrecks of many equations.

3.    Within the interior of solid media, the density of the ether varies but the rigidity remains constant.

The battle ground of the elastic etherists has been the behaviour of light in crystalline solids. These problems center around the assumptions that have to be made to account for certain technical polarization phenomena, for partial reflection, and for the peculiar property of *double refraction* possessed by all crystallized minerals except those whose fundamental form is the cube. This last mentioned phenomenon was discovered by Erasmus Batholinus (1625-1698) a Danish philosopher, about the year 1669.[13] While experimenting with a crystal of Iceland spar he made the interesting observation that a beam of light incident upon the crystal was broken up into two pencils, one of which obeyed the ordinary laws of refraction and the other a new law, for which no theory had been devised.

These subjects are unfortunately too technical to be reviewed here in detail but it will suffice to say that while the assumption of a uniform rigidity in a labile ether of crystalline substances combined with the hypothesis of an aelotropic density seems to be adequate to explain the phenomena of partial reflections, it is wholly unable to

---

[12]Baltimore Lectures, page 12 (1884).
[13]Experimenta cristalli Islandici disdiaclastici (1669).

account for double refraction. In fact, it seems as though the contrary assumption would have to be made, in which the density remains fixed but the rigidity varies for different directions.

We shall not pass judgment upon the elastic theory of the ether, but its present status seems to be that of a pageant of immense historical interest only. It may be that, in the revolution of physical ideas which we are now experiencing, we shall once more return to an ether to which substantial reality by analogy with elastic matter is to be given, but that hope today seems a very remote one.

### 5. *Maxwell's Ether and the Electro-Magnetic Theory of Light.*

We turn next to the ether of James Clerk Maxwell whose great treatise on the theory of electricity and magnetism, published in 1871, clothed Faraday's tubes and fluxes of force in the garment of differential equations and led directly to the discovery of wireless communication. Maxwell was born near Edinburgh and attended both Edinburgh University and Trinity College, Cambridge, from which he came out second wrangler, the first place being held by E. J. Routh, the author of numerous works on dynamics. Maxwell then lectured at Cambridge, and later filled appointments as professor both at Aberdeen and King's College, London. He retired to private life in 1865, but in 1871 became professor of physics at Cambridge. During his short life of forty-eight years he made contributions of the very highest importance both in the kinetic theory of heat and the theory of electro-magnetism. He is, perhaps, the giant among the giants of that great age of physics.

The postulates of Maxwell's ether will now be stated:

1. The ether is *space-filling,* that is to say, it is an entity of unlimited extension.

2. The ether is so *extremely tenuous* that it pervades all matter.

3. The ether is the *seat of energy* and *conveys energy* from place to place. In Maxwell's immediate thoughts this energy was electro-magnetic in character, but the enlargement of the postulate to include all energy is certainly not contrary to the spirit of his conjectures.

Upon these postulates Maxwell erects the superb structure of his electro-magnetic theory of light. In a famous passage in his treatise Maxwell explains the concept in the following words:[14]

---

[14]Electricity and Magnetism, vol. 2, 3rd ed. (1904), p. 432.

When light is emitted, a certain amount of energy is expended by the luminous body, and if the light is absorbed by another body, this body becomes heated, showing that it has received heat from without. During the interval of time after the light left the first body and before it reached the second, it must have existed as energy in the intervening space.

According to the theory of emission, the transmission of energy is effected by the actual transference of light-corpuscles from the luminous to the illuminated body, carrying with them their kinetic energy, together with any other kind of energy of which they may be receptacles.

According to the theory of undulation, there is a material medium which fills the space between the two bodies, and it is by the action of contiguous parts of this medium that the energy is passed on, from one portion to the next, till it reaches the illuminated body.

The luminiferous medium is therefore, during the passage of light through it, a receptacle of energy. In the undulatory theory, as developed by Huygens, Fresnel, Young, Green etc., this energy is supposed to be partly potential and partly kinetic. The potential energy is supposed to be due to the distortion of the elementary portions of the medium. We must therefore regard the medium as elastic. The kinetic energy is supposed to be due to the vibratory motion of the medium. We must therefore regard the medium as having a finite density.

In the theory of electricity and magnetism adopted in this treatise, two forms of energy are recognized, the electrostatic and the electrokinetic and these are supposed to have their seat, not merely in the electrified or magnetized bodies, but in every part of the surrounding space, where electric or magnetic force is observed to act. Hence our theory agrees with the undulatory theory in assuming the existence of a medium which is capable of becoming a receptacle of two forms of energy.

In order to appreciate the full significance of these ideas one must familiarize himself with two very interesting quantities associated with matter which are called respectively the *coefficient of magnetic permeability* and the *dielectric constant*. The first of these quantities measures the susceptibility of matter to conducting lines of magnetic force. For example the magnetic permeability of iron is very much greater than that of air, because magnetic forces travel through iron much more easily than they do through air. The dielectric constant plays a similar rôle for electrical forces and is thus a measure of the capacity of a medium to conduct electrical lines of force. In more technical language the dielectric constant, or inductive capacity, as it is sometimes called, is that "quantity in an insulator which determines the charge taken by a conductor imbedded in it when charged to a given potential." In the so-called electro-magnetic units of physics the magnetic permeability for the ether is assumed to be unity and in electrostatic units the dielectric constant for the ether is also unity.

The question to which Maxwell devoted his attention was this: Does any connection exist between the magnetic permeability and the dielectric constant of the ether? Upon the basis of his postulate of an ether, capable of storing and transmitting energy, Maxwell was able to show that the square root of the reciprocal of the product of the two coefficients was of the dimensions of a velocity. But to what did this velocity belong and could any meaning be attached to such a statement?

It was the truly magnificent insight of Maxwell that led to the answer. If both the magnetic permeability and the dielectric constant are reduced to the same system of units, *the velocity just defined is numerically equal to the velocity of light.*

With this discovery the electro-magnetic theory of light was born! At last the dream of Faraday who wished to connect the mystery of light with the lines of electric and magnetic forces had become a reality. Can we wonder at the enthusiasm with which this great discovery was greeted by most of the physicists of his day? Alas, as in all other human activities, it is impossible to record a majority, for it may be doubted whether Lord Kelvin, himself ever gave the electro-magnetic theory his allegiance.[15] This identification of light with electro-magnetic forces in the metaphysical ether must rank with Newton's discovery of the gravitational origin of the tides. No higher encomium is possible than this.

But one very significant thing, in the light of the philosophical course which we pursue, must be pointed out here. The ether of Maxwell had lost a large part of its rational existence. Its density and its elasticity were no longer proper subjects of investigation. The same reason that prevented the ether of MacCullah from gaining adherents prevailed also for Maxwell's ether, with this difference that the approach to the concept had come through dielectric constants and magnetic permeabilities. It had historical dignity and conceptual reality from Faraday's tubes of force.

But the truth can not be disguised. Maxwell's ether is essentially Maxwell's set of equations; its reality resides far more in the subjective image created by these formulas than in any attempt to

---

[15]For an account of this interesting unwillingness of Lord Kelvin to accept the views of Maxwell see Thompson's: Life of Lord Kelvin (loc. cit.), p. 1024.

give it objective existence by analogy with properties of matter. This set of equations, to be sure, is derived by picturing fluxes of Faraday's tubes of force through caps over conducting circuits, and by comparing the number of lines of electric and magnetic forces which enter a given region with the number which emerge, but do these images help us in any way to describe the reality of the ether? Upon this point there may be grave doubt.

### 6.  The Ether of Stokes.

In the next chapter we shall consider the problem of the aberration of light which has been omitted from our introductory considerations. This is obviously not the place to consider the theory of the ether as it relates to the motion of material particles through it. We can, however, record the postulates of an ether which was designed by George Gabriel Stokes (1819-1903) to explain phenomena connected with the motion of ponderable bodies relative to the ether entangled with them.[16]  This ether had imperfections which were considered by H. A. Lorentz and Max Planck, both of whom suggested ways in which they should be modified.[17]

The postulates of Stokes' ether may be formulated as follows:

1.  The ether is a tenuous medium filling all space.

2.  It is the seat of energy and conveys energy from place to place by vibrations analogous to displacements in an elastic body.

3.  The ether near the earth is dragged along by it so that on the earth's surface there is an exact equivalence between the ether velocity and the velocity of the earth.

4.  At some distance from the earth the ether is at rest.

5.  The ether is *irrotational*.

This hypothesis is a very important one because of its mathematical implications, but it is difficult to explain in simple language. It means that the infinitesimal particles of which the ether may be thought to consist do not rotate. Consider for example, that the iron of a magnet is composed of an immense number of tiny magnets which in a magnetic field are able to orient themselves independently of one another in the direction of the lines of force. If the magnet thus conceived is rotated in a magnetic field all the elementary particles will also rotate, and the motion of the elements of the bar

---

[16]On the Aberration of Light, Phil. Mag. (3), vol. 27 (1845), p. 9; Mathematical and Physical Papers, vol. 1, pp. 134-140.

[17]Stoke's theory of aberration in the supposition of a variable density of the ether. Amsterdam Proceedings, (1898-1899), p. 443; also see, The Theory of Electrons, p. 173.

will be rotational. On the contrary, there will be no individual motion of the particles, if no magnetic field be present, and the rotation of the bar, thus considered, will be irrotational.

6. The ether has a variable density and at the surface of the earth is 60,000 times as dense as in empty space.

This last postulate was added by Planck to replace the postulate originally made by Stokes that the medium was incompressible, which led to a contradiction with the fifth assumption. In commenting upon this rather remarkable postulate, Lorentz makes the following statement:[18]

In this department of physics, in which we can make no progress without some hypothesis that looks somewhat startling at first sight, we must be careful not rashly to reject a new idea, and in making his suggestion Planck has certainly done a good thing. Yet I dare say that this assumption of an enormously condensed ether, combined, as it must be, with the hypothesis that the velocity of light is not in the least altered by it, is not very satisfactory. I am sure, Planck himself is inclined to prefer the unchangeable and immovable ether of Fresnel, if it can be shown that this conception can lead us to an understanding of the phenomena that have been observed.

### 7. The Wraith-Like Ether of Lorentz.

Perhaps the last formal attempt to endow an ether with consistent properties was that given by H. A. Lorentz in his "Theory of Electrons," in which the Dutch physicist returns to the original ether of Fresnel, the stagnant ocean which forms the substratum of undulatory transfers of energy. According to Lorentz the ether may be thought of as endowed with the following properties:[19]

1. The ether pervades all matter. It "not only occupies all space between molecules, atoms or electrons," but "it pervades all these particles."

2. The ether is always at rest. "We can reconcile ourselves with this, at first sight, somewhat startling idea, by thinking of the particles of matter as some local modifications in the state of the ether. These modifications may of course very well travel onward while the volume elements of the medium in which they exist remain at rest."

3. The ether is the seat of the electric and magnetic forces.

---

[18]The Theory of Electrons, pp. 173-174.
[19]The Theory of Electrons, p. 11.

4. The ether has none of the properties of an elastic solid. It possesses neither mass, density, nor elasticity.

5. It has no structure.

6. It cannot be experienced sensuously except as it serves as a medium for the propagation of energy.

7. It is not a framework by means of which we can measure the velocities of material particles.

When one reflects carefully on these postulates he is struck by their negative character. The material ether has disappeared and we are left with an approximately metaphysical entity. As one reflects on the gradual dissipation of the material properties of the ether from the vigorous elastic medium of Cauchy to the thin wraith of Lorentz, he is reminded of Mark Twain's description of the vanishing of the "Mysterious Stranger.":

He thinned away and thinned away until he was a soapbubble, except that he kept his shape. You could see the bushes through him as clearly as you see things through a soapbubble, and all over him played and flashed the delicate iridescent colors of the bubble, and along with them was that thing shaped like a window-sash which you always see on the globe of the bubble. You have seen a bubble strike the carpet and lightly bound along two or three times before it bursts. He did that. He sprang—touched the grass— bounded—floated along—touched again—and so on, and presently exploded—puff! and in his place was vacancy.

Is there any physical reality to the Lorentz ether? Does it exist in any sense? Have we the same degree of physical apprehension of it that we have for the concepts of entropy, or action? The only answer that the writer knows to this delicate question is best expressed in the following brief debate between two masters of modern physical science:

H. A. LORENTZ: (For the affirmative) I cannot but regard the ether, which can be the seat of an electromagnetic field with its energy and its vibrations, as endowed with a certain degree of substantiality, however different it may be from all ordinary matter.[20]

L. SILBERSTEIN: (For the negative) One fails to see what properties, in fact, it (the Lorentz ether) still has left to it, besides that of being a colorless seat (we cannot even say substratum) of the electro-magnetic vectors. . . . The ether, having been deprived of many of its precious properties, was at any rate already so nearly non-substantial, that the first blow it had to sustain from modern re-

---

[20]The Theory of Electrons, p. 230.

search knocked it out of existence altogether. . . . Still, substantial or not, for the theory of Lorentz we are now considering, it is *something*, namely its unique system of reference. So long, therefore, as it was thought that there is such a unique system, Lorentz's all-pervading medium could continue its scanty existence.[21]

## 8. *The Ether as the Primary Atom.*

In the foregoing history of attempts to construct an ether we have held strictly to the physical point of view, in which our attention is sharply focused upon the problem of how energy gets from the sun to the earth through the high vacuum of interstellar space. It would not be entirely out of place to record another concept, which turns our thoughts toward chemical aspects of the problem.

This novel picture of the ether was given by that distinguished discoverer of the periodic properties of the elements Dmitri Ivanovich Mendeléeff (1834-1907). However novel his speculations may seem, we must remember that Mendeléeff's reputation rests upon his power of prophecy, and one can not wholly discredit the speculations of such a man, founded as they are upon his rich experiences during the great years of the nineteenth century.

Mendeléeff was born at Tobolsk, Siberia, the youngest of seventeen children. At the age of twenty-two he went to St. Petersburg to study natural science and from thence to Heidelberg in 1860, where he started a laboratory of his own. Returning to St. Petersburg the following year he became professor of chemistry in the technological institute of that city in 1863. In 1890 he resigned his professorship to become director of the Bureau of Weights and Measures three years later, a position that he held until his death, in 1907, the same year that saw the passing of Lord Kelvin.

Mendeléeff's chief renown rests upon his discovery of the periodic law of the elements. He had noticed that when the elements were arranged according to the size of their atomic weights they naturally fell into groups and series, those in each group having similar properties. Thus the chemical properties of lithium, sodium, and potassium as one triad, or chlorine, bromine, and iodine as another, are very similar, and the atomic weight of the middle element in each is approximately the average of the atomic weights of the other two. A. E. B. de Chancourtois, who anticipated Mendeléeff in some aspects of the periodic theory, thought of the elements as being ar-

[21]The Theory of Relativity, 2nd ed. (1924), London, p. 42.

ranged on a helix, those in each group being similarly situated upon it. The great achievement of Mendeléeff was his prediction and description of three new elements to fill vacancies in his table. These elements, to which he gave the names ekaboron, ekaaluminum, and ekasilicon, were discovered within fifteen years after their prediction, gallium in 1871, scandium in 1879, and germanium in 1886. The greatest book written by Mendeléeff was his "Principles of Chemistry," which has had many editions and has been translated into numerous languages.

The ether of the Russian chemist grew out of a strong conviction that ether was a material entity and the primary element of nature. He did not mean by this that the ether was to be regarded as "the constituent principle out of which the chemical atoms are formed," but rather as itself the first of the elements, indivisible and untransmutable. Mendeléeff was somewhat loath to publish this novel idea, and it was not until 1902, when advancing years forced him to the issue, that he undertook to give a systematic development of his postulate.[22]

His position is explained in the following quotation:

If ether were producible from atoms and atoms could be built up from ether, the formation of new unlooked-for atoms and the disappearance of portions of the elements during experiment would be possible. A belief in such a possibility has long been held in the minds of many by force of superstition; and the more recent researches of Emmens to convert silver into gold, and those of Fittica (1900) to prove that phosphorus can be transformed into arsenic, show that it yet exists. In the fifty years during which I have carefully followed the records of chemistry, I have met with many such instances, but they have always proved unfounded. It is not my purpose to defend the independent individuality of the chemical elements, but I am forced to refer to it in speaking of the ether, for it seems to me that, besides being chemically invalid, it is impossible to conceive of ether as a primary substance, because such a substance should have some mass or weight and also chemical relations—mass in order to explain the majority of phenomena proceeding at all distances to the infinitely great, and chemical relations in order to explain those proceeding at distances infinitely small or commensurable with the atoms.[23]

The ether of Mendeléeff has the following properties:

1. It is a gas, like helium or argon, incapable of chemical combination with any element.

---

[22] Principles of Chemistry, Appendix 3, An Attempt towards a Chemical Conception of the Ether, Third English edition, (1905), vol. 2, pp. 509-529.
[23] P. 512.

If the ether is a gas it must have weight, but its power of penetrating all matter is so great that it is impossible to determine its mass experimentally. "It does not require the recognition of a peculiar fourth state (of matter) beyond the human understanding (Crookes). All mystical, spiritual ideas about ether disappear."

2. It is the lightest gas with a high penetrating power and an extremely high velocity.

Mendeléeff does not attempt to place his new element in the series with hydrogen but invents a new series of zero-th order and calls the ether element the unknown "x." He calculates its atomic weight to be between $9.6 \times 10^{-7}$ and $5.3 \times 10^{-11}$, where the atomic weight of hydrogen is assumed to be unity. He discards the second value in favor of the first for the very interesting reason, in view of our recent quantum theory of energy, that "it would in some measure answer to a revival of the emission theory of light." Adopting the first value, an atomic weight approximately one millionth that of hydrogen, the atoms of the new element would have the considerable velocity of about 2250 kilometers (1400 miles) per second.

Can these views be thought of as only those of a bright imagination, colored by a periodic view of the elements of nature, or is there any basis for scientific credence in this age of bewildering mystery? It appears to the writer that there is something quite prophetic, when we reflect upon the quantum theory and cosmic radiation, in the following passage of the noted chemist:[24]

It seems to me that the optical and photo-radiant phenomena, not to mention the loss of electrical charges, indicate a material flow of something which has not been weighed, and it appears to me that they might be understood in this manner, for peculiar forms of the entrance and egress of ether atoms should be accompanied by such disturbances in the etherial medium as give the phenomena of light.

## 9. *Is there an Ether?*

We have now surveyed hastily and without the aid of mathematics, that bright torch of truth, some of the most important theories of the ether. These theories excepting that of Mendeléeff, have been subjected to the searching scrutiny of calculation and laboratory data. From them, one by one, their material properties have been gradually removed until but a shadow connects them with sensuous experience. The ether of Lorentz preserves its existence

---

[24]Loc. cit., p. 528.

as an imperative of human reason, which demands that something must exist for the conveyance of energy from place to place and for the possibility of conceiving lines and tubes of force.

The aim of this book is to exhibit the metaphysical character of the postulates of material science. Certainly the baffling problem of the ether forces this sharply upon us. During the early years of the nineteenth century there was a certain tangible reality in the ether because the difference between its properties and the properties of ordinary matter was merely one of degree. Today scarcely a vestige of this shadowy reality remains, and yet the physical entities that led to its invention cry out for some kind of rational explanation, which appears to be denied them.

Do we want to believe in action at a distance or forces which work through the medium of a complete vacuum? Do we want to believe that energies flow from place to place without the intervention of any kind of transmitting medium? What shall we say about the potential energy of the lifted stone or the electrical energy of the Leyden jar? Is the curious concept of action which the earth minimizes in its annual swing around the sun, to be regarded as a thing without a real existence? What shall we say about the Foucault pendulum and its evidence of the existence of a cosmic inertial frame?

Are we seeing mysteries where there are none? I think not. The problem may be resolved, perhaps, by assuming a new definition of reality. Is it necessary for a physical entity, in order to have reality, to be sensuous or even to have an analogy with material things? If we are willing to answer this question in the negative, then we have committed ourselves to what may be regarded as a metaphysical philosophy. To be sure we must look at the methods of the mathematicians and safeguard our concepts by a lower bound beyond which we shall not go, else this admission will involve us in all manner of esoteric mysticisms.

Let us, for example, state as a basis for the new metaphysics the postulate that physical entities may exist which are of transcendental character in the sense that they can not be explained on the basis of analogies with material objects or other models of sensuous character. Let us require, however, that any proposition in the new physics which has no sensuous basis for reality must be capable of a mathematical formulization the implications of which can be reduced to terms that may be checked with experimental evidence. In other words, let us assume that the ether of Maxwell is identical with the equations of Maxwell and has objective reality only in so far as these equations check with the data of experience. Newton's action at a distance is Newton's potential function, out of which flow the long formulas of Leverrier and Simon Newcomb, with their prediction of the motions of the planets.

Have we asked too much, or is there still a craving of the human spirit for a closer bond with the mysterious forces and the radiant energies of phenomena? In the next chapter we shall further explore the postulate of an ether as it relates to the problem of matter in motion, and perhaps we can see through the glass a little less darkly than at the present time.

# CHAPTER IV.

## DOES MATTER DRAG THE ETHER?

### 1. *Huygens and the Wave Theory of Light.*

THE wise Sir Francis Bacon (1561-1626) in his essay on Truth paraphrases Lucretius in the following words:

It is a pleasure to stand upon the shore and to see ships tossed upon the sea; a pleasure to stand in the window of a castle, and to see a battle and the adventures thereof below: but no pleasure is comparable to the standing upon the vantage ground of Truth, and to see the errors, and wandering, and mists, and tempests, in the vale below.

In the pages of the last chapter, from the vantage point of time, we have reviewed the heroic struggle of those who would endow the ether with the properties of a material substance. At present these efforts have seemed to be without avail. Like the action at a distance of Newton, the action of Maupertuis, and the entropy of Clausius, the reality of this physical entity is elusive. On the assumption of an elastic ether every postulate with regard to density, elasticity, and rigidity led to contradiction with experiment. The ether of Stokes and Planck had to be 60,000 times as dense at the surface of the earth as it was in empty space; the ether of Maxwell was merely the seat of electro-magnetic forces and their energy; its reality consisted in a set of equations; the ether of Lorentz had become a sort of spectral entity the tangible properties of which were its extension and its ability to convey energy from place to place.

In this chapter we shall look at the problem from another angle. Let us postulate an ether, and endow it with but a single property, namely that of undulation. We frankly confess that this leads us face to face with a dilemma. We may either conceive of a thing that has no substantive being but yet has the ability to propagate a wave, or we may postulate that energy gets about according to mathematical laws of our subjective creation. The second possibility has been repellent to rational philosophy until recently, but on the assumption that, like the arsenic eaters of the Alps, one can get used to anything, there seems to be a more general acceptance of this metaphysical position.

The whole situation reminds one of the embarrassing circumstance in which Alice once found herself while adventuring through the looking glass. She had met Humpty Dumpty, and wanting to make a pleasing impression upon the stranger, discovered that she was facing a dilemma of first magnitude.

"What a beautiful belt you've got on!" Alice suddenly remarked. . . . "At least," she corrected herself on second thought, "a beautiful cravat, I should have said—no, a belt, I mean—I beg your pardon!" she added in dismay, for Humpty Dumpty looked thoroughly offended, and she began to wish she hadn't chosen that subject. "If I only knew," she thought to herself, "which was neck and which was waist!"

In the last chapter little was said about the rival theories of light propagation and the optical properties of moving bodies. It was, in truth, the struggle between the undulatory theory of the Dutch physicist Christian Huygens (1629-1695) and the corpuscular theory of Sir Isaac Newton that forced the concept of the ether into scientific thinking. Has the struggle ceased? Today the supreme effort of those who seek to match their formulas against the evidence of the laboratory is to decide between the corpuscular theory (now called the quantum theory) and the wave theory of energy. One of America's physicists recently pictured the struggle as a football game, but he might appear unduly optimistic to some in regarding the game as now being in its fourth quarter.

Huygens, who was born at The Hague, received his early education from his father, later studied at Leiden under Frans Van Schooten, and completed his formal discipline in the juridical school at Breda. Some of his early work fell into the hands of Descartes, who predicted a brilliant future for him. In 1660 and 1663 he went to Paris and to London and in 1666 he accepted a flattering offer from Louis XIV to make his residence in Paris. From then until 1681 he resided in the stimulating atmosphere of the Bibliotheque du Roi, where many of his ideas were developed. He returned to his native city in 1681 partly from considerations of health and partly because of the revocation of the Edict of Nantes. The interests of Huygens were many and varied. He improved the telescope of Galileo by partly overcoming chromatic aberration, and with it discovered the sixth satellite of Saturn and explained the varying appearance of the planet as due to a ring. He studied the nebula

of Orion and invented the pendulum clock. His magnum opus was
the "Horologium oscillatorium," published in 1673, but his chief
renown rests upon a little volume entitled a "Traité de la lumière,"
completed in 1678 but not published until 1690. In this beautiful
little treatise he elaborates the undulatory theory of light which had
already been advanced by Robert Hooke (1635-1703) in 1668 and by
Ignace Pardies (1636-1673) in 1672, and states that fundamental
law of optics which is now known under his name.

The theory of the undulatory character of light assumes that light
is propagated in waves. In the early history of the theory, as has
already been explained in the preceding chapter, the waves were
regarded as similar to those of sound which are longitudinal. But
in the later theory they were thought of as transverse vibrations such
as may be created in the deformation of rigid elastic bodies. The
old question persists: In what are these waves moving?

Huygens, the chief exponent of the wave theory in the early
history of the subject, explains his postulates in the following words:

It is inconceivable to doubt that light consists in the motion of
some sort of matter. For whether one considers its production, one
sees that here upon the earth it is chiefly engendered by fire and
flame which contain without doubt bodies that are in rapid motion,
since they dissolve and melt many other bodies, even the most solid
bodies; or whether one considers its effect, one sees that when light
is connected, as by concave mirrors, it has the properties of burning
as the fire does, that is to say it disunites the particles of bodies. This
is assuredly the mark of motion, at least in the true philosophy, in
which one conceives the causes of all natural effects in terms of
mechanical motions. This, in my opinion, we must necessarily do,
or else renounce all hopes of ever comprehending anything in physics.

And as, according to this philosophy, one holds as certain that
the sensation of sight is excited only by the impression of some
movement of a kind of matter which acts on the nerves at the back
of our eyes, there is here yet one reason more for believing that
light consists in a movement of matter which exists between us and
the luminous body.

Further, when one considers the extreme speed with which light
spreads on every side, and how, when it comes from different regions,
even from those directly opposite, the rays traverse one another
without hindrance, one may well understand that when we see a
luminous object, it cannot be by any transport of matter coming to
us from this object, in the way in which a shot or an arrow traverses
the air; for assuredly that would too greatly impugn these two
properties of light especially the second of them. It is then in some
other way that light spreads; and that which can lead us to compre-

hend it is the knowledge which we have of the spreading of sound in the air.[1]

Huygens' principle which seems to have come unscathed through the modern scrutiny of first principles merely asserts that each element of a wave front progressing through a uniform medium is to be itself regarded as the origin of a secondary wave, and the wave front which represents the total disturbance is the envelope of all these secondary disturbances. This happy thought allowed Huygens to explain refraction and reflection, where his contemporaries had failed.

## 2. The Corpuscular Theory of Light.

The corpuscular theory, on the other hand, assumes that light consists of tiny pellets or corpuscles shot out with the velocity of 186,000 miles per second from the radiating source. Today we have slightly changed the theory by calling the corpuscles "quanta" and we regard them as bits of energy rather than as small material particles.

The chief exponent of the corpuscular or emission theory of light was Newton, who, however, curiously enough, postulated the existence of an ether at the same time that he rejected the undulatory theory of Hooke and Huygens.[2] With Newton there existed an all pervading ether capable of propagating vibrations; its density was conceived of as variable, being greatest in inter-stellar space. But the vibrations can not be thought of as light, because of difficulties which he saw in explaining rectilinear propagation on this hypothesis. Therefore he conceived of light as being "something of a different kind propagated from lucid bodies. They that will, may suppose it an aggregate of various peripatetic qualities. Others may suppose it multitudes of unimaginable small and swift corpuscles of various sizes, springing from shining bodies at great distances one after another; but yet without any sensible interval of time, and continually urged forward by a principle of motion, which in the beginning accelerates them, till the resistance of the etherial medium equals the force of that principle, much after the manner that bodies let fall in water are accelerated till the resistance of the water equals the force of gravity. But they that like not this, may suppose light any other

---

[1] Treatise on Light, translated by Silvanus P. Thompson (1912), pp. 3-4.
[2] Extracts from Newton's "Opticks" are reproduced by T. Preston in his "Theory of Light," 3d ed. London (1901), pp. 20-21, to "show how much more closely than is generally supposed" Newton's theory of light resembles the undulatory theory now accepted.

corporeal emanation, or any impulse or motion of any other medium or etherial spirit diffused through the main body of ether, or what else they can imagine proper for this purpose. To avoid dispute, and make this hypothesis general, let every man here take his fancy; only whatever light be, I suppose it consists of rays differing from one another in contingent circumstances, as bigness, form, or vigour."[3]

### 3. *The Phenomenon of Interference.*

The eighteenth century saw the almost complete triumph of the emission theory, supported as it was by the authority of Newton. But at the end of that century and during the early years of the next a tremendous revolution started, which caused a complete reversal of the situation. Thomas Young (1773-1829), a native of Somersetshire, England, and trained in medicine, commenced to advance the wave theory in a series of papers dating from 1799. The famous contribution made by Young was his suggestion of the phenomena of interference.

Borrowing an illustration used in a similar connection by Newton, Young explains his ideas in the following historic passage:

Suppose a number of equal waves of water to move upon the surface of a stagnant lake, with a certain constant velocity, and to enter a narrow channel leading out of the lake; suppose then another similar cause to have excited another equal series of waves, which arrive at the same channel, with the same velocity, and at the same time with the first. Neither series of waves will destroy the other, but their effects will be combined; if they enter the channel in such a manner that the elevations of one series coincide with those of the other, they must together produce a series of greater joint elevations; but if the elevations of one series are so situated as to correspond to the depressions of the other, they must exactly fill up those depressions, and the surface of the water remain smooth. Now I maintain that similar effects take place whenever two portions of light are thus mixed; and this I call the general law of the *interference* of light.[4]

The phenomenon of interference can be witnessed by anyone who will drop two stones into a smooth body of water. The waves from the two sources spread out with a certain velocity in two circles, which finally join and break up into crests and valleys of varying heights and depths. There is in point an interesting note taken from

---

[3]Royal Society, Dec. 9, 1675.
[4]Young's Works, vol. 1, p. 202.

the diary of William Thomson, later Lord Kelvin, which was written while on a continental tour when he was sixteen years of age:[5]

Reached the bar at the mouth of the Maas, near Brill, at about 4 1/2 o'clock in the morning, where we had to lie until 10. The vessel rolled greatly from side to side, but the rolling was intermittent, as every two or three minutes it calmed down and then rose again with perfect regularity. This probably arose from two sets of waves of slightly different lengths coming in in the same direction from two different sources.

Those who have ever had the hardihood to take a canoe out on a lake when it is rough will know that the skill in the sport consists in being able to guess the time and amplitude of those great, wet rollers which are the culmination of a series of little waves. And just as water waves tend to amplify and annul one another when crests and valleys coincide, so also will light waves (if such things really exist) intensify and interfere with one another.

The ideas of Young did not, however, meet with cordial response in England, and a fierce attack launched in the Edinburgh Review by Henry Brougham, afterwards Lord Chancellor of England, successfully discredited the new theory of interference.

The case was otherwise in France, however, for Young's concept was thoroughly explored in a series of brilliant memoirs by Augustin Fresnel (1788-1827). The story is one of the dramas of the history of science. Fresnel had had the good fortune to be opposed politically to Napoleon and when the latter returned from the island of Elba in 1815 for his celebrated hundred day sojourn in the empire, Fresnel was given a period of enforced idleness. O solitude, "the best nurse of wisdom"! how little we appreciate your virtues! In these later days our Voltaires and Fresnels are allowed to waste their genius in the activities of modern life; Swift's paradox that a "wise man is never less alone than when he is alone" has seldom been realized by those who might somewhere endow sanctuaries consecrated to seclusion. It is well occasionally to reflect that Newton's greatest work was done when the plague drove him away from Cambridge.

But to return to our story. During this period of arrest, Fresnel busied himself with the wave theory of light and in an early memoir advanced a theory of diffraction similar to that of Young. By a diffraction phenomenon we mean an optical phenomenon caused by a deviation in the rectilinear propagation of light. For example, if

---

[5] Life of Lord Kelvin (loc. cit.), vol. 1, p. 16.

a ray of light passes through a small opening or past the edge of an opaque obstacle there will appear slight deviations in its path. The first observations on diffraction were made by F. M. Grimaldi (1618-1663), who had noticed that there was some illumination within the geometrical shadow of an opaque body.[6] Newton had repeated with a little variation the experiment of Grimaldi and had observed the iris-colored bands which bordered the image of two knife edges set very close together, between which light is transmitted to a screen.

Young had attempted to explain diffraction on the basis of his interference theory by assuming that there was interference between the light which passed very close to the knife edges and that which was reflected from them. Fresnel also fell into this error in his first paper,[7] but not satisfied with his explanation he reexamined the theory and in 1816 presented to the Academy a supplement to his original paper, in which the real explanation was made,[8] namely, that the diffraction phenomena are due to the interferences between the secondary waves emitted from the unobstructed part of the original wave. His calculations were made on the basis of Huygens' principle.

## 4. The Diffraction of Light.

In the meantime the corpuscular theory had gained new vigor from an explanation on dynamical principles of the double refraction phenomenon in Iceland spar, this explanation having been advanced by no less a person than Pierre Simon Laplace (1749-1827) who was then at the height of his mental vigor and influence. The Academy, hoping to establish the corpuscular theory beyond further criticism, proposed "Diffraction" as the subject of the prize to be awarded in 1818.

Fresnel, under this spur, developed his theory with great vigor and presented his ideas in a large memoir in 1818 for the prize of the Academy.[9] The judges, however, were three ardent advocates of the corpuscular theory, Laplace, Poisson, and Biot, and to face such a committee with a manuscript following the tradition of Huygens and Young seemed like a joust with windmills. However, the mathematical ability of Poisson in reality won the victory for the

---

[6]In a posthumous work entitled: Physico-mathesis de lumine, coloribus, et iride. Bologna (1665). In particular, see Book 1, prop. 1.

[7]Annales de Chemie (2), i (1816), p. 239; also Oeuvres complètes d'Augustin Fresnel, Paris (1866), in three vols. with introduction by Emile Verdet (1824-1866), vol. 1, p. 89.

[8]Oeuvres, vol. 1, p. 129.

[9]Mémoire de l'Académie, vol. 5 (1826), p. 339; Oeuvres, vol. 1, p. 247.

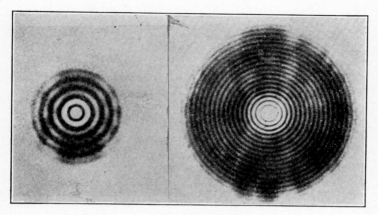

PLATE IV

Patterns made by light diffracted around steel spheres. The Arago white spot is to be seen in the center of each pattern. From the Physical Review, vol. 7 (1916), p. 548.
(a)                                    (b)

 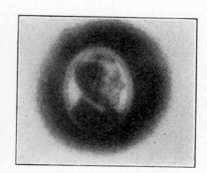

PLATE V

Picture (b) is a reproduction of (a) made by diffracting the light around a steel ball. From the Physical Review, vol. 3 (1914), p. 242.

young theorist. While reading the manuscript Poisson noticed that the methods of Fresnel could be extended to the case of diffraction by an opaque disk, and he easily showed that if the path of a ray of light were occulted by such an obstacle there would appear in the exact center of the shadow a white spot whose intensity would equal the intensity of the incident ray.

What a breathless moment in the history of science! Was not this *reductio ad absurdum* of the great Poisson the very weapon to turn upon the hosts of the corpuscular army? The experiment was made by Arago, and there in the center of the shadow of the disk was the white spot predicted by Poisson. The prize was given to Fresnel.

The two patterns appearing in Plate IV were made by light which diffracted around steel spheres placed in the path of the incident beam.[10] The white spot which so discomfited the proponents of the corpuscular theory is clearly exhibited in the center of the discs. The second set of pictures (Plate V) shows a photographic transparency of the war president (a) from which was made a diffraction photograph (b) in which the usual lens of the camera was replaced by a steel ball. How the early theorists would have marvelled to know that some day actual photographs would be made with a ball of steel placed directly across the path of the beam of light.

The consequences of diffraction have, of course, been thoroughly explored in the later history of the subject. Eugene von Lommel (1837-1899), in a series of classic papers, reduced many of the diffraction problems to calculation and was able to show the exact correspondence between mathematical principles and objective experiment.[11]

The question always lurks in the background of physical speculation, however, that if matters could only be pushed a few decimal places further, then the discrepancy between the theory and its application would be revealed. In Newton's theory of universal gravitation the behaviour of the planet Mercury has been a disturbing element. Why should that smallest of the planets, swinging in its rapid course about the sun, present an anomaly difficult to account for on the hypothesis of Newton's laws? Why does its perihelion advance 43 seconds per century, so that the time of Mercury's transits across the face of the sun fails to accord with the exact calculations

---

[10]M. E. Hufford: Some New Diffraction Photographs, Physical Review, vol. 3, 2nd ser. (1914), pp. 241-243.

[11]Die Beugungserscheinungen einer kreisrunden Öffnung und eines kreisrunden Schirmchens, Abb. der K. Bayer, Akad. der Wissenschaften, vol. 15 (1884), pp. 233-328.

of Leverrier and Newcomb, based upon the mathematical theory into which the slight perihelion correction has not been introduced? While this discrepancy exists, unexplained by the discovery of the planet Vulcan or by some other plausible disturbance within the reach of Newton's theory, there will always be a reasonable doubt as to the limits to which his assumptions can be applied.

What is the story with regard to diffraction and the wave theory of light? Recent calculations have been made to check the radii of a

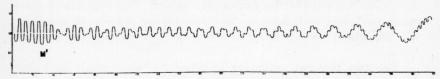

FIG. 2

Diagram showing the structure of a diffraction pattern. The horizontal axis corresponds to the radius of the photograph with the center at the point zero. The vertical axis measures the intensity of the light and dark bands of the pattern.

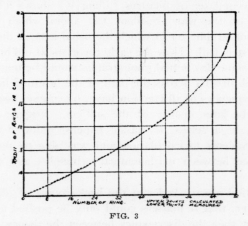

FIG. 3

Diagram showing the striking agreement between theory and experiment in the case of diffraction. The measured and calculated radii of the diffraction rings of the pattern form a single line.

pattern of seventy rings, made by diffracting light through a circular orifice.[12] The details of the experiment are very simple. A tiny pin point of monochromatic light is placed at one end of a tube 106 feet in length and the resulting beam is allowed to fall upon a photographic plate at the other end. Midway between the source and the screen is set a metal plate containing a hole slightly more than an

[12]The Diffraction of Light by a Circular Opening and the Lommel Wave Theory, M. E. Hufford and H. T. Davis, Physical Review, vol. 33 (2nd ser.) (1929), pp. 589-597.

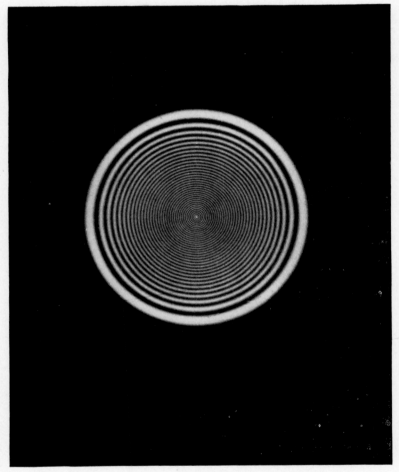

PLATE VI

inch in diameter, through which the beam passes and from whose edges it is diffracted. The beautiful pattern with its seventy rings is reproduced in the accompanying photograph, Plate VI. But the question in which we are interested is this: Do the position and intensity of the rings accord with the theory of Fresnel? The answer is contained in the two accompanying diagrams (figures 2 and 3). In the first of these the intensity on the vertical axis is computed for every value of the radius of the plate on the horizontal axis. That is to say the value marked zero corresponds to the center of the diffraction pattern and the last value recorded on the horizontal axis corresponds to the final darkening of the plate at the outer edge of the ring system. The vertical axis measures the intensity of the light creating the rings, a dark band on the diffraction photograph corresponding to a crest of the irregular curve and a light band corresponding to a hollow. The tiny undulations which make up the later rings are evidence of the fine structure of the pattern, although these small variations in the intensity are masked in the actual photograph because of the long exposure required to produce the picture.

And what is the answer to our question? Does the Fresnel picture of the wave correspond with the actual facts investigated over so long a range? The second diagram shows the exceptional agreement between the radii measured from the actual diffraction pattern and the radii computed from the crests and hollows of the intensity diagram. We may thus conclude that the wave theory of diffraction, regarded as a purely subjective creation, agrees with remarkable exactness with the objective experiments.

But the old question persists: Does this prove that there is an ether? Was Lorentz correct when he said that, for all the arguments of his contemporaries, he still felt that there was an objective reality to the ether concept? Does diffraction prove it or does diffraction only increase our bewilderment, as we try to organize the phenomena of the world on a basis agreeing with rational intuitions? Can the ether, robbed of all of its substantive properties and endowed with a transcendental function in which our measure of belief merely depends upon our inability to believe anything else, be regarded as belonging to the domain of reality?

### 5. *The Puzzle of Aberration.*

Having discussed the controversy between the wave theory and the corpuscular theory of light, we shall now turn to a brief review of several experiments which have had a profound influence upon the progress of physical science.

The first of these was the discovery in 1728 by James Bradley (1692-1762) of the *angle of aberration*.[13]  If one goes out in a rain when there is no wind, he must, nevertheless, hold his umbrella in front of him to keep from getting wet.  The drops of rain, which are in reality falling straight down, appear to be approaching at an angle due to the fact that one is in motion.  As a matter of fact if the velocity of the falling rain drops were known one could actually calculate his walking speed from the angle at which the rain appears to strike his umbrella.  This is the phenomenon of aberration which is often illustrated by the picture of a ball thrown through the window of a moving car.  If the car is moving fast enough the ball will enter a window in the front and will pass out through a window in the rear.  To a passenger its path will appear to have been a diagonal across the car.

In exactly the same way a ray of light from a distant star appears to come into the atmosphere of the earth at an angle with the star's true position due to the motion of the earth through space.  Of course, if the earth had not been moving in an ellipse, this fact would never have been discovered, because the angle of aberration would always have been a constant and would have forever eluded our efforts to detect it.  It was only discovered when Bradley found that the star Gamma in the head of the constellation of the Dragon which had appeared in one direction at Christmas time was in a different direction in July.

At first Bradley was much perplexed over this discovery of the apparent displacement of the stars at different times in the year, until he casually observed a flag floating at the mast head of a ship; when the ship changed its course, the flag flew in a different direction. Hence the explanation of the cause of aberration as due to the elliptical motion of the earth in space occurred to him.

This illustration of the flag is an example of the force of little things and the power of elementary analogies.  One of the impressive facts in science is this ability of the race to make progress in the explanation of mysterious phenomena by models of simple things. Lord Kelvin devised his vortex theory of the atom, one of the excitements of the latter years of the last century, by observing the behaviour of rings of smoke.  You are familiar with the story of

---

[13]Account of the new discovered motion of the Fix'd Stars, Phil. Trans., vol. 35 (1728), p. 637.

Archimedes and his discovery of the specific gravity of metals by his loss of weight in the bath tub. What a pity that some one in the early days of science did not reflect upon the vortical behaviour of water flowing out of a bowl! He might well have wondered how the elementary parts of the fluid were able to decide which way to whirl. The situation would have appealed to him as similar to that of Buridan's ass which starved between two equal mounds of hay. Reflections based upon this very elementary experiment might have led to the discovery of the rotation of the earth. One sometimes wonders how many other simple things there are around us which could, by analogy, be built up into beautiful structures of constructive thought.

Let us pause here just a moment to see what a remarkable fact this discovery of aberration is. In the last chapter it was shown how Galileo might have proved an absolute rotation of the earth by means of a pendulum suspended from the dome of a cathedral and set in vibration over a piece of ruled paper on the floor. What a marvellous fact he could have deduced from Bradley's constant of aberration. Focusing his telescope upon Polaris in December and again in July he would have been able to bring incontrovertible evidence to show that the earth moved about the sun. Perhaps some of the humiliation of that early science could have been avoided by this one fact.

In the early days much weight was thrown against the Copernican theory that the earth moved around the sun because the so-called parallax of the stars could not be measured. By the annual or heliocentric parallax we mean the angle ⊙ S E where ⊙ is the sun, S the star and E the earth. This angle is so exceedingly small that a stellar parallax was not measured until 1838, when F. W. Bessel found one for 61 Cygni.[14] The largest known parallax is that for Alpha Centauri, which has a parallax of .76″, thus being at a distance of 4.3 light years from the earth. The angle of aberration, on the other hand has a magnitude of 20.″47, which, as you see, is of an entirely different nature from the angle of parallax. Parallax depends upon the relative distance between two bodies; the angle of aberration depends upon an absolute revolution only. Let us suppose that the sun, the moon, the planets and all the stars were blotted from the sky, but let one beam of light be started somewhere in the universe. From this one external source of energy, Galileo might

---

[14]See a letter from Professor Bessel to Sir J. Herschel, Oct. 23, 1838, Monthly Notices of the Royal Astronomical Soc., vol. 4, pp. 152-161.

have demonstrated that the earth had something corresponding to an absolute revolution in space. This is a poetic thought and one perhaps as mysterious as the absolute rotation which we discussed in the last chapter. In other words, we are again faced by the question of revolution about what? Can it be that these phenomena of the revolution and rotation of the earth are but evidences of a mysterious relationship of matter with a seat of energy which we have called the ether?

In the days of Bradley the corpuscular theory of light was then the accepted theory and stellar aberration was easily explained by the analogies just cited. When the wave theory commenced to gain the upper hand, under the researches of Young and Fresnel, the situation assumed a different aspect, and the question was immediately asked how a ray transmitted by vibrations in the ether could be affected by the elliptical motion of the earth. The analogy of the man in the rain storm no longer had force. The answer to the question may be stated thus: If we are willing to admit a stagnant ether, that is to say, an ether which never moves and is unaffected by the motion of the earth through it, then it is possible to explain aberration just as well on the wave theory as on the corpuscular postulate. Unfortunately the proof of this statement is mathematical and must be omitted. We should carefully note this fact, however, that to explain aberration we are partly committed to what is called the "stagnant ether" theory. In the last chapter when we were not concerned with the optical properties of moving bodies this postulate was not advanced, but the phenomenon of aberration brings it clearly into view. Young has picturesquely put the concept in the following words:[15]

Upon considering the aberration of the stars, I am disposed to believe that the luminiferous ether pervades the substance of all material bodies with little or no resistance, as freely perhaps as the wind passes through a grove of trees.

In commenting upon this statement, Silberstein remarks: "This picturesque analogy fitted altogether the case of air, which behaves very nearly like a vacuum, but not glass or water, for which the 'grove of trees' had to be replaced by a rather dense thicket."[16]

Hence the critical phenomenon of aberration when applied to the movement of the earth as determined from the light of the stars

---

[15]Experiments and Calculations relative to physical optics, Philosophical Transactions (1804), pp. 1-16, in particular p. 12.
[16]Theory of Relativity (1924), p. 35.

could be explained equally well on either the wave theory or the corpuscular postulate. Any one left to choose between the two theories on the basis of this phenomenon alone would, we believe, have chosen the latter, since it is so much easier on intuitional grounds to think of light in terms of rapidly moving material particles than as a transverse vibration in a metaphysical medium.

## 6. Does Matter Drag the Ether?

However, an unexpected and brilliant victory was soon to be won by the forces under the banner of the wave theory. The question was asked: What would happen to the aberration angle if one used a telescope whose tube was filled with water rather than with air? As anyone knows who has ever tried to spear fish, light bends when it enters an optical medium which is denser than air. Should there not, therefore, be found a difference in the angle of aberration due to the fact that the speed of light in water is less than it is in air? This very reasonable view led to experimentation by Arago, who found no change in the aberration constant for the case of glass,[17] and in 1871 by Sir G. B. Airy (1801-1892), royal astronomer at Greenwich, who tested the water telescope with the same result.[18]

What strange phenomenon was this? Arago, as a member of the corpuscular party, was much perplexed and his attempt at an explanation drove him to a curious hypothesis. He conceived that the source of light sends out particles with an infinity of different velocities but that out of these none but one endowed with a certain velocity has the power of exciting our sense of sight. Hence, if a swarm of particles fell upon the telescope full of water, they would all be retarded to a certain extent, and those particles which had been traveling too rapidly in the air telescope to affect our sense of sight would now move down into the visible region. This strange hypothesis soon involved Arago in a maze of difficulties from which he could not extricate himself, and he wrote a letter to Fresnel. Fresnel's reply is one of the famous documents in physical literature and part of it is quoted below:[19]

---

[17]See Biot: Astro. Phys., 3d ed., v, p. 364.

[18]On a supposed alteration of the amount of Astronomical Aberration of Light produced by the passage of the Light through a considerable thickness of Refracting Medium, Proc. Royal Soc. of London, vol. 20, pp. 35-39.

[19]Lettre d'Augustin Fresnel à François Arago, sur l'influence du mouvement terrestre dans quelques phénomènes d'optique, Annales de Chem. et de Phys., vol. 9, p. 57, cahier de septembre, 1818; Oeuvres, vol. 2, Paris (1868), pp. 627-636. See also Silberstein's "Theory of Relativity, pp. 60-62.

Through your beautiful experiments upon the light of the stars, you have proved that the movement of the earth has no sensible influence upon the reflection of rays which come from the stars. . . .

You have asked me to examine the question whether the result of these observations can be reconciled more easily with the system which makes light consist of vibrations in a universal fluid. It is all the more necessary to give the explanation in this theory, since it ought to apply equally well to terrestrial objects; for the velocity with which the waves are propagated is independent of the movement of the bodies from which they emanate.

If one admits that our globe impresses its movement on the ether in which it is enveloped, one would easily conceive why the same prism always refracts light in the same manner whatever side it arrives from. But it seems impossible to explain the aberration of the stars on this hypothesis; up to the present time at least I have been able to conceive that phenomenon clearly only by supposing that the ether passes freely through the globe, and that the velocity communicated to this subtle fluid is only a small part of that of the earth; it does not exceed the hundredth part, for example.

However extraordinary this hypothesis may at first sight appear, it is not in contradiction, it seems to me, with the idea that the greatest physicists have made concerning the extreme porosity of matter. One may demand, in truth, since a very thin opaque body intercepts light, how it happens that there exists a current of ether through our globe. Without pretending to reply completely to the objection, I can remark, however, that these two types of movements are of a nature too different for us to be able to apply to the one that which we observe relative to the other. The movement of light is not a current, but a vibration of the ether. One can imagine that the small elementary waves into which light is divided in passing through a body are, in certain cases, out of phase when they reunite, by reason of the difference in routes passed over or from the unequal hindrances which they encountered in their journey; this it is which obstructs the propagation of the vibrations, or changes their nature in such a way as to remove the property of illumination, such as we find in a very striking way in black bodies; whereas the same circumstances do not prevent the establishment of a current of ether. One increases the transparency of hydrophane by moistening it, and it is evident that the placing of the water between the particles, which favors the propagation of luminous vibrations, should be, on the contrary, an additional small obstacle to the establishment of an ether current; this demonstrates the great difference which exists between these two types of movements.

The opacity of the earth is not a sufficient reason to deny the existence of an ether current between the molecules, and one may suppose sufficient porosity in order that it may communicate to this fluid only a very small part of its movement.

By aid of this hypothesis, the phenomenon of aberration is as easily conceived in the theory of undulations as in that of emission; for there results some displacement of the telescope while the light is moving through it: or, by my hypothesis, the luminous waves do not partake sensibly of the movement of the telescope, which I suppose directed toward the true place of the star: hence the image of this star finds itself behind the thread placed at the focus of the lens by a quantity equal to that passed over by the earth while the light passed through the telescope.

It is now my affair to explain, on the same hypothesis, why refraction does not appear to vary with the direction of light rays due to terrestrial movement.

The concluding passages of this remarkable letter give a technical account of the consequences of his hypothesis, answering the question of Arago, and explaining why no change in the angle of aberration is discovered with a telescope filled with water or some other medium denser than air. In order to make his explanation he introduced the concept of a partial *ether drag* for optical media which has been the subject of discussion and experiment ever since.

Putting the matter as simply as possible, Fresnel's theory was that the excess, and only the excess, of the ether contained in any ponderable body over that in an equal volume of free space is carried along with the full velocity of the body; the remainder of the ether within the space occupied by the material, like the whole of the free ether outside, is stationary with respect to the fixed stars.

Stating this proposition in other words, Fresnel believed that matter in some way imprisons a small amount of ether over and above what it is entitled to as a geometrical body in free space, and the ether thus entrained or captured belongs to and travels with it. This poetic notion can be put a little more technically by saying that matter contains within it as its own ether an excess equal to $n^2-1$ of the total ether displacement, where n is the index of refraction. Thus for air, where $n=1$, the excess of the ether is zero; for water the index of refraction equals $4/3$; hence excess ether imprisoned within this fluid is $16/9-1=7/9$. The next time you look at a glass full of water, reflect that, in Fresnel's belief, both the glass and the water have tangled up within their atoms some of this mysterious substance which we have called the ether. In some way there has been a condensation within their atoms and perhaps this condensed ether is the framework upon which their intricate structure of electrons and protons has been constructed.

## 7. *Fizeau's Proof of Fresnel's Theory.*

It was natural that careful experiments should be made to test the theory of Fresnel, and during the years 1871-1872 Sir G. B. Airy in the observatory of Greenwich made measurements on Gamma Draconis with a water telescope, as has already been related. His calculation of the constant of aberration agreed within experimental error with the constant determined by means of the air telescope. This, of course, was only an indirect proof of the correctness of the hypothesis of Fresnel; we turn next to the beautiful experiment performed by H. Fizeau in 1851[20] and later repeated under very careful conditions with certain modifications by Michelson and Morley in 1886.[21] The latter date was just four years after that historical event when F. Lindemann proved that a circle could not be squared.[22] I dare say that if you searched carefully in the newspapers of that day you would not find any mention of this historical event. A

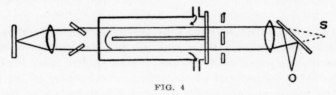

FIG. 4

problem that had baffled many of the best mathematical minds since the time of Euclid was that year actually proved to be impossible of solution. It was also the year when Lommel published his classical papers on the diffraction of light, already mentioned above, and two years before Hertz discovered the wireless waves predicted by Clerk Maxwell. The world did not know it, but that period was an important one in the history of thought.

Returning to the experiment of Fizeau let us see whether or not the ether is actually entangled in matter. Referring to figure 4 we see that a beam of light from a narrow slit 0 was allowed to fall upon a plane mirror and hence was reflected in two beams, a lower and an upper one, around the indicated circuit, by means of a system of

[20]Sur les hypothèses relative à l'éther lumineux, et sur une expérience qui parait demontrer que le mouvement des corps change la vitesse avec laquelle la lumière se propage dans leur intérieur. Comptes rendus, vol. 33 (1851), pp. 349-355; Annales de Chemie, vol. 57 (1859).

[21]Influence of Motion of the Medium on the Velocity of Light, American Journal of Science, vol. 31, pp. 377-386. See also, Michelson: Light Waves and their Uses, Chicago (1907), p. 155, and: Relative motion of the earth and the luminiferous ether, American Journal of Science, vol. 34 (1887), pp. 333-345; Phil. Mag., vol. 24 (1887), p. 449; Journ. de Phys., vol. 7 (1888), p. 444.

[22]Uber de Zahl π, Mathematische Annalen, vol. 20 (1882), pp. 213-225.

mirrors and lenses. The beams after their journey were reunited at the point S where they could be observed. Now in the course of their travels the two rays passed through a jacket through which water was forced at a high rate of speed. In the experiment the water ran at a rate of about eight meters per second or approximately 19 miles an hour. It is clear from the diagram that one of the beams would always go with the current and the other always against it, so that if the ether were actually dragged along by matter according to the law of Fresnel we should find the wave fronts arriving at different times at the point S. This fact would be exhibited by a set of interference fringes.

If water has no effect upon the propagation of light, then the two beams of light will reunite at S without interference. If, however, Fresnel is correct and water exerts a drag upon the ether, then interference should be produced at S and we should find the plate crossed by interference fringes. The answer is that Fizeau obtained a sensible displacement when water moved two meters per second, and a measurable displacement for seven meters. Using eight meters per second and calculating the dragging coefficient for comparison, Michelson and Morley obtained the value .434 which is sufficiently close to the calculated value of .438 to vindicate the Fresnel theory.

## 8. Is there an Ether Wind?

With this background we are now upon the threshold of the momentous experiment from which the theory of relativity finally emerged. This experiment bears the names of A. A. Michelson (1852-1931) and E. W. Morley (1838-1923) who announced their results in the year 1887. The object of the experiment[23] was to determine whether or not the motion of the earth through the stagnant ether of Fresnel and Young could be determined. The analogy with a boat makes the object of the experiment clear. If one is upon a boat in the middle of Lake Michigan and wishes to determine whether or not he is in motion the simplest suggestion is to throw a log overboard and interpret its drift as a measure of the velocity with which the water is slipping past the vessel. The log used in the experiment about to be described was nothing but an interference fringe determined in the following manner.

---

[23]On the Relative Motion of the Earth and the Luminiferous Ether, Philosophical Magazine, vol. 24 (5) (1887), pp. 449-463.

From a source S (fig. 5) a beam of light is sent into the ether in the direction of the motion of the earth. At the point D part of the light passes through a small hole and part of it is reflected in a direction perpendicular to the motion of the earth. By means of mirrors the two parts of the beam are reunited at D and reflected and transmitted to the point 0, where they form an interference figure. By means of a very simple calculation in algebra one can show that the difference in length between the two paths is equal to $D \times V^2/C^2$, where D is the distance of each reflecting mirror from the point where the beams were divided, V the velocity of the earth, and C the velocity of light. If the entire apparatus be turned around so that the beam of light goes in a direction opposite to the motion of the earth, then the direction of the interference shift is changed and the total displacement is equal to $2DV^2/C^2$.

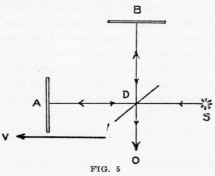

FIG. 5

In the original experiment the apparatus which we have described was set upon a massive stone floating on mercury placed in a cast-iron trough which was cemented into a low brick pier. The main difficulties encountered in the experiment were the distortion of the apparatus produced by rotating it and its extreme sensitiveness due to vibration. The latter was so great that the interference fringes were seen only at brief intervals even when the observers worked at two o'clock in the morning.

The result was as follows. Using as a measure the length of a wave of sodium light, the value of 2D, about 22 meters, was equal to $3.7 \times 10^7$. Also the value of $V^2/C^2$ was $10^{-8}$. Hence the expected value of the shift was $3.7 \times 10^7 \times 10^{-8} = .37$ of a fringe width. In no case did the actual displacement of fringes exceed .02, and probably it was less than .01, which was less than 1/40th of the expected value.

The experiment was repeated by E. W. Morley and Dayton C. Miller in 1905[24] with considerably increased accuracy, and they concluded that, if there were a shift of any kind, it was something like .0076, which is not greater than one two hundredth of the computed value.

A much more elaborate set of experiments on this interesting question was undertaken by Miller in the years from 1921 to 1925 both at the famous observatory on Mount Wilson and at Cleveland.[25] Miller had not been satisfied with the conclusion reached in 1905 and was not entirely convinced that the small positive shift discovered was due entirely to experimental error. From these very intricate new measurements Miller concluded that there exists a positive shift, much smaller, however, than that demanded by the stagnant ether theory, but nevertheless a shift which varies both with the time of day and with the altitude at which the experiment is performed.

Miller's experiment was an exceedingly arduous one, the variations studied every minute, and the results difficult to interpret. From a statistical study of the proper motions of the stars astronomers have arrived at the conclusion, subject of course to considerable error, that the solar system has a drift in space which is approximately twelve miles per second in the direction of the constellation Hercules. If this velocity is compounded with the earth's velocity of 18.6 miles per second in its orbit a change in the total drift of the earth is found at different times in the year, and this change should have revealed itself through variations in the interference fringes. The results obtained by Miller showed no such annual change; the assumption was made by him that astronomers were in error both with regard to the direction of solar drift and its absolute magnitude. Miller's explanation was, in fact, that the earth had a cosmic drift perhaps twenty times as great as that calculated statistically from the proper motions of the fixed stars, and this drift is toward the constellation of the Dragon rather than toward Hercules. The magnitude of this great velocity is thus sufficiently large to mask the slight variation that would be occasioned by compounding it with the smaller orbital motion of the earth.

Miller's investigation of the effects of altitude upon his experiment is not conclusive and perhaps somewhat contradictory. You

[24]Extract from a letter dated Cleveland, Ohio, Aug. 5th, 1904, to Lord Kelvin, Phil. Mag., vol. 8 (6), 1904), pp. 753-754; also, An Experiment to detect the Fitz-Gerald-Lorentz effect, Phil. Mag., vol. 9 (6), (1905), pp. 680-685.

[25]Ether-Drift Experiments at Mount Wilson, Science, vol. 61 (1925), pp. 617-621; Proc. of the Nat. Academy of Science, vol. 11 (1925), pp. 306-314; Significance of the Ether-Drift Experiments of 1925 at Mount Wilson, Science, vol. 63 (1926), pp. 433-443.

will recall from the preceding chapter that the theory of Stokes and Planck assumes the ether to be stagnant in outer space but in motion at the surface of the earth. On this hypothesis we should expect to find the ether drift increasing with altitude. In 1925 Miller reached the conclusion: "The ether-drift experiments at Mount Wilson during the last four years, 1921 to 1925, lead to the conclusion that there is a relative motion of the earth and the ether at this observatory of approximately nine kilometers per second, being about one-third the orbital velocity of the earth. By comparison with the earlier Cleveland observation, this suggests a partial drag of the ether by the earth, which decreases with altitude."[26] This interesting conclusion, confirmatory of the postulates of Stokes and Planck, was denied the following year when Miller stated: "The evidence now indicates that the drift at Mount Wilson does not differ greatly in magnitude from that at Cleveland and that at sea-level it would probably have the same value."[27]

The last statement of the preceding paragraph is also in agreement with an experiment made in 1925 by R. Tomascheck, at an altitude of 11,342 feet on the Jungfrau in the Alps.[28] Tomascheck was repeating the experiment originally performed in 1903 by Trouton and Noble,[29] who sought to determine a motion of the earth through the ether by measuring the torque exerted by the ether wind upon a suspended electrical condenser. His results, like those of the original experimenters, were negative. The elusive ether refused to reveal itself in anything so tangible as a velocity with respect to moving matter. Further corroboratory evidence of this conclusion is furnished in the negative results obtained in 1928 by R. J. Kennedy working under the direction of Michelson, who repeated his original experiment at the astronomical observatory at Mount Wilson with a much more sensitive apparatus than that originally used. The source of the small positive shift obtained by Miller was not revealed in this experiment.[30]

[26]Science, 1925, p. 621.
[27]Science, 1926, p. 443.
[28]Annalen der Physik, vol. 78 (1925), pp. 743-756.
[29]F. T. Trouton and H. R. Noble, The Mechanical Forces Acting on a Charged Electric Condenser Moving Through Space, Phil. Trans. of the Royal Soc., (A), vol. 202 (1904), pp. 165-181.
[30]For this evidence and a comprehensive conference on the entire problem of ether drift see: Conference on the Michelson-Morley experiment, Astrophysical Journal, vol. 68 (1928), pp. 341-402.

## 9. Optical Proof that the Earth Rotates.

One must not imagine, however, that all attempts to measure velocities fail, for there is one striking class of phenomena for which one can always expect to get positive results. These phenomena involve accelerated velocities. We have already examined in the last chapter the surprising fact that the absolute rotation of the earth can be detected within the closed walls of a building; we have tentatively advanced the proposition that the explanation of this cosmic phenomenon may be intimately connected with the reality of the energy of rotation. We have seen in the present chapter how the orbital velocity of the earth is revealed in the constant of aberration where again we are dealing with a phenomenon in which a large sum of kinetic and potential energy is involved. Any experiment which has for its goal the absolute measurement of accelerated velocity appears always to give a positive result wherever such accelerations actually exist. It is a striking fact that the Foucault pendulum at the equator is powerless to detect the rapid velocity of matter upon this rim of the whirling earth, but at any other latitude reveals the velocity of the particles. An important experiment, which depended for its result upon the relative acceleration of particles at different latitudes was performed by A. A. Michelson and H. G. Gale at Chicago and reported in 1925.[31]

The Michelson and Gale experiment was performed by sending beams of light in different directions through a tube constructed in the form of a rectangle. The tube which was more than a mile in total length was first reduced to a partial vacuum. The two beams of light were then reflected around the rectangular circuit in opposite directions and reunited so as to form an interference fringe.

Now this experiment might be expected to give a negative result, if the Stokes-Planck ether described in the preceding chapter were the true picture of reality, for the ether trapped within a heavy pipe buried in the earth might very well be dragged along with the system. Rays of light in such a stagnant medium would reunite without interference. On the other hand if the postulate of an ether wind passing through even the most solid of material substances were the correct one, then we might expect, were it not for the Michelson-Morley experiment, a positive result exhibited by an interference fringe, because the light beam in one direction would be retarded over

[31]The Effect of the Earth's Rotation on the Velocity of Light, The Astrophysical Journal, vol. 61 (1925), pp. 137-145.

the other, due to passing over equal paths in different latitudes. At the lower latitude the slower beam would move against the velocity of the earth and at the higher latitude with it. This differential, though small, was sufficiently large to yield a theoretical shift of .236 of a fringe or 1/200,000 of an inch, an amount within experimental reach.[32]

The value actually found by the experimenters was .230 of a fringe, that is to say this figure was approximately the average of the 300 odd readings made. Those, however, who would see in this experiment a contradiction with the original Michelson-Morley result must reflect that in the Michelson-Gale experiment the velocity measured was one associated with the acceleration of matter, since the effect made use of was the change of velocity with latitude. In other words the only result achieved was another vindication of the statement: "the earth rotates," and not in any sense a demonstration of the existence of an ether wind.

## 10.  The Paradoxical Ether.

We are now upon the threshold of relativity. This theory was originally devised to explain the interesting paradox which we have exhibited in the preceding paragraphs. The constant of aberration is clear proof that the earth has a velocity with respect to the framework of the fixed stars ; the Michelson-Morley experiment is similar evidence that the earth is at rest with respect to the postulated ocean of ether which conveys the vibrations of light.

In order to extricate ourselves from the difficulty we might postulate an ether dragged by the earth and stagnant in the interstellar spaces, but to make this concept acceptable to rational intuitions we must add the irrational assumption that the density at the surface of our planet is 60,000 times as great as that remote from gravitating matter. "Truth," said Mark Twain, "is the most precious thing we have ; therefore let us use it sparingly." But even if this fanciful density were to be assumed, the experiment of Michelson and Gale, with their pipes buried in the ground, or the experiment of Tomaschek in the high Alps is strong evidence that the dragging theory of the ether must be abandoned.

Fresnel enjoys the uncanny reputation of almost flawless prediction and his theories have withstood the careful scrutiny of those

---

[32]For a detailed mathematical analysis of the considerations which enter here see Silberstein's Theory of Relativity (loc. cit.), p. 376 et seq. See also, Phil. Mag., vol. 8 (6), (1904), p. 716 and Journal of the Optical Society, vol. 5 (1921), p. 291.

who have erected the structure of relativity. With Fresnel the ether was a stagnant ocean, whose particles flow unimpeded through solid matter as easily as wind rushes through the branches of a tree, save that matter itself imprisons as part of its corporeal substance a quantity of this universal entity. This theory is in contradiction with no experiment except that the ether wind eludes discovery.

Do we yet believe in the reality of the ether? Whenever we try to give it material properties, weigh it, calculate its density, endow it with elasticity and rigidity, measure its flow through the pores of solid matter, we are completely baffled. But when we look with reflective glance upon the beautiful rings of a diffraction pattern and view a photograph taken within the shadow of a ball of steel, is our disbelief not greatly shaken? How can we explain these mysteries?

Do you now think that physical science is confined to the pursuit of decimal points and the exploration of a tangible reality by instruments of precision? Do you not see in this mysterious impasse a bond with metaphysics? Are you justified in stating that ether is or is not a real thing because its substantive properties have seemed to vanish and only that single property of undulation remains by means of which we explain the phenomenon of diffraction?

This scrutiny of the assumptions of physics has been attempted recently by several philosophers, but none of them essays the task more ably than N. R. Campbell, whose treatise entitled "Physics, the Elements" published in 1920, is singularly free from either formulas or description of experiments. Campbell puts the matter squarely in the following paragraph:[33]

But is it true that metaphysics can be avoided wholly in an attempt to probe to the foundations of science? (Now and henceforth I propose to use the word metaphysics, not as a mere term of abuse, but to denote the study which those who accept the status of metaphysician think valuable. So far as I can make out, the study consists in the investigation of reality and existence.) At some stage in our inquiry we must stop and accept judgments without argument; is it certain that these judgments will not be found to be metaphysical? Or again, are we sure that the process of reasoning by which we develop our conclusions from these fundamental judgments does not depend on the acceptance of doctrines that are distinctively metaphysical?

Campbell accepts the general opinion that science does not in any way depend upon metaphysical concepts, and his answer may very

[33]Physics, the Elements. Cambridge (1920), p. 11.

probably be predetermined by his definitions.  But the concept of the
ether, existing for Maxwell in a set of mathematical equations, and
for those who look at diffraction, existing as a scaffolding for the
application of the principles of Huygens, Young, and Fresnel, and
for those who look upon the negative result of the Michelson-Morley
experiment, existing as an historic wraith haunting the laboratories
of light, this concept of the ether presents the most elegant of
metaphysical questions.  Who would want to settle the delicate problem and either give to ether an objective reality or deny it?

Perhaps these speculations leave you feeling like Alice.  "Fan
her head!" the Red Queen anxiously interrupted.  "She'll be feverish
after so much thinking."

# CHAPTER V.

## TIME, SPACE, AND THE FOURTH DIMENSION.

### 1. *The Ether Paradox.*

SAYS Goethe through the mouth of Mephistopheles:

A downright paradox, no doubt,
A mystery remains alike to fools and sages.

In the last chapter we arrived at a very perplexing place in the development of physics. We reflected upon the phenomenon of aberration and were led to the belief that light was an undulatory motion in the luminiferous ether and that the ether itself was so tenuous that it passed through solid matter like wind through the branches of a tree. We were told by Fresnel that ether condenses within atoms of ponderable matter and is carried along by them in a matter that can be calculated as soon as we know the value of the coefficient of diffraction. We then found out that the most delicate instrument in the world could not detect a significant amount of relative velocity between the moving earth and the stagnant ether. Well do we understand the lamentations of Odysseus "for on the one hand lay Scylla, and on the other mighty Charybdis in terrible wise sucked down the salt sea water."

The situation that confonted science at the time of the Michelson-Morley experiment reminds us of a situation in which Alice found herself, according to the opinion of the White Queen.

A spirited argument had just been held between Alice on the one hand and the two queens on the other, when the Red Queen said:

"Even a joke should have some meaning. . . . You couldn't deny that, even if you tried with both hands."

"I don't deny things with my *hands*," Alice objected.

"Nobody said you did," said the Red Queen. "I said you couldn't if you tried."

"She's in that state of mind," said the White Queen, "that she wants to deny *something*—only she doesn't know what to deny!"

"A nasty, vicious temper," the Red Queen remarked; and then there was an uncomfortable silence for a minute or two.

Let us state the problem otherwise. Suppose that we are sailing in a vessel on Lake Michigan during a rain storm and as we tack across the lake first in one direction and then in another we notice that the rain appears to come from different quarters. One would naturally interpret this to mean that our boat is in motion first in one direction and then in another, even if we have no other means of determining its motion. But in order to have a check upon our conclusion suppose we toss a log overboard and watch it fall behind the ship. If the log doesn't show a relative motion with respect to the boat we should naturally be very much surprised and should experience that same perplexity that science felt in the years following the Michelson-Morley experiment. The constant of aberration was almost conclusive evidence that the earth was in motion with respect to the ocean of ether postulated for the undulation of light, but the experiment of Michelson and Morley appeared to show that the earth was at rest with respect to this same ocean of ether surrounding it.

But one must be careful about jumping too hastily to conclusions. Even simple situations must be scrutinized for their hidden paradoxes. Evident propositions may lose some of their obviousness when approached from other angles. The following illustration is taken from the writings of that bright philosophical mind, Philip E. B. Jourdain (1879-1919), whose untimely death brought to abrupt close a chain of logical speculations which promised brilliant fruitage. Let us examine the obviously correct statement that it is better to be occasionally right than always to be wrong. An exception is easily pointed out. Let us merely reflect upon the case of two clocks, one of which has stopped and the other of which is always ten minutes fast. The first clock is certainly correct twice each day, but the second is always wrong, yet none of us would prefer the first clock to the second.[1]

How can we explain the paradox of an earth at rest with respect to the ether ocean and yet in motion? If we are to be true scientists in the sense of the dictum of Poincaré we must seek for that "harmonious order of the parts . . . which a pure intelligence can grasp." In another place he says that if there be one explanation of a given body of natural phenomena, then there is an infinite number of such explanations. "But every proposition may be generalized in an infinity of ways. Among all the generalizations possible we must choose, and we can only choose the simplest. We are therefore led to act as if a simple law were, other things being

---

[1] The Philosophy of Mr. B*rtr*nd R*ss**ll, Chicago (1919), p. 32.

equal, more probable than a complicated law. Half a century ago this was frankly confessed, and it was proclaimed that nature loved simplicity; she has since too often given us the lie. Today we no longer confess this tendency, and we retain only so much of it as is indispensable if science is not to become impossible."[2]

The most classical example of this dictum is the warfare between the followers of Ptolemy and those of Copernicus with regard to the motion of the planets. Ptolemy asserted that the earth was the center of the universe and that all the planets and the sun moved around it. However, in order to explain their motions he was led into complex paths. The motion of the sun around the earth would appear to be an ellipse, but the motion of Jupiter would seem to consist of a series of loops. The apparent or geocentric motion of the planets is a combination of two motions, the first of which is that of a body moving once a year upon the circumference of an ellipse of small eccentricity equal to the earth's orbit, and the second that of the center of the ellipse carried around the sun in the real orbit of the planet and in the planet's period. A motion of this kind is called epicycloidal.

The most powerful argument in favor of the Copernican system is not the criterion of reality, but that of simplicity. Its appeal rests upon the fact that the complexities of the Ptolemaic picture disappear when we assume that the sun is the center of the planetary system and all the planets move about it. The complicated epicycles become ellipses in the familiar Copernican system.

But suppose that we ask which of these systems is the correct one. Naturally we should choose the simpler because there is something in the rational point of view which makes us want to assume that nature is fundamentally simple. Without the check of the angle of aberration which we discussed in the last chapter, or a knowledge of the parallaxes of the stars, it would be difficult to maintain that one system was necessarily more rational than another, without first invoking the postulate of simplicity. As a matter of historical fact Tycho Brahe was led to choose the Ptolemaic system rather than that of Copernicus, first on the basis of scriptural authority, and second because the parallax of the stars was beyond the refinements of his telescope to observe.[3] Today, as Poincaré would say, we should be under the necessity of choosing the simplest of the hy-

---

[2] From Science and Hypothesis in The Foundations of Science (loc. cit.), p. 120.
[3] To be quite accurate we must observe that the system finally adopted by Tycho was a mixture of those of his predecessors. The sun moved around the earth in his cosmology but the other planets moved around the sun. See Russell-Dugan-Stewart's: Astronomy (Revision of Young's Manual), (1926), vol. 1, p. 245.

potheses among all those that might be made which were not in contradiction with experiment.

The remarks that have just been set down with regard to the formation of hypotheses may seem trivial indeed, but they contain, nevertheless, an important point of view. The toilers in the laboratory are on the road to the experimental truth about phenomena, but experiments are difficult to make and can be brought to bear only upon certain ideal phases of the problem. Hypotheses are necessary as supplementary aids to truth, guides, so to speak, to further investigation. Their implications, often wholly unsuspected in the original statement, must be investigated by mathematical equations. Consider, for example, the problem of the age of the earth, about which there is yet not full accord between physicists, mathematicians, astronomers, and geologists. Lord Kelvin, one of the most eminent mathematical physicists first to investigate the problem, assumed that the earth was a molten ball with a temperature throughout of 3,900 degrees centigrade, and made other auxiliary hypotheses with regard to thermal coefficients.[4] On the further assumption that the earth's surface was maintained at approximately zero temperature he sought to answer the question how long a time would elapse before the crust would be in a sufficiently stable condition for the oceans to form. His problem was to find from his hypotheses how long it would take the earth to cool to that point at which the geothermal gradient would have a constant value of one degree in 27.76 meters. Was Lord Kelvin's answer of 100,000,000 years an incorrect one? By no means! This conclusion followed inevitably from his hypotheses and the answer could be changed to anything one pleased by merely manipulating the original assumptions. Simplicity and physical intuitions guided Kelvin's choice. In this later period, with new assumptions as to the radio-activity of the earth's crusts, and other concepts of energy, a different answer to the problem has been obtained. The assumptions in the one case made the guess of Kelvin; the assumptions in the other lead to our guess.

## 2.  *The Contraction Hypothesis.*

With this introduction into the philosophy of explanations, let us examine the motion of the earth with speculations as to a possible explanation of the fundamental disagreement between aberration and the Michelson-Morley experiment. Wherein is the flaw in our

---

[4]Math. and Physical Papers, vol. 3, p. 295. See also Smithsonian Report (1897), p. 337. For a resumé consult Becker: Smithsonian Miss. Coll., v. 56, No. 6 (1910).

hypotheses? Is it in our notion of an ether wind or is it bound up more fundamentally with our concepts of velocity?

The simplest explanation that presents itself is to deny the evidence of the original ether drift experiments, but the skepticism of Miller has not been justified by his subsequent repetition of the experiment. The critique of this argument made in the last chapter reduces to a small figure the probability that assumption of experimental error is the ultimate explanation.

A second argument, advanced somewhat facetiously by Bertrand Russell to explain a related paradox in the theory of radiation, is that nature is irrational. Why should we not expect to reach contradictions in nature? What makes us so sure that there is a rational explanation for phenomena? When we read the sad history of human thought in its struggle against superstition it is clear that man in the mass is fundamentally irrational. Perhaps there is a basic cause for this behaviour. As a matter of fact it seems as difficult to explain why we expect rationality in the phenomena of nature as it is to explain our belief in the laws of probability. There is an intimate connection between these two things. Our belief that the sun will rise tomorrow is a rational belief merely because the records of history as far back as we can trace them contain the records of this phenomenon. The probability that the sun will not rise upon a particular day in the not too distant future is certainly incalculably small. And yet who would want to predict for a million years hence? We look upon the records of the sky and we find there occasional references to those great bursts of light caused by the appearance of cosmic cataclysms. The astronomical journals merely state that a "nova" has been observed. The new star flares for a few days and is gone, but there is indelibly written upon our minds a personal application in that magnificent spectacle. Who knows the mystery of our sun?

The third explanation was made early by G. F. Fitz Gerald (1851-1901) and H. A. Lorentz and is called the contraction hypothesis.[5] From it the latter derived his famous equations of the Lorentz transformation, which were important stepping stones that Einstein used in reaching his celebrated theory.

Hendrik Antoon Lorentz was born in Arnheim, Holland in 1853 and died in 1928. His magnum opus was his mathematical study of

[5] Sir Oliver Lodge communicated the suggestion of Fitz Gerald to Nature, vol. 46 (1892), p. 165. It was adopted by Lorentz in a communication to the Amsterdam Academy. Verslagen d. Kon. Ak. van Wetenschappen (1892-3), p. 74. See also, Theory of Electrons, p. 195.

the phenomena of the electron, that tiny particle of negative electricity which, together with the positive proton, is thought to be the ultimate constituent of matter. The electron is so small that it has to be studied by means of the mathematical interpretation of certain experiments on the behaviour of light, X-rays, wireless radiations, etc. One of these experiments explained by Lorentz was the so-called *Zeeman effect*. If a source of light be placed in a strong magnetic field and the spectrum examined, it will be found that lines which were solid in the unmagnetized spectrum, have now been divided into several parts or components. The great achievement of Lorentz was to trace this phenomenon to its source and to show how a modification in the vibrations of the electrons of the radiant matter was created by the magnetic field.[6] These investigations shared with the work of Zeeman the Nobel prize for physics in 1902. His contributions to scientific literature are the following: The theory of electrical and optical phenomena in moving bodies; the theory of electrons; and eight volumes of lectures on modern physics.

What was the explanation of Fitz Gerald and Lorentz? It was absurdly simple. When matter is in motion with respect to the ether it becomes shorter than when it is at rest. Nature is in a great conspiracy to prevent us from discovering our motion through the etherial framework of space. We move and the atoms of our substance shrink together in such a way as to defy the detection of absolute velocity. The hypothesis can be stated in terms of a simple formula which says that if a body at rest in the ether has a length L, its length while moving with a velocity v is equal to $(1 - v^2/2\ c^2)$ L, where c is the velocity of light. What a strange hypothesis? And why the mysterious appearance of the velocity of light? Just because our original experiments were performed by investigating the motions of this elusive entity, is that sufficient reason why its velocity should have so fundamental a part in the conspiracy of nature? Does this hint at a fundamental constant in the structure of the universe? Are there numbers, perhaps, which bound other activities of nature just as 460 degrees below zero bounds the heat content of material bodies? Are we justified in suspecting that this apparently limitless universe of time and space and matter may, conceivably, be bounded in other of its material dimensions?

Let us examine the contraction hypothesis further. The appearance in the formula of the velocity of light explains why this phenomenon has escaped the observation of early experimenters.

<hr>

[6]See Theory of Electrons, Chap. 3.

The solar system with its velocity in space, probably not greater than fifty miles a second, would not be appreciably affected by the contraction, but for an electron with a velocity in the neighborhood of half that of light, the contraction would amount to an eighth of its total length. It is thus a matter of relative velocity. During the summer months we are longer than during the winter months. We shrink in size on a railroad train when it is in motion. If we were wise we should purchase all our necessities involving length in the summer months and be sure that the material was not turned across our cosmic path when it was measured.

## 3.  *The Lorentz Transformation.*

Lorentz pushed these ideas to their logical conclusion and derived what are called the equations of the Lorentz transformation. These equations are really quite simple when one understands them, which leads us to the remark that such a statement is merely a critique of understanding. It is possible that the reader has experienced the unpleasant necessity of attending a series of lectures where the material was either obscurely presented or too abstract for him to grasp. And then perhaps some day the lecturer presented a section with which the listener was conversant from previous experience. With what minute detail the lecturer appeared to enlarge upon his theme. Little obscurities were carefully explained. If he had used one tenth the care in explaining the great deeps over which he had been sailing, the lectures would have blossomed into clarity. It seems to be a tendency of the human mind to befog difficulties by calling them easy. There are numerous examples where mathematicians start with the following encouraging remark: "It is easily proved," or perhaps, if the difficulty is particularly bad, "it is very easily proved" or "it is obvious." Laplace, sometimes called the French Newton, was not noted for the clarity of his writing. J. B. Biot who assisted him in revising his celestial mechanics for the press once appealed to him to clear up some obscure analysis in a proof, and after trying in vain to reconstruct his argument, Laplace is reputed to have said: "I am confident that the result is correct; let us therefore say that the conclusion follows obviously from the premises." (Il est facile de voir).[7]

In order to explain the Lorentz transformation let us first consider such an object as the top of a table and let us give it a location in

---

[7] See F. Cajori: A History of Mathematics, 2nd ed. New York (1919), p. 262.

space and time. This naturally leads us to the concept of a fourth dimension where the fourth dimension is to be regarded as time.

This idea is not to be looked upon as wholly a contribution of the present century, for it goes back a long distance into the history of scientific thought.[8] One of the first references to time as the fourth dimension is found in the article on "Dimension" written by J. d'Alembert (1717-1783) for Diderot's famous Encyclopédie. In this article d' Alembert remarks:

I have said above that it is not possible to conceive of more than three *dimensions*. A witty man of my acquaintance believes that one may, however, regard duration as a fourth (sic) *dimension*, and that the product of time (sic) by solidity, will be in some manner (sic) a product of four *dimensions;* this idea can be debated, but it has, it seems to me, some merit, even if it serves only that of novelty.

It has been conjectured that the "homme d' esprit" mentioned by d' Alembert may have been J. Lagrange (1736-1813), the great analyst, who was then, however, only eighteen years of age. At any rate it is significant that Lagrange later, in making application of his theory of analytic functions to the subject of mechanics, gives that most fruitful interpretation of the geometrical character of time which modern science now employs. Lagrange remarks:[9]

Let us now employ the theory of functions in mechanics. Here the functions are essentially with respect to time, which we shall always designate by t; and as the position of a point in space depends upon the three rectangular coordinates x, y, z, these coordinates, in the problems of mechanics, are regarded as functions of t. Thus one is able to look upon mechanics as a geometry in four dimensions, and the analysis of mechanics as an extension of the analysis of geometry.

Returning to our consideration of the table top, let us place a clock upon it and thus endow it with a place in the four dimensional manifold which creates the framework of objective nature. The German mathematician H. Minkowski (1864-1909) called the tetrad of values x, y, z, t a *world point*.[10] That is to say a point of the

[8]See for example an article by R. C. Archibald: Time as a Fourth Dimension. Bulletin of the American Mathematics Society, vol. 20 (1914), pp. 409-412.

[9]Théorie des fonctions analytiques. Paris (1813), 1st section of part 3: Application de la théorie des fonctions á la mécanique. Oeuvres, vol. 9 (1881), p. 337.

[10]Raum und Zeit. Physik. Zeitschrift, vol. 10 (1909), pp. 104-111; Jahresberichte der Deutscher Math-Vereinigung, vol. 18 (1909), pp. 75-88; also Werke, vol. 2 (1911), pp. 431-444.

world is to be regarded as a material particle at a certain instant of time. Suppose that we watch this particle in its travels throughout the period of its existence. The variations in x, y, z, and t would generate what we might call a *world line*. Suppose further that a large number of these material particles are collected together to form a body of finite dimensions in space and that we draw through each particle its world line. The collection of world lines thus made constitutes a *world tube,* or as Minkowski first called it, a space-time filament. It is interesting to try to visualize the world tube for such an object as a firecracker. If one sees these world lines in the four dimensional manifold before the match is applied they are all compact. But at the instant of explosion a great bubble is generated in the tube, whose film spreads farther and farther apart as we go along the time dimension of the figure and as the particles are scattered to the four winds. Those to whom these ideas are novel might reflect upon the rather neat way in which H. G. Wells has put the matter in his romance, The Time Machine (1898), where he makes his Time Traveler say: *"There is no difference between Time and Space except that our consciousness moves along it."*

Returning once more to our table top, let us try to calculate its world point. But this, we shall discover, is a difficult thing to do, because somehow or other we think that we must define the point in terms of something else, which for convenience we call axes. Let us explore the matter further. Suppose we first refer the position of the table top to the axis of the earth, whose position we know in something resembling an absolute way from the Foucault pendulum experiment. But we also know from the constant of aberration that the earth is revolving around the sun; perhaps it might be better to transfer our original axis to a more stable one passing through the diameter of the sun and perpendicular to the ecliptic or path that the earth follows. But even that axis won't do. As we make careful observation on the stars we are surprised to find that those in the direction of the constellation Hercules seem, on the average, to be moving in our direction, while the stars at the opposite pole are apparently receding. The observation is naturally interpreted to mean that the sun itself is not motionless in space, but has a drift in the general direction of the constellation Hercules. Hercules can be observed by those who care to know the direction of our cosmic passage just below the dragon and the little bear, according to the scheme given on the next page.

We can't, therefore, use the sun as a fundamental axis so we turn to the frame-work of the fixed stars. Since these so-called fixed stars are themselves in motion, it again becomes a matter of statistical averages, based upon the proper motions of celestial objects, to locate a set of axes passing through the center of gravity of the stars. From present revelation in astronomy we believe that the stars belonging to our galaxy, that is to say all the stars visible to our telescopes, form a spiral nebula, whose constituent particles are probably in motion with respect to a center of gravity. Let us take this center perhaps 52,000 light years from us, to use a recent estimate of Harlow Shapley,[11] and erect a set of axes there. But unfortunately we have not yet reached the solution of our problem

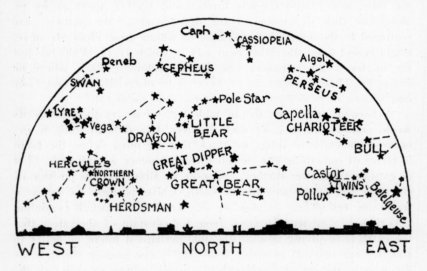

because modern astronomers report the discovery of about a million such galaxies within the reach of our telescopes and certainly our galaxy is in motion with respect to them. Hence we must move again and erect our axes at the center of gravity of the super galaxy of the spiral nebulae. But this super galaxy may in turn be but an atom in another galaxy of higher order and so we must move on and on without getting any where.

Our perplexity is the same as that of Alice in a conversation with the Mock Turtle and the Gryphon whom she had met upon her adventures in wonderland.

---

[11]Star Clusters by H. Shapley, New York (1903), p. 177.

"And how many hours a day did you do lessons?" said Alice, in a hurry to change the subject.

"Ten hours the first day," said the Mock Turtle, "nine the next, and so on."

"What a curious plan!" exclaimed Alice.

"That's the reason they're called lessons," the Gryphon remarked, "because they lessen from day to day."

This was quite a new idea to Alice, and she thought it over a little before she made her next remark. "Then the eleventh day must have been a holiday."

"Of course it was," said the Mock Turtle.

"And how did you manage on the twelfth?" Alice went on eagerly.

"That's enough about lessons," the Gryphon interrupted in a very decided tone. . . .

We have had enough about absolute axes in space. Lorentz, however, thought of these axes as being fixed in the great ocean of ether. Let us bear with him for a while. Let us suppose that the ocean of ether is at rest with respect to the framework of the fixed stars. Let us suppose, further, that our table is fixed with respect to the axes that we have chosen. Let us place an object upon the table. We can then determine its world point to be x, y, z, and t with regard to the axes that we have chosen and the clock beside it. Let us now place a second table beside the first and set it upon wheels so that it can be moved with whatever velocity we may choose to give it. Now suppose that we place a second object on the second table and a clock beside it. The two tables are identical in space and time except that one is slightly displaced, say a distance A, in the y direction. This displacement we shall disregard, since it has no bearing upon the argument of Lorentz. The second object has the same world point as the first excepting for y, that is to say $x' = x$, $y' = y + A$, $z' = z$, $t' = t$, where the primes refer to the second point.

Now suppose that the second table is set in motion with a velocity V in the direction x with respect to the first. We fix our attention upon the world point of the object on the table. What happens to it? Sir Isaac Newton who was not bothered by these ideas, and those of us who want to talk in rational terms would say that the new world point of the second object is merely $x' = x + Vt$, $y' = y + A$, $z' = z$, $t' = t$. These simple equations merely state in the language of common understanding that the second object is in motion with respect to the first.

Not so, says Lorentz, for the time and space of the moving object contract according to the laws of the postulated conspiracy of nature. The new world point of the second object is not that of Newton or of rational intuitions, but is modified by the hypothesis of contraction into the following: $x' = (x + V t) / \sqrt{(1 - V^2 / c^2)}$, $y' = y + A$, $z' = z$, $t' = (t - V x/c^2) / \sqrt{(1 - V^2 /c^2)}$, where c is the velocity of light.

What an amazing speculation this brings to view! Well may we heed the advice of the White Queen and commence to practice our belief in impossible things. What is the meaning of the constant $c$ which appears so strangely in these equations? What has the speed of light to do with the movement of one table top with respect to another through the mysterious ether? How can the speed of light be related to the framework of the fixed stars?

If we regard these transformations more closely we are surprised to see what would happen if we start the second table with the speed of light. The world point immediately jumps to infinity, which is merely a nice mathematical way of saying: "Hold on, you can't make that table go as fast as light, because nothing except light can go that fast." In other words the speed of light is the ultimate relative velocity of matter.

But see what has happened to time! If you think it strange that space should be so related to the velocity of light, what opinion must you have of time? Time has become all tangled up with space and the mysterious velocity, and the only way to return to normalcy is to set V equal to zero and stop your table top. Of course all of this is difficult to believe, but we must reflect that a theory which would explain why the ether moved past the earth in one experiment and then did not move in another, would of necessity differ from our ordinary intuitions. You really have to practice thinking such things.

What Lorentz really meant was this: If we assume this relationship to exist between the space and time variables of two objects, one moving with respect to another, then the Michelson-Morley experiment can be explained as a contraction of matter in the direction of its motion. Two beams of light, one parallel to the motion of the earth through space and the other perpendicular to it, will be reunited without creating an interference fringe. In other words the distorting of matter, due to its motion through space and calculated according to the space and time transformations of Lorentz, is

enough to account exactly for the disappearance of the small amount
of time which should have exhibited its existence as an interference
fringe in the famous experiment.

A truly magnificent confirmation of the views of Lorentz is to be
found in a mathematical experiment which was made upon Maxwell's equations of electromagnetic radiations. You will recall from
the historical outline of the preceding chapter that Maxwell, years
before the excitement arose regarding the Michelson-Morley experiment, had succeeded in defining a mathematical ether whose reality
was more in Maxwell's equations than in any substantial model. It is
quite evident that no farseeing physicist of that day could have anticipated the theory of the Lorentz transformation in setting up his
mathematical structure. The equations of Maxwell came directly
and simply out of considerations of the fluxes of the Faraday tubes
of electric and magnetic forces.

Let us now change these celebrated equations of the English seer
from one set of time-space variables to another.[12]  In other words
let us see what change in the experiments with electromagnetic
radiations might be anticipated by an experimenter in a moving
laboratory according to the equations of Maxwell. The mathematical
problem is not difficult to perform, but the result has a profound
implication. The Maxwell equations in terms of the new time and
space are the same as the Maxwell equations in terms of the old
four-dimensional manifold. In other words the Lorentz transformation was lurking within these magical symbols all the time and might
have been anticipated years before, had anyone thought to ask the
question forced so spectacularly to attention by experimental evidence.
This is a powerful argument in favor of the Maxwell theory and a
mighty bridge from the old physics to the new. The optical properties
of a laboratory moving with unaccelerated velocity through space
are identical with those of a laboratory at rest, provided, of course,
there can be any meaning attached to these common terms "moving"
and "at rest."

### 4.  Einstein and the Subjective View.

With these mystical ideas before us, we now come to the fourth
explanation, which, if it does not appeal to you, can be replaced by
one of the other three alternatives mentioned above or can be dis-

[12]For a mathematical treatment of this invariance, see Silberstein: Theory of
Relativity, chap. 8, in particular note 1, p. 225.

carded in favor of one of your own.  The great man who conceived this explanation is Albert Einstein.

Einstein was born of Jewish parents at Ulm, Württemberg, May 14, 1879.  His boyhood was spent at Munich, where his father, who owned electro-technical works, had settled.  The family migrated to Italy in 1894, while Albert remained in Switzerland and attended a cantonal school in Aaron.  He attended lectures while teaching mathematics and physics at the polytechnical school at Zürich until 1900.  After a year as tutor at Schaffhausen he was appointed examiner of patents at the patent office at Berne, where, having become a Swiss citizen, he remained until 1909.  He took his Ph. D. degree at Zürich and during this period began to publish his remarkable papers.  It was in 1905 that his fundamental memoir, establishing the special theory of relativity appeared.[13]  In 1909 he was appointed extraordinary professor of theoretical physics at Zürich and in 1911 accepted the chair of physics at Prague, only to return to Zürich as full professor the following year.  In 1913 a special position was created for him in Berlin as director of the Physical Institute.  His relativity theory, begun in 1905, was accepted in Germany by 1912.  It was followed in 1915 by that magnificent monument of human genius, the general relativity theory.[14]  Although in some ways this appears to be the most significant of his theories, his work on the Brownian movement of molecular particles and on the photo-electric and other phenomena of the quantum theory, in the opinion of some, has been equally fundamental and far reaching.  He was awarded the Nobel prize in 1921.  In 1929 a short paper in the Prussian Academy of Sciences brought the forces of electricity and magnetism within the geometrical scope of his general relativity theory.[15]

The postulates of the simple relativity theory were formed to explain the Michelson-Morley experiment.  It is that theory which we shall now review rather than the more comprehensive doctrine by means of which Einstein approached the mystery of action at a distance.

To many who approach the theory of relativity the basic assumptions often seem strange and mysterious.  They are contrary to ordinary modes of thought.  Popular writers on the subject have

---

[13]Zur Electrodynamik bewegter Körpern, Ann. der Physik, vol. 17 (1905), p. 891.

[14]Die Grundlage der allgemeinen Relativitätstheorie, Ann. der Physik, vol. 49 (1916), p. 769.  With M. Grassmann: Entwurf einer verallgemeinerten Relativitätstheorie und einer Theorie der Gravitation, Zeitschrift der Math. Phys., vol. 63 (1914), p. 215.

[15]Zur Einheitlichen Feldtheorie, Sitzungsberichte der Preuss. Akad. der Wissen., Phys.-Math. Klasse, (1929).

often stressed the paradoxes and emphasized unrealities, but there is nothing essentially bizarre in the theory except its overthrow of conventional belief. If one has sufficient mental agility to take the equations of Maxwell as a definition of an objective ether, or if one does not find the reality of action too difficult to assume, then the postulates of Einstein are not essentially beyond his grasp. We must always remember that we are enquiring into the acts of nature with a mind which has evolved through ages of superstition and blind belief; would it not be an amazing coincidence to find that intuitions evolved through these ages of ignorance should finally be found to accord with the verities of physical law. One would then surely incline to the pessimism of Mark Twain who concluded: "It is all a dream—a grotesque and foolish dream. Nothing exists but you. And you are but a *thought*—a vagrant thought, a useless thought, a homeless thought, wandering forlorn among the empty eternities!"

In an earlier chapter we have broached this point of view, but it will be worthwhile to emphasize it further. As we look about us the universe steals in through the medium of our five senses and by some strange psychological process the world points and the world lines are catalogued in our brain. Then out of this assemblage of points and lines we make an ordered arrangement which we think of as rational belief. We see a penny tossed and notice that it falls either heads or tails. Without making a single experiment we arrive at the conclusion that if 10,000 pennies were tossed, then approximately 5,000 of them will be heads. Nay more than that, without performing a single experiment we can predict with rare accuracy that the limits of deviation will be 4,900 and 5,100. The point is this that we are projecting upon an objective world of pennies and penny tossing a subjective creation. Without the necessity of experimental check we create a set of laws expressed in mathematical language which are to apply to the world of nature. How do we know that this mathematical picture gives us the true aspect of nature?

The answer to this question is that it doesn't. Paradoxical as it may seem, there are no laws in nature that rest upon a more secure foundation logically than the laws of chance. In one of the most beautiful documents in the literature of mathematical physics Clerk Maxwell has developed the entire subject of thermodynamics by the application of the laws of chance to a collection of spherical molecules in random motion. And yet carried far enough we find that the laws of chance lead us to the following belief, which I quote from the treatise of J. H. Jeans: "The Dynamical Theory of Gases."[16]

To borrow an illustration from Lord Kelvin, if we have a bar of iron initially at uniform temperature, and subject neither to external disturbance nor to loss of energy, it is infinitely probable that, given sufficient time, the temperature of one half will at some time differ by a finite amount from that of the other half. Or again, if we place a vessel full of water over a fire, it is only probable, and not certain, that the water will boil instead of freezing. And moreover, if we attempt to boil the water a sufficient number of times, it is infinitely probable that the water will, on some occasions, freeze instead of boil. The freezing of the water, in this case, does not in any way imply a contravention of the laws of nature: the occurrence is merely what is commonly described as a "coincidence," exactly similar in kind to that which has taken place when the dealer in a game of whist finds that he has all the trumps in his hand.

The subjective creation which we have made without experiment and wholly dependent upon our human logic leads us to this strange belief. To amplify it a bit further, let us consider the case of playing the game of bridge. Four hands of thirteen cards are dealt. Do you realize as you pick them up that you are faced by an historical event. This is probably the first time in the history of the world, and perhaps will be the only time in recorded history that that particular distribution of cards in four hands has been played. Have you ever heard of a table at which each player held every card in a single suit? One case has been reported by Arne Fisher in his Theory of Probabilities.[17] "What would," as Czuber remarks, "D'Alembert have said to an actual reported case in 'Grunert's Archiv' where in a game of whist each of four players held 13 cards of one suit?" The numerical probability of such an event is $(635013559600)^{-4} = 1 : 16,260,233 \times 10^{40}$. In the case of the vessel of water the boiling or freezing depends entirely upon the distribution of the velocities of the constituent molecules and the rare event might happen where all of the swiftly moving molecules and all of the slowly moving ones became separated into two groups. Part of the water would then boil vigorously and the other part freeze.

So much for the mathematical structure by means of which we want to interpret the laws of nature. Nature always seems to avoid conformity to these rigorous models and the strange situation in physics with regard to the quantum theory of energy can be traced

---

[16] 3rd ed., p. 181.
[17] P. 52.

to a point at which energy refuses to behave in a statistical way. Our laws of chance appear to yield to some different mode which has seemed the very antithesis of logical intuition.

## 5. *The Velocity of Light as a Basic Constant.*

Let us return to Einstein's method explaining the fact that the earth moves through the ether according to aberration and yet does not move through the ether according to the ether-drift experiment of Michelson and Morley.

Einstein's postulates may be summarized as follows:

1. In empty space the relative velocity of one material particle with respect to another can not exceed the speed of light.

There is vastly more in this postulate than would appear at first sight. For some mysterious reason the speed of light is a basic constant in the physical universe. This is an important consideration, because light impulses are among the most fundamental contacts that we have with reality. If they did not escape us we should never lose the past; if we could move with greater velocity than light, time might be reversed and the peculiar "one wayness" of duration thus destroyed. To speak of direction, however, involves logical pitfalls, even when applied to the three dimensional continuum of space. At this instant you are certainly at one point in the universe, although it is impossible to give it an absolute location; in the next instant you are certainly not less than twenty miles from that point, and there is no irrefragable reason to believe that you ever will or ever could return to that same point in space again.

Clerk Maxwell, whom we have exhibited in preceding pages as an eminent British physicist, has left behind a not insignificant amount of verse. But while Maxwell was not a Shelley, the physicist has put the problem of time picturesquely in the following lines:[18]

What! has Time run out his cycle, do the years return again?
Are there treasure-caves in Dreamland where departed days
    remain?

Did you ever reflect what would happen if you could actually move through space with a velocity exceeding that of light? Time in so far as it depends upon the propagation of light would be reversed. Camille Flammarion (1842-1925), the imaginative French astronomer, in his charming volume "Lumen" makes an observer leave the earth with such a velocity. For him time has reversed itself

---

[18]Life of James Clerk Maxwell by Lewis Campbell and W. Garnett, London (1882), p. 600.

and he sees the effect before the cause. The universe has a new basis which, from our point of view, is wholly irrational. Who, in such a situation, could meditate upon the reasons for the movements of history? How could he explain the phenomenon of Galileo before his inquisitors, after having first beheld the magnificent cosmology of Newton? A short quotation from Flammarion's novel furnishes both entertainment and food for reflection.

When I recognized the field of Waterloo, I saw at first a number of dead bodies stretched upon the ground. Beyond them I saw Napoleon arriving *backwards* holding his horse by the bridle. Then I saw the dead soldiers come suddenly to life and spring to their feet, the horses came to life again at the same time and their riders sprang into the saddle. As soon as two or three thousand men were thus resuscitated, they gradually reformed their ranks. The two armies began to fight with fury. In the center of the French army I perceived the Emperor, surrounded by his soldiers. The Imperial Guard had come to life again! At the end of the day not a single man was killed or even wounded—not a uniform was torn. Two hundred thousand corpses, come to life, marched off the field in perfect order. And the result of this strange battle was not to vanquish Napoleon, but on the contrary to restore him to the throne.

But the idea is not wholly modern for we read the following conversation in the *treatise* of Lewis Carroll.

"Living backwards!" Alice repeated in great astonishment. "I never heard of such a thing!"

". . . but there's one great advantage in it, that one's memory works both ways."

"I'm sure mine only works one way," Alice remarked. "I can't remember things before they happen."

"It's a poor sort of memory that only works backwards," the Queen remarked.

"What sort of things do *you* remember best?" Alice ventured to ask.

"Oh, things that happened the week after next," the Queen replied in a careless tone. "For instance, now," she went on, sticking a large piece of plaster on her finger as she spoke, "there's the King's Messenger. He's in prison now, being punished: and the trial doesn't even begin till next Wednesday: and of course the crime comes last of all."

Well, at any rate, we have admitted a lot, but perhaps not too much in admitting the first postulate of Einstein. One consequence is that we have shut out from our material world a tremendous number of events. Suppose, for example, that an event happened ten years ago on Polaris. Does that event belong to the history of this planet? Is it a past event? By no means. Since it takes light many years to make the journey from Polaris to the earth, that event has not yet happened. We do not mean figuratively, but actually. Since nothing can travel faster than light, we are bound to a limited universe of events. The thing becomes more vivid if we talk in terms of sound instead of light. If our only means of communication with reality were through sound, our active past would be tremendously limited. We should always dwell in the present by merely moving in one direction with the speed of sound. The significance of this point of view is made manifest in the well-known story of the soldier who was asked about his feelings when he heard his first shell. "Well," said he, "I heard that shell twice. Once when it passed me and once when I passed it." That shell was once in his active past and once again out of it.

The relativists frequently speak of a four-dimensional cone in which we live. The axis of the cone is time and the generatrix is the path traced by a beam of light. Without mathematics this statement is only a pleasing fancy; with mathematics it becomes an analytical device of power.

The whole matter may, perhaps, be summarized in a modern version of a Mother Goose rhyme which is an imitation of a limerick frequently quoted in this connection:

> Hi diddle diddle, the cat and the fiddle,
> The cow jumped over the moon,
> Going faster than light, she sped through the night,
> And returned on the preceding noon.

### 6. *The Geometry of Light Rays.*

Another postulate of the new theory follows:

2. A straight line is the path of a beam of light.

If you are willing to admit this statement then you have committed yourself to an objective rather than to a subjective geometry. You have broken definitely with the mathematicians. A straight line is the shortest distance between two points, although it is a little difficult to conceive of strictly mathematical points.

Perhaps this aspect of geometry has never occurred to you. But reflect for a moment upon the proposition to which you were committed by the first definition of Euclid's elements. "That which has position but not magnitude is called a point." Have you ever tried to count all the points on a straight line? The attempt is very illuminating and will forever remove any notion that you may have had that points are arranged upon a line like beads upon a wire. Consider, for example, the totality of rational points between zero and one. There will be a point at $1/2$, another at $1/3$, another at $2/3$, etc., until we have enumerated all the points. This sequence is customarily written as follows:

$0/1$, $1/1$, $1/2$, $1/3$, $2/3$, $1/4$, $3/4$, $1/5$, $2/5$, $3/5$, $4/5$, . . .

It is clear that every rational point will appear in this array, since every integer appears in the denominator and the numerators are made up of all the integers prime to the integers below the bars of the fractions.

One striking thing to be noticed about this sequence is the fact that it is what is technically referred to as *denumerable;* in other words we can make a one-to-one correspondence between its terms and the terms of the sequence formed from the positive integers. This fact is revealed by merely writing the integers successively below the terms of the series of fractions. It is thus clear that there will be an infinite number of such terms.

The reason for interpolating this discussion into a theme devoted to objective phenomena is to exhibit the vast difference in point of view between the pure mathematician and the pure physicist. We can but compare the statement of Oliver Heaviside, master of electromagnetic waves, that "mathematics is reasoning about quantities," with the toast once proposed by H. J. S. Smith (1826-1883), who found fame in the theory of numbers, "Pure mathematics: may it never be of any use to any one."[19] The author has profound sympathy with both. When we are dealing with an objective theory geometry can become the subject of laboratory investigation; when we are dealing with pure reason, on the basis of a set of consistent postulates, we need have nothing at all to do with objective reality; nay more, objective reality may, in fact, prove to be a disturbing element, if allowed to intrude upon the delicate thread of pure reason.

But to return once more to our subjective points. Let us give the first point in the rational sequence written down above the length, let us say, of the wave of sodium light, which is, in spite of its minuteness, billions of times longer than any point, since, by definition, the point hasn't any dimension whatsoever. Let us assign to the

---

[19]F. Cajori: History of Mathematics (Loc. cit.), p. 442.

next point one half of this length, to the next point one fourth, etc. until all the points have been given a dimension. Of course, one may reflect, the last points in the sequence will have assigned to them a very small length, indeed; but we can counter with the observation that no matter how small the length may be it is infinitely greater than any which the point has by fundamental hypothesis.

Let us now add together all these lengths assigned to the rational points, a problem which one can solve very readily by a simple mathematical formula. What a strange fact emerges! This sum is found to be equal to but twice the wave length of sodium light, which when compared with the total length of the line, is nothing at all. We have evidently forgotten something, and that something we are told is found in our neglect of the so-called irrational points, such as $1/\sqrt{2}$ or $\pi - 3$. To be sure A. Hurwitz, a mathematician of great power, has proved that if you name any number, no matter how small, for example, $10^{-G}$, where G is a million billion, there will always exist numbers in the sequence of the rational points which are closer to $1/\sqrt{2}$ or $\pi - 3$, or any other irrational number, than the small number which you named.[20] The delicate logic required in avoiding this objection it is obviously not possible for us to investigate here.

But how shall we count up all these neglected irrational points, assuming their subjective existence to have been proved, since we have already exhausted our integers in counting the rational points? A little matter of that sort is all in the day's logic. Why, of course, invent a transfinite cardinal number. When you get to infinity in the sequence of integers commence again with a new cardinal to which we shall assign the name *aleph-zero*.[21] The definition of this magical symbol is simply: aleph-zero is the first cardinal number that is not finite. With it you will be able to enumerate all the points in the line and thus found the beautiful theory of the mathematical continuum. From such a point of view geometry, with its Euclidean points and its lines constructed from them, is a magnificent creation of logical reasoning, but there is no argument by means of which one can show that it should have the slightest objective reality. Mathematicians, as in the case of Smith cited above, not infrequently resent having their beautiful science debased by application.

If these be proper observations, there is no reason why geometry

[20]Über die angenäherte Darstellung der Irrationalzahlen durch rationale Brüche. Math. Annalen, vol. 39 (1891), pp. 279-284.
[21]See Chapter 7 for further elucidation of this point.

might not be re-defined for the world of objective reality. Where the subjective and the objective views merge, as they do in most of the cases where mathematics is involved to explain phenomena, science is vastly enriched; but basicly the two ideas, as we have viewed them here, are essentially incompatible. It is dangerous to raise the question: Which should we follow in the teaching of geometry?

Euclid begins with the definition:[22]

That which has position and length but neither breadth nor thickness is called a line. A line which lies evenly between points on it is called a straight line.

Einstein would have us replace this by stating:

A straight line is the path of a beam of light.

Euclid makes geometry a creation of the mind. Two straight lines cannot intersect in more than one point.[23]   A finite straight line may be produced at either extremity to any length.

Einstein makes geometry a discovery of nature. We study objective geometry not with a pencil and paper and a clear head but by instruments of scientific precision. By experiment we can discover something about the space of reality and not about the space constructed out of subjective points. The following quotation from Maxwell may well be regarded as symbolic of the new instruction in geometry:[24]

> The lamp-light falls on blackened walls,
> And streams through narrow perforations,
> And long beam trails o'er pasteboard scales,
> With slow-decaying oscillations.
> Flow, current, flow, set the quick light-spot flying,
> Flow, current answer light-spot, flashing, quivering, dying.

The author, however, does not want to be misunderstood in this connection. His purpose is not to cast the slightest discredit upon those beautiful subjective geometries founded by Euclid, Lobatchevski, and Riemann; they are the logical treasures of our race. Nor does he want to be understood as seriously suggesting that the

---

[22]Elements of Geometry.  Book 1, definitions 2 and 6.
[23]Elements, Postulates 1 and 4.
[24]Life of Maxwell (loc. cit.), p. 631.

geometry of Euclid, with its abstract points and lines, should be discarded for the study of geometrical optics. He is only striving to put picturesquely a point of view, that nature has a geometry of light rays and that man has three geometries constructed upon logical postulates. The interesting question is not which of these subjective geometries is true but which has the closest relationship with the geometry of space in which straight lines are rays of light. If, for example, we are striving to picture velocities geometrically by vector diagram, which geometry is to be regarded as the nearest model to the facts of objective reality? Does it surprise us to know that it is the non-Euclidean geometry of Lobatchevski?[25]

### 7. Light and Time.

Let us now turn to a third postulate inherent in Einstein's philosophy. It should be remarked first, perhaps, that no attempt is being made, in this enunciation of the foundations of the special theory of relativity, to reduce the system of postulates to a minimum, and some will be found to overlap others previously stated. Striking consequences of the new doctrine may thus be exhibited separately.

3. If a man A is separating from a second man B, with any uniform velocity whatsoever, provided of course, that it does not exceed the speed of light, then a beam of light observed by both men will appear to have the same velocity.

This strange remark can be put rather picturesquely by assuming that A and B are replaced by separating beams of light. Then the velocity of one with respect to the other is still no greater than the speed of light. A little more sense appears in this remark when you reflect that time stands still for a beam of light. Since, by our first postulate, the speed of light is the absolute boundary of velocity, it is clear that a remarkable consequence must follow when this velocity is actually attained.

Look out at the stars on some clear evening and then reflect: How very old the light from some of you must be! The light has been travelling for hundreds of years and hence is hundreds of years old. But this is not so. Light never loses its youth. You could never find a quantity of old light. The light that arrives tonight from Polaris is just as young as the day when it was radiated from its electron.

In this connection George Birkhoff tells the story of a youth who

---
[25]See section 10.

started out upon a journey to one of the distant stars in a projectile which moved with the speed of light.[26] For him time stood still and he was forever young. Approaching the star he makes use of its gravitational field to reverse his direction and hence returns to earth again. When he arrives he is still young while his comrades have become old men. The nature of relativity is revealed in the explanation of this paradox. Suppose that the young man lost sight of the earth in his flight and looked out of his projectile through a window. Would he be conscious of his great velocity? Suppose that he sets up a Michelson-Morley experiment and tries to detect his velocity through the ether. Would he find any? As far as he is concerned he is motionless in the ether. His clocks go on in the same manner as before. His age increases and he is unconscious of his great velocity. Only when he looks back at the earth he will say: How rapidly the earth is receding from me. The clocks there seem to be standing still. My comrades there are perpetually young while I am growing old. You see it is all in the point of view. It is only when the young man turns around again that things will begin to happen. Events on the earth will seem to speed up. The years will roll by with incredible rapidity and his comrades will grow older, until, when he arrives again he will find that all of them have grown old together. The explanation of the paradox is thus seen to lie in the reversal of the direction of motion, which would, of course, be inconceivably hard to accomplish. The special theory of relativity does not examine into the nature of the geometry of fields of acceleration, which would certainly have to be invoked in any question of the reversal of direction.

Humpty Dumpty evidently had some such thing in mind when he was discussing ages with Alice. She had just replied to his question: "How old did you say you were?"

"Seven years and six months!" Humpty Dumpty repeated thoughtfully. "An uncomfortable sort of age. Now if you'd asked *my* advice, I'd have said 'Leave off at seven'—but it's too late now."

"I never ask advice about growing," Alice said indignantly.

"Too proud?" the other enquired.

Alice felt even more indignant at this suggestion. "I mean," she said, "that one can't help growing older."

"*One* can't, perhaps," said Humpty Dumpty; "but *two* can. With proper assistance, you might have left off at seven."

---

[26] The Origin, Nature, and Influence of Relativity, New York (1925), pp. 102-3.

He was evidently thinking of Einstein when he made these remarks, although this is not explicitly recorded in the treatise.

## 8. *The Postulate of Relativity.*

We proceed to another postulate, which may be stated as follows:

4. If a man A is observing the activities of a man B, who is in relative motion with a velocity V, the clock of B will seem to be telling the time $T\sqrt{1 - V^2/c^2}$, where T is A's time and c is the velocity of light, and the units of length will appear to be $L\sqrt{1 - V^2/c^2}$, where L is the length used by A. Conversely B will have the same opinion of the faulty behaviour of the time and length of A.

This strange postulate is the basic assumption of the special theory of relativity. It means that there is no such thing as an absolute velocity; nature will not recognize such a thing. We are taught by astronomers to believe here on the earth that we are moving with an orbital velocity of 18.6 miles per second around the sun and that the solar system as a whole has a drift of approximately twelve miles per second in the direction of the constellation Hercules.

"Absurd," says Nature, "there isn't any such thing as velocity. You only imagine these things."

"But look at aberration," you reply indignantly, "of course we are in motion."

"Wrong again," says Nature, "that doesn't prove that you are in motion. It only shows that you are turning around. It measures the kinetic energy of revolution. It shows that you have different relative positions with respect to the sun, but not that you have an absolute velocity. There isn't any such thing as motion in the absolute sense; of course you don't move. You only think that you do and you wouldn't think that if it weren't that the sun's gravitational field leads to that illusion."

In other words, there isn't anything with respect to which you can be in absolute motion. Is it the ether? If you knew that there existed an ether it might be with respect to it, but the reality of the ether is a delicate philosophical question. Is it the fixed stars? We know that they are not fixed. Is it the center of gravity of the galaxy? We suspect that that isn't fixed with respect to the centers of gravity of the totality of other spiral nebulae. Is it the center of gravity of the hyper galaxy? We don't seem to find any stopping place when we try to find a point through which to place our axes.

It makes us feel a little bit like Captain Stormfield on his trip to heaven: "So, as I said, when I had been tearing along this way about thirty years I began to get uneasy. Oh, it was pleasant enough, with a good deal to find out, but then it was kind of lonesome, you know. Besides, I wanted to get somewhere."

Nature in a convincing way says that velocity is an illusion. Since there are no axes in the heavens to which we can refer velocity, of course we shouldn't expect velocity to be real.

### 9.   The Concept of Space-Time.

Another postulate may be stated as follows:

5.   The hypotenuse of a triangle in four dimensions is unaffected by relative velocity.

Perhaps this statement makes you feel like Humpty Dumpty who had just asked:

"How many days are there in a year?"

"Three hundred and sixty-five," said Alice.

"And how many birthdays have you?"

"One."

"And if you take one from three hundred and sixty-five, what remains?"

"Three hundred and sixty-four, of course."

Humpty Dumpty looked doubtful. "I'd rather see that done on paper," he said.

One of the delightful remembrances of elementary geometry, when time has sufficiently obscured the difficulties and the struggles in the haze of reminiscence, is the Pythagorean theorem which asserts that the sum of the squares of the legs of a right angle triangle is equal to the square of the hypotenuse. The legend goes that Pythagoras was so jubilant over the discovery of the proof of this pretty theorem that he sacrificed a hundred oxen to the gods.[27] In symbols this theorem may be written $L^2 = X^2 + Y^2$.

But Pythagoras in his considerations was dealing with a subjective triangle based upon the postulates which later became the foundations of the geometry of Euclid. No notion whatsoever was in his mind with regard to a velocity associated with his triangle. But in this later age when the behaviour of objective lengths focuses the attention upon velocity, we are led to ask what would happen if we tried to teach the Pythagorean theorem upon a moving platform to

---

[27] F. Cajori: History of Mathematics, p. 18.

a class at rest, (as classes usually are)? To the class the length would seem to change according to the law stated in the fourth postulate. Length in the two dimensional manifold of the surface of the blackboard has no absolute quality which we should desire for our theorem.

Now strangely enough there is a length, if we wish to stretch this term into the fourth dimension of time, which preserves its identity unchanged by relative motion. This novel length may be written in symbols, $L^2 = X^2 + Y^2 - c^2T^2$, where c is the velocity of light. This is the modern version of the theorem of Pythagoras. The hypotenuse of the space-time triangle does not alter with velocity. In terms of mathematics it is an *invariant* with respect to the Lorentz transformation, as may be proved by merely substituting the values of X, Y, and T from the equations of the transformation previously given. This length is the reality; the other is but a beautiful subjective creation.

H. Minkowski, to whom these ideas are due, wrote, in an inspired moment, the following:[28]

The views of time and space, which I have set forth, have their foundation in experimental physics. Therein is their strength. Their tendency is revolutionary. From henceforth space in itself and time in itself sink to mere shadows, and only a kind of union of the two preserves an independent existence.

To be quite clear in this matter one is tempted to quote the following dimensional equation:

$$186{,}300 \text{ miles } = \sqrt{-1} \text{ seconds.}[29]$$

In a certain sense we have made great progress; but in another we may seem like the boy who came rushing in to his father one evening and said: "Dad, I made thirty dollars today." His father, was interested. "Yes," said the young financier, "I traded two ten-dollar cats, for a fifty-dollar dog." In our adventure toward explaining the mysteries of space and time we have apparently traded two mysteries for one.

## 10. *The Law of Addition of Velocities.*

We proceed next to the explanation of several significant conclusions which are derived without difficulty from the relativity

---

[28]Raum und Zeit. Physik. Zeitschrift (1909), vol. 10, p. 104; Werke, vol. 2 (1911), p. 431.
[29]Raum und Zeit. Werke, vol. 2, p. 441.

postulates. The first of these is the frequently quoted theorem relating to the addition of velocities. It may be stated thus:

1. If A's velocity with respect to B is U and B's velocity with respect to C is V, A's velocity with respect to C is not $U + V$, but $(U + V) / (1 + UV/c^2)$, where c is the velocity of light.

To put the matter a little more simply, the conclusion states that if a man is walking at the rate of four miles per hour down the aisle of a railway coach which is moving at the rate of 45 miles per hour, his velocity relative to the ground is not 49 miles but a small fraction less.

It is very interesting to test the matter in the case of separating beams of light. Suppose we calculate how fast opposite points on a spherical wave of light are separating. Setting U and V in the formula both equal to c we reach the delightful conclusion that the sum of the two velocities is equal to the original velocity c. In other words the two points on the spherical waves, moving in opposite direction with the speed of light, are separating with the speed of light.

The conclusion explains a difficult passage in the treatise of Lewis Carroll:

Alice never could quite make out, in thinking it over afterwards, how it was that they began: all she remembers is, that they were running hand in hand, and the Queen went so fast that it was all she could do to keep up with her: and still the Queen kept crying "Faster! Faster!", but Alice felt she *could not* go faster, though she had no breath left to say so.

The most curious part of the thing was, that the trees and the other things round them never changed their places at all: however fast they went, they never seemed to pass anything. "I wonder if all the things move along with us?" thought poor puzzled Alice. And the Queen seemed to guess her thoughts, for she cried "Faster! Don't try to talk!"

Not that Alice had any idea of doing *that*. She felt as if she would never be able to talk again, she was getting so much out of breath: and still the Queen cried "Faster! Faster!" and dragged her along. "Are we nearly there?" Alice managed to pant out at last.

"Nearly there!" the Queen repeated. "Why we passed it ten minutes ago! Faster!" And they ran on for a time in silence, with the wind whistling in Alice's ears, and almost blowing her hair off her head, she fancied.

"Now! Now!" cried the Queen. "Faster! Faster!" And they went so fast that at last they seemed to skim through the air, hardly touching the ground with their feet, till suddenly, just as Alice was getting quite exhausted, they stopped, and she found herself sitting on the ground, breathless and giddy.

The Queen propped her up against a tree, and said kindly, "You may rest a little, now!"

Alice looked round her in great surprise. "Why, I do believe we've been under this tree all the time! Everything's just as it was!"

"Of course it is," said the Queen. "What would you have it?"

"Well, in *our* country," said Alice, still panting a little, "you'd generally get to somewhere else—if you ran very fast for a long time as we've been doing."

"A slow sort of country!" said the Queen. "Now, *here*, you see, it takes all the running *you* can do, to keep in the same place. If you want to get somewhere else, you must run at least twice as fast as that!"

This very difficult problem of the addition of velocities has been beautifully elucidated in terms of the non-Euclidean geometry of Lobatchevski and Bolyai. You will recall from an earlier discussion that the characteristic of this geometry was its assumption that more than one line can be drawn through a point so as to be parallel to another line. One conclusion to which this assumption leads is that the sum of the angles of a triangle is less than the sum of two right angles, this departure from Euclid being determined by the lengths of the sides of the triangle. It is clear that the law of the addition of velocities does not accord with our ordinary Euclidean geometry, where the sum of two velocities, regarded as vectors, is assumed equal to the vector joining their two extremities so as to form a Euclidean triangle the sum of whose angles equals a hundred and eighty degrees. All of this is changed in the new philosophy. The vector diagram of velocities now must form a triangle in non-Euclidean space the sum of whose angles is less than two right angles. For the case of the orbital velocity of the earth the departure from Euclidean geometry, measured in terms of the so-called angle of parallelism, is exactly equal to the angle of aberration, namely $20''.6$. Unfortunately this beautiful representation can not be further explored here because of its technical difficulties, but this fact at least can be appreciated. We have through many years been committed so thoroughly to the geometry of Euclid that we have come to look upon it as absolute representation of objective nature.[30] But careful experimental scrutiny of the meaning of velocity forces us

---

[30]As a matter of accuracy it should be pointed out that the non-Euclidean geometry of velocities is applied to what has been called the addition of *rapidities*, i. e. a (the rapidity) = arc tanh $v/c$, where $v$ is the relative velocity and $c$ the speed of light. See Silberstein's: Theory of Relativity, (loc. cit.), chap. 6, in particular, p. 178.

to the conclusion that there is a slight departure from the postulates of Euclid when we examine the geometry of the mathematical representations of this elusive concept. The equally logical, but intuitively more difficult, subjective creation of Lobatchevski and Bolyai is a closer representation of objective discoveries.

### 11.  Mass and Velocity.

Another conclusion easily derived from the postulates of Einstein relates to the relationship between mass and velocity. This connection is simply stated:

2.  Mass increases with velocity.

A few years ago a huge meteorite fell in Siberia. So large and so tremendously swift was it that it destroyed a vast forest covering many square miles. But that event which was only a local happening might have been a world catastrophe provided the meteorite had struck the earth with a velocity close to that of light. Why are such velocities not found in nature among the ponderable bodies? One answer to this question is, perhaps, that a body increases in mass as it speeds up. If a body were subject for a long time to an attractive force it would gradually increase in velocity and it might appear that that speed had no upper bound. We have just seen, however, that nothing can exceed the speed of light; there must be some sort of limitation imposed. One way of accomplishing this is to assume that the mass of a moving object increases and for very high velocities approximating the speed of light attains a mass which is nearly infinite. Hence we reach the dictum that finite forces are limited as regards the velocities which they can create.

The relationship already recorded for length and time is found in this phenomenon also, and we have the result that the mass of an object moving with velocity V is equal to $M/\sqrt{1 - V^2/c^2}$ , where M is its mass at rest and c is the velocity of light.

The picturesque names of *transverse mass* and *longitudinal mass* have been given to the mass at rest and the mass in motion respectively.

Is there experimental evidence to show that such differences in mass actually exist? A. H. Bucherer[31] and W. Kaufmann[32] have made extensive investigations of the variation in mass which takes place in high speed electrons as determined by measuring the de-

[31]Messungen an Becquerelstrahlen, Phys. Zeitschrift, vol. 9 (1908), pp. 755-760.
[32]Über die Konstitution des Elektrons, Ann. der Physik, vol. 19 (1906), pp. 487-553.

flections in the electronic particles caused by variable electric and magnetic fields. These experiments amply confirm the deductions of the relativity theory in the case of these high speed particles in whose motion such variations would have an appreciable magnitude.

### 12. *The Identification of Mass and Energy.*

Another conclusion, whose special significance will be pointed out in a later chapter, may be stated as follows:

3. Mass (M) and energy(E) are connected by the equation $E = M c^2$, where c is the velocity of light.

Before we can comment upon the importance of this simple statement, which may ultimately prove to be the most significant contribution of the theory of relativity, we must call to mind two great doctrines which developed out of the speculative thought of the later eighteenth and early nineteenth century. These doctrines are respectively *the conservation of matter* and *the conservation of energy*.

In the writings of a number of early philosophers we find the proposition advanced that matter can be neither created nor destroyed, but it was left to the great French chemist, Antoine Laurent Lavoisier (1743-1794) to show by experiment in the laboratory that matter merely changes its form when subjected to physical or chemical transformations. Lavoisier, born in Paris, was elected in 1768 to the Academy of Science and the following year was appointed farmer-general of the revenue. His activities in this political capacity drew an undesirable attention to him during the violent years of the French Revolution, and in May, 1794, he was condemned to die under the guillotine. A petition presented in his favor to the revolutionary council elicited the reply: "the Republic has no need for scientists." Lavoisier was guillotined at the Place de la Révolution on May 8, and one is left to reflect upon the melancholy words of Lagrange: "Only a moment was necessary to make this head fall, and a hundred years perhaps will not suffice to reproduce such another one."

The principle of the conservation of energy was enunciated almost simultaneously by Julius Robert Mayer (1814-1878), an obscure physician of Heilbronn, Germany, James Prescott Joule (1818-1889), an English physicist famous for his numerous contributions to thermodynamics, and Herman L. V. von Helmholtz (1821-1894). Mayer's discovery of this principle is exceedingly interesting because of the apparent remoteness of the original observation and the con-

sequence which his philosophic speculation was able to construct.
Thus Mayer recounts his historical adventure:[33]

In the summer of 1840, on the occasion of bleeding Europeans
newly arrived in Java, I made the observation that the blood drawn
from the vein of the arm possessed, almost without exception, a
surprisingly bright red color.
This phenomenon riveted my earnest attention. Starting from
Lavoisier's theory, according to which animal heat is the result of
a process of combustion, I regarded the twofold change of color
which the blood undergoes in the capillaries as a sensible sign—as
the visible indication—of an oxidation going on in the blood. In
order that the human body may be kept at a uniform temperature,
the *development* of heat within it must bear a quantitative relation
to the heat *which it loses*—a relation, that is, to the temperature of
the surrounding medium; and hence both the production of heat
and the process of oxidation, as well as the *difference in color of the
two kinds of blood,* must be on the whole less in the torrid zones than
in colder regions.

His reflections upon this phenomenon finally led him to the
proposition that "an invariable quantitative relation between heat and
work is a postulate of the physiological theory of combustion." What
a tremendous leap from the red blood of European visitors in Java
to a great cosmic principle. How one marvels at the power of
imagination "which bodies forth the form of things unknown."
Not less interesting is the story of the reception of Joule's
theory when it was first presented to the English scientists. The
story is given as follows in Joule's own words:[34]

It was in the year 1843 that I read a paper "On the Calorific
Effects of Magneto-Electricity and the Mechanical Value of Heat"
to the chemical section of the British Association assembled at Cork.
With the exception of some eminent men, among whom I recollect
with pride Dr. Apjohn, the president of the section, the Earl of
Rosse, Mr. Eaton Hodgkinson, and others, the subject did not
excite much general attention; so that when I brought it forward
again at the (Oxford) meeting in 1847 the chairman suggested that,
as the business of the section pressed, I should not read my paper,
but confine myself to a short verbal description of my experiments.
This I endeavored to do, and discussion not being invited, the communication would have passed without comment if a young man
had not risen in the section, and by his intelligent observations created
a lively interest in the new theory.

---

[33]The Mechanical Equivalent of Heat (1851).
[34]Scientific Papers, vol. 2, p. 215; see also Thompson's Life of Lord Kelvin, vol. 1,
p. 263.

This young man was William Thomson, later Lord Kelvin, with whom Joule had a long and lasting friendship. At almost the same time Helmholtz, who had just announced the same principle in a masterly paper entitled: "On the Conservation of Force," was struggling for recognition against the skepticism of the leading physicists of Germany.

The principle of the conservation of energy asserts that within a closed region of space the total supply of energy is neither increased nor destroyed but remains constant. It may change its form, and it may become inaccessible, as when the supply of free energy in a thermal system runs down its temperature gradient, but the energy is never lost. It has merely concealed itself in the internal movements of the individual molecules of matter.

But what a revolution is seen in the equation of Einstein. Mayer, Joule, and Helmholtz showed that work and heat energy were equivalent; Einstein shows that energy and matter are the same. There are not two laws, one conserving matter and the other energy, but one law wherein the totality of energy and matter is conserved.

Mass and energy are, therefore, essentially alike; they are only different expressions for the same thing. The tremendous possibilities in this relationship can be pictured by means of a few figures. Let us consider a single gram of mass which is a very small quantity, since it would require nearly half a thousand grams to make a single pound. Replacing the velocity of light in the equation by its proper numerical value we obtain the astonishing answer that this insignificant amount of matter is equivalent to 6.63 times $10^{13}$ foot-pounds of energy. Stating this otherwise, we mean that this tiny bit of matter is the equivalent of the amount of energy which would run a thousand four horse-power engines for an entire year.

The energy lost by the sun through radiation in a single year, according to the Einstein formula, may also be computed without difficulty, and we find that it is equivalent to an amount of matter weighing $1.5 \times 10^{20}$ grams, which is approximately equal to one fifty-millionth the mass of the earth.[35] On this estimate the sun could continue to radiate at its present rate for fifteen trillion years before its total supply of energy would be exhausted.

---

[35]See Sir James Jeans: Astronomy and Cosmogony, Cambridge (1928), p. 108 and Silberstein's: Theory of Relativity, p. 256.

### 13.  *The New Metaphysics.*

In the special theory of relativity we catch a glimpse of the new reality.  Physics, with its galvanometers and its mirrors, has found itself facing the vision of a vast metaphysical doctrine.  Time and space, which were formerly but thoughts for the philosopher in his subjective musing, now assume the most important aspects of reality.  They are fused together into a four-dimensional framework which is not to be regarded as space alone nor as time alone, but as the single entity of space-time.

And what shall we say about the objective reality of this picture?  We have created a material geometry whose elements are rays of light.  No longer may we build our mathematical picture of the objective world on logical principles alone.  In so far as we shall want to talk about the geometry of nature, the delicate question of choice between the three branches of geometrical postulation is no longer one of inclination but is forced upon us by the evidence of laboratory experiment.

But whether or not the new philosophy repels us by its difficulty and by its disregard of what we think of as rational intuition, there is certainly one virtue that it preeminently possesses.  It has exhibited the power of synthesizing isolated theories.  The conservation of matter and the conservation of energy are revealed as but two aspects of a single problem.  Time and space no longer enter our equations as unrelated variables, but are henceforth to be regarded as parts of a single thing.

In the light of the new knowledge, if you would become a student of physics you must first become a geometer.  Wise and far sighted, indeed, was Plato who put above the entrance to his school: "Let no one ignorant of geometry enter my door."

# CHAPTER VI.

## WHAT IS GRAVITATION?

### 1. *The Problem of Knowledge.*

IN THE last chapter we investigated an interpretation of two experimental facts, the first of which told us, through the constant of aberration, that the earth moved in space, and the second, through the ether drift experiment, that the earth was at rest with respect to the postulated medium by means of which radiant energy is propagated. This explanation involved us in a speculation as to the relationship between objective nature and the baffling concepts of space and time. For the first time in the history of thought these twin entities emerge as objective things. Subjective geometry begins to assume an aspect of reality. But there must already have occurred to the reader the thought that these new ideas are thrusting upon us with renewed force the old question of epistemology: What is knowledge?

This question is not wholly divorced from racial characteristics, as has been pointed out by Poincaré. "They (the English) are always to hold, so to speak, one foot in the world of senses, and never burn the bridges keeping them in communication with reality. . . . The Latins seek in general to put their thoughts in mathematical form; the English prefer to express it by material representation. . . . For a Latin, truth can be expressed only by equations; it must obey laws simple, logical, symmetric and fitted to satisfy minds in love with mathematical elegance. The Anglo-Saxon to depict a phenomenon will first be engrossed in making a *model,* and he will make it with common materials, such as our crude, unaided senses show us them. He also makes a hypothesis, he assumes implicitly that nature, in her finest elements, is the same as in the complicated aggregates which alone are within the reach of our senses. He concludes from the body to the atom."[1]

What is knowledge? We feel that it can be gained only through those sensations which enter through our five senses. Reason is merely a bridge from one sensation to another. It is a guide to the interpretation of relations between sensations. We acquire a set of

---

[1]Preface to "The Foundations of Science," p. 4.

data from the laboratory and translate it into the language of mathematics; the transformations suggested by reason lead us to conclusions which we must test by new experiments with sensuous apparatus. The theory of relativity gained general recognition only when the predicted deflection of light past the limb of the sun had been found by astronomers from observations during an eclipse. One must reflect with thanksgiving that the Creator of the universe has given the earth a moon so fortunately situated that its shadow periodically obscures the entire disk of the sun. What a cosmic calamity it would have been had the orbit of the moon been but a few thousand miles greater than it is! There are some who wish to make us believe that Venus, the "star of evening," may be inhabited by intelligent beings, whose development may be greater than our own. But we must first reflect upon their great handicap living within the perpetual clouds of a planet which has no moon to reveal the secrets of the universe.

Will it be necessary for us to make a new definition of knowledge and will there always be a nebulous region between that which is known and that which is unknown so that boundaries can never be established? Are we satisfied to regard the ether as something forever barred from sensuous experience but with a kind of reality exhibited in the fact that the forces and energies which it was designed to carry are completely defined in terms of a set of equations? Must we look upon the atom as something material, round, perhaps, and solid like a marble of infinitesimal size? Must we know its weight and its radius, its velocity and its inertia? Must we be able to count its numbers in a given quantity of matter and think of it merely as a primary substance, differing only in dimension from the material with which we are in daily contact? Are we satisfied to give up this substantial image for a set of mystical equations? Are we willing to let the reality of nature disappear in a manner mindful of the philosophies of Hume and Berkeley and preserve its objective existence in the partially subjective equations of logical intuitions? "What is Truth?" said jesting Pilate; and would not stay for an answer.

There is at least a partial reply to these difficult questions in the following quotation from Poincaré:[2]

Does the harmony the human intelligence thinks it discovers in nature exist outside of this intelligence? No, beyond doubt a reality

---

[2]Foundations of Science, p. 209.

completely independent of the mind which conceives it, sees or feels it, is an impossibility. A world as exterior as that, even if it existed, would for us be forever inaccessible. But what we call objective reality is, in the last analysis, what is common to many thinking beings, and could be common to all; this common part, we shall see, can only be the harmony expressed by mathematical laws. It is this harmony then which is the sole objective reality, the only truth we can attain; and when I add that the universal harmony of the world is the source of all beauty, it will be understood what price we should attach to the slow and difficult progress which little by little enables us to know it better.

## 2. Newton and Gravitation.

We turn from these delicate considerations to one of the most perplexing mysteries of the universe. What is gravitation?

Gravitation is traditionally defined as a force which is exerted upon each particle of matter by every other particle of matter, according to the famous law of inverse squares. In other words every particle of matter attracts every other particle of matter directly as the product of the masses and inversely as the square of the distances between them. The discovery of this law is attributed by universal consent to Newton, although it existed somewhat nebulously in the minds of a few of his contemporaries and immediate predecessors. For example Sir Francis Bacon had advanced the theory that gravitation decreased both outward and inward from the surface of the earth and had proposed to check this idea by placing clocks run by weights at the top of a high steeple and in the bottom of a deep well and comparing their rates with a clock run by an iron spring at the surface of the earth.[3] This experiment was actually performed two centuries later by Ph. von Jolly.[4] Robert Hooke (1635-1703) had attempted as early as 1662 to detect the loss of weight which would be sustained by an object lowered with a piece of thread from a convenient place upon Westminster Abbey, but the delicacy of the experiment masked his results and he reported negatively. In 1682, five years before the publication of Newton's Principia, Hooke read before the Royal Society a paper entitled "A Discourse on the Nature of Comets," in which he considered gravitation to be a principle of all matter, propagated through a universal medium, and varying inversely as the square of the distance.

---

[3] Novum Organum, Book 2, section 36.
[4] Die Anwendung der Waage auf Probleme der Gravitation, Abh. Bay. Akad. Wiss. Cl. 2., vol. 13, Abth. 1, pp. 157-176; vol. 14, Abth. 2, pp. 3-26.

The genesis of the idea of gravitation in the mind of Newton makes an interesting story. The following account is given by Voltaire, who learned it from Catherine Barton, a favorite niece of Newton, and is the source of the famous "apple story" so frequently related in this connection.[5]

"But being retired in 1666, upon account of the Plague, to a solitude near Cambridge," says Voltaire, "as he was walking one day in his garden, and saw some fruits fall from a tree, he fell into a profound meditation on that gravity, the cause of which had so long been sought, but in vain, by all the philosophers, whilst the vulgar think there is nothing mysterious in it. He said to himself, that from what height soever in our hemisphere those bodies might descend, their fall would certainly be in the progression discovered by Galileo; and the spaces they run through would be the square of the times. Why may not this power which causes heavy bodies to descend, and is the same without any sensible diminution at the remotest distance from the center of the earth, or on the summits of the highest mountains, why, said Sir Isaac, may not this power extend as high as the moon?"

Now it happened that Johannes Kepler (1571-1630), after a profound study of the data on the motions of the planets collected by Tycho Brahe, had come to three important conclusions which are known in astronomy today as Kepler's laws:

The first of these asserted that the planets move sensibly in ellipses with the sun at the focus; the second that the line connecting a planet with the sun passes over equal areas in equal times; the third that the cubes of the mean distances of any two planets from the sun are to each other as the squares of their periods.

The first law is clearly an addition to the statement of the Copernican theory of planetary motions. The sun is at the center of the system and the planets move about it in ellipses. The second law, often referred to as the law of areas, accounts for the acceleration of the planets' velocity at certain times in the year. For example, in the winter time the earth moves more rapidly in its orbit than during the summer, due to its closer approach to the sun and the necessity for greater velocity in order that the requirement of the law of areas should be fulfilled. The third law, called the harmonic law, was especially pleasing to Kepler and he expresses himself in

---

[5] Éléments de la philosophie de Newton, Part 3, chap. 3.

the following famous exultation. Can we not indulge him this ecstasy who first found in the tables of Tycho the magnificent relationship which binds all the planets together into a single system?

It is not eighteen months since I got the first glimpse of light, three months since the dawn, very few days since the unveiled sun, most admirable to gaze upon, burst upon me. Nothing holds me; I will indulge my sacred fury; I will triumph over mankind by the honest confession that I have stolen the golden vases of the Egyptians to build up a tabernacle for my God far away from the confines of Egypt. If you forgive me, I rejoice; if you are angry, I can bear it; the die is cast, the book is written, to be read either now or by posterity, I care not which; it may well wait a century for a reader, as God has waited six thousand years for an observer.[6]

The problem that confronted Newton was to find a single hypothesis which would exhibit these laws as aspects of a unifying principle. This he thought that he had found in the assumption of a cosmic force varying inversely as the square of the distance. But unfortunately when Newton proceeded to apply his theory to the relationship between the earth and the moon he encountered an arithmetical disagreement, which for sixteen years kept this immortal discovery from the light. In making his calculations of the relationships existing between the earth and its satellite, Newton used the value of sixty miles for the length of a degree of arc upon the earth's surface, which led to a contradiction between the calculated and observed value of the gravitational acceleration at the surface of the earth. This disappointment led him to lay "aside at that time any further thought of the matter" until 1684, when there was brought to his attention a new determination of the length of a degree of arc which had been made by Jean Picard near Paris. This new value was 69 1/2 English miles instead of the 60 previously used, and when Newton made this substitution in his formulas, the two values, theoretical and observed, were found to agree. The Newtonian theory of gravitation was a reality.[7]

---

[6]Harmonicis mundi, book v. Concluding sentence of the Prooemium. For admirable accounts of the life and work of Kepler see, M. Bertrand: Kepler: His Life and Works. Translation by C. A. Alexander. Report of the Smithsonian Inst. (1869), pp. 93-110; also Sir Oliver Lodge: Pioneers of Science (1919), chap. 3.

[7]An alternative explanation of the long delay between discovery and publication has been advanced by J. C. Adams and J. W. L. Glaisher. This explanation asserts that while the numerical verification of the theory was fairly complete in 1666, Newton hesitated to publish until he had proved the theorem that a spherical body attracts an external particle as though the entire mass were concentrated at its center. Glaisher remarks: "No sooner had Newton proved this superb theorem—and we know from his own words that he had no expectation of so beautiful a result till it emerged from his mathematical investigation—than all the mechanism of the universe at once lay spread before him." See F. Cajori: A History of Physics, Revised ed. (1929), pp. 66-67.

Newton now turned his whole attention to perfecting his work and during the next two years he was wholly absorbed in the task. Various stories are told of his preoccupation during this period, his absent-mindedness, even his forgetfulness of meals. At what cost are magnificent structures of thought evolved!

The curious incident of the discovery of Newton's monumental work is of perennial interest. According to the story[8] Sir Christopher Wren, Robert Hooke, and Edmund Halley had been discussing the subject of gravitation, and Wren offered the other two a prize of "a book worth forty shillings" if either of them could prove that a body moving under the law of inverse attraction would be an ellipse. The prize was not collected; Halley paid a visit to Newton and asked him if he knew how to approach this perplexing problem. Newton replied that he had already solved it, but in searching through his papers was unable at the moment to discover his solution. In a short time, however, he sent the paper to Halley together with other extensions of his ideas on motion.

Halley immediately made the Royal Society aware of what he had discovered and Newton was asked by the Society for permission to publish the manuscript. Newton gave his consent, and the Society put the matter in the hands of Halley, whose interest and insistence finally forced Newton to complete his great work and prepare it for publication. The first edition entitled "Philosophiae Naturalis Principia Mathematica" appeared in 1687 at the expense of Halley himself, who always regarded his discovery of the monumental contribution with peculiar pride and pleasure.

### 3. Properties of Gravitation.

Let us now turn our attention to some of the experimental properties of gravitational force.

1. Weight is proportional to mass.

This simple statement contains a profound truth. Why should weight, that is to say the gravitational force at the earth's surface, depend wholly upon inert mass? Even wise Aristotle thought otherwise, and for many centuries the universities, following his authority, taught that a heavy weight and a light one fell with different velocities. We have already recorded in another place how Galileo refuted his colleagues in the University of Pisa by dropping two objects of unequal weight from the famous leaning tower, but did

---

[8]See Sir David Brewster: Life of Sir Isaac Newton, chap. 11, second ed., p. 138.

this demonstration win admiration for himself and acceptance of the theorem? It merely served to demonstrate the courageous spirit of Galileo, because to drop those iron weights lost him more friends and put him in more jeopardy of life than if he had thrown them at random in the market place. One can but perpetually marvel at the attitude of the human mind toward newly discovered truth. The first reaction seems to be to decide whether one is for or against a new doctrine in the light of its immediate effect. The evidence must be examined only secondarily.

Are we wishing to see in this now commonly accepted fact of the equivalence of inertial mass and weight a new mystery or should it be an expected consequence of our rational concept of matter? I think that most people upon reflection will agree that the proportionality between weight and mass is a remarkable phenomenon. Why should a bar of lead, for example, possess exactly the same attractive force as a piece of glass of equal inertial mass? Is the mystery of inertia identical with the mystery of gravitation? Are they but aspects of the same thing?

Certainly this would appear to be the case if one gives close scrutiny to the three laws of motion upon which Newton built his mechanics.[9]

Law I. Every body perseveres in its state of rest or of motion in a straight line, except in so far as it is compelled to change that state by impressed forces.

Law II. Change of motion is proportional to the moving force impressed, and takes place in the direction of the straight line in which such force is impressed.

Law III. Reaction is always equal and opposite to action; that is to say, the actions of two bodies upon each other are always equal and directly opposite.

The concepts of force and inertia are inextricably entangled. Suppress one from your formulas and anything that you may say about the other is meaningless. Acceleration and inertia are but the active and passive aspects of the behaviour of matter in the continuum of space and time. The implications of these laws permeate the entire structure of dynamics. Force is proportional to acceleration and the factor of proportionality is mass. But weight, evidence of the reality of the attractive influence of gravitation, is a constant force and hence proportional to mass.

[9]Principia, Axiomata.

The truth of the law of Galileo has been investigated by the most accurate of modern instruments and recent measurements upon the possible variations in the gravitational constant between platinum, copper, water and asbestos have resulted in the conclusion that the variation can not exceed one part in 20 billion.

Another fact to which attention must be directed refers to the determination of the so-called constant of gravitation. This may be stated as follows:

2.   The gravitational pull between two spheres, each of one gram mass, and placed so that their centers are one centimeter apart, is equivalent to a force equal to $6.658 \cdot 10^{-8}$ of a dyne.

In a treatise whose main object is the examination of the philosophical structure of modern physics such a statement as that just written down may appear entirely out of place. This is not a review of the specific numerical consequences of experimental evidence. But we are making an inquiry into the nature of physical reality, and it must be of the first order of importance to know whether the hypothetical force postulated by Newton is merely a fortuitous guess as to the geometrical behaviour of nature, or whether there is actual evidence of the reality of the gravitational force.

Those who have had the misfortune of slipping upon an icy sidewalk may derive small solace from the reflection that the cause of their discomfiture is a force of inconceivably small magnitude. For example two iron balls one hundred feet in diameter, if placed a little more than half a mile apart, would exert upon each other a force less than a three ounce weight. Our own comparatively small weight is derived from the accumulation of force from the entire mass of the earth.

The reality of this force has been demonstrated by a number of early experimenters, a few of whom will be mentioned briefly. Pierre Bouguer about 1740 undertook to determine the density of the earth by measuring the variation of the second pendulum observed at Quito, Ecuador, approximately 9,000 feet in elevation and again at the Isle of Inca at sea level. Bouguer found that the variation did not follow exactly the inverse-square law of gravitation, and he attributed the difference to the pull exerted by the lofty plateau upon which Quito is built. Making an estimate of the density of the attracting rocks he arrived at a value for the density of the earth which was, when we consider the difficulties of measurement, naturally considerably in error.[10]

Later he made another interesting attempt to show the reality of the force of gravitation by determining the horizontal pull of Chimborazo, a mountain 20,000 feet in height. His method was to find the deflection caused in a plumb line due to the proximity of the mountain, the deflection to be measured by the zenith transit of a star observed in the neighborhood of the mountain and again at a distance from it. As in the other experiment the results attained exhibited a large error. Much distress was experienced by the experimenters from the weather conditions near the mountain. Bouguer wrote: "I shall not speak of the cold and the other discomforts we had to put up with; snow covered our tent and all the ground around as far as 800 or 900 toises (a toise = 6.4 feet) below us, and we lived in fear of being buried under its weight. It needed constant vigilance in order to avoid it."[11] The great achievement accomplished by these hardy adventurers was to show that the force of gravitation is not a subjective concept but existed as a real measurable property of rocks.

A similar attempt to estimate the density of the earth by computing the constant of gravitation was made in 1774 by Nevil Maskelyne, who measured by a zenith telescope the deflection of a plumb line on the north and south sides of Schihallien in Perthshire, Scotland.[12]

More exact determinations of the density of the earth were made in 1854 by Sir G. B. Airy, who employed for his purpose the variations in a pendulum clock lowered to the bottom of a mine shaft. The experiment was carried out in England at the Harton pit near South Shields, the effective depth being 1250 feet.[13] A similar experiment was also tried in 1882-1883 at the Adalbert shaft at Pribram in Bohemia and in 1885 at the Abraham shaft near Freiberg by R. von Sterneck, but the results were necessarily rendered inaccurate by the great difficulty of estimating the density of the different strata through which the shafts were cut.[14]

---

[10]An account of his long labors is published in "La Figure de la Terre," Paris (1749). A translation of section 7 is given by A. S. Mac Kenzie in "The Laws of Gravitation," New York (1900), pp. 23-44.

[11]From "La Figure de la Terre," sec. 7.

[12]An Account of observations made on the mountain Schihallien for finding its attraction, London Phil. Trans. (1775), pp. 500-542.

[13]Monthly notices of the Royal Astr. Soc., vol. 15 (1855), pp. 35-36, 46, 125-6; Ann. de Chim. et de Phys. (1855), vol. 43, (3), pp. 381-3; Arch. des Sc. Phys. et Nat. (1855), vol. 29, pp. 188-191.

[14]Untersuchungen über die Schwere im Innern der Erde, Mitth. Mil.-Geog. Inst. Wien, vol. 2 (1882), pp. 77-120; vol. 3 (1883), pp. 59-94; vol. 4 (1884), pp. 89-155; vol. 5 (1885), pp. 77-105; vol. 6 (1886), pp. 97-119.

The most effective way of determining the gravitation constant is by the direct measurement of the attraction between two carefully constructed masses in the laboratory. Here the difficulty of the experiment is on the other foot. The masses are exactly known, but the force is very small; in the case of the mountain the force is comparatively large, but the density is difficult to determine.

The first experiment of this kind was carried out by Henry Cavendish (1731-1810), prince of experimenters, who perfected an apparatus originally designed by Rev. John Mitchell.[15] This device consisted of a wooden arm made so as to combine great strength with little weight. The arm was suspended by a small wire in a horizontal position, and at each extremity there was hung a lead ball approximately two inches in diameter. Close to these two weights were suspended two larger lead balls eight inches in diameter and the whole apparatus was then enclosed in a sealed room and observed from without by means of a telescope. When the relative positions of the balls were varied by means of a device controlled from outside the room, the variation in attractive force caused a vibration in the system composed of the smaller weights and these vibrations, interpreted by a torsion formula, were then used to determine the force of gravitation.

This experiment has been frequently repeated, a sensible improvement being effected in 1895 by C. V. Boys,[16] who replaced the metal wires of a Cavendish apparatus by delicate quartz fibres. His experiment, subsequently repeated in 1896 by K. Braun,[17] with results agreeing with those of Boys to four significant figures, is today regarded as giving the most accurate determination of the gravitational constant.

R. von Eötvös in 1896 perfected an apparatus now generally used by geologists in the practical application of the torsion balance to mineral and oil explorations.[18]

The conclusion to be drawn from these facts is that we are dealing in the subject of gravitation with a measurable force whose objective existence can be demonstrated in the laboratory. It is not

[15]Experiments to Determine the Density of the Earth, London Phil. Trans. (1798), part II, pp. 469-526.

[16]On the Newtonian Constant of Gravitation. Trans. Royal Soc. of London (A) (1895), vol. 186, pp. 1-72.

[17]Die Gravitations Constante, die Masse and mittlere Dichte der Erde nach einer neuen experimentellen Bestimmung, Denkschr. Akad. Wiss. Wien. Math.-naturw. classe, vol. 64 (1896), pp. 187-258-c.

[18]Untersuchungen über Gravitation und Erdmagnetisms, Wied, Ann. vol. 59 (1896), pp. 354-400. A careful account of the history and developments in this subject up to 1900 is given in "The Laws of Gravitation" by A. S. MacKenzie.

akin to the mystical creation of the ether, whose substantial property is an elusive necessity of reason. The force of gravitation will affect the torsion balance; the ether will react upon no material instrument; the force of gravitation is not a creation of Newton's imagination, with reality only in the equations which determine the orbits of the planets; the ether derives its principal right to a place in science from the equations of Maxwell.

Let us turn to a perplexing question. Why does gravitation fail to have any substantial attribute except that exhibited by the torsion balance? Why does neither heat, cold, chemical structure, nor the screening influence of other matter have the slightest effect upon this mysterious quantity? Are we after all justified in assigning more reality to gravitation than to the ether? The ether is the postulate medium by means of which a vibrating electron on the surface of the sun is able to influence a radiometer in our laboratory; gravitation is a measurable force acting upon two material bodies. Neither appears to have any other substantial characteristic. Are we justified in assuming reality for the one and denying it to the other?

Let us examine these negative characteristics of gravitation a little more closely.

3. The force of gravitation is unaffected by temperature. This was a surprising conclusion, since gravitation is essentially a property of matter and the form and structure of matter are intimately associated with its heat content.

Extremely delicate measurements have been made to test this negative characteristic of gravitational force. J. H. Poynting and P. Phillips counterpoised a mass of 208 grams on a balance, varied its temperature from —186° to 100° centigrade, and found that if there were a change it was less than one part in a billion per degree change for the range from 0° to 100° and less than one in ten billion for the negative range.[19] More recent measurements made in 1916 by P. E. Shaw are somewhat in disagreement with these figures. Working with a range of temperature from 15° to 250° centigrade, he found a positive temperature effect on gravitation, which is, however, not larger than twelve parts in a million per degree.[20]

These experiments are necessarily extremely difficult because of the minuteness of the difference sought for and the many sources

---

[19]Proc. of the Royal Soc. (A) vol. 76 (1905), p. 445. A similar result was obtained by Southerns in 1906. *Ibid.* vol. 78.

[20]Consult: The Newtonian Constant of Gravitation as affected by Temperature. Transactions of the Royal Society, vol. 216 A (1916), pp. 349-392.

of experimental error. A safe conclusion to draw is that the temperature effect, if it exists at all, is very small.

Another significant fact about gravitation is this:

4. Matter is transparent to gravitation.

This is to say there is no appreciable effect upon the gravitational constant if a material screen of any sort be placed between two gravitating objects. There is an interesting speculation in the entertaining story of H. G. Wells: "The First Men in the Moon" as to what would happen if a screen opaque to gravitation could be discovered. Mr. Cavor, the scientist of the tale, had found a method for manufacturing such a screen.[21]

He showed me by calculations on paper which Lord Kelvin, no doubt, or Professor Lodge or Professor Karl Pearson, or any of those great scientific people might have understood, but which simply reduced me to a hopeless muddle, that not only was such a substance possible, but that it must satisfy certain conditions. It was an amazing piece of reasoning. Much as it amazed and exercised me at the time, it would be impossible to reproduce it here. "Yes," I said to it all, "yes. Go on!" Suffice it for this story that he believed he might be able to manufacture this possible substance opaque to gravitation out of a complicated alloy of metals and something new—a new element I fancy—called, I believe, *helium,* which was sent to him from London in sealed stone jars. Doubt has been thrown upon this detail, but I am almost certain it was *helium* he had sent him in sealed stone jars. It was certainly something very gaseous and thin. If I had only taken notes. . . . There seemed no limit to the possibilities of the scheme; whichever way I tried, I came on miracles and revolutions. For example, if one wanted to lift a weight, however enormous, one had only to get a sheet of this substance beneath it and one might lift it with a straw. My first natural impulse was to apply this principle to guns and iron-clads and all the material and methods of war and from that to shipping, locomotion, building, every conceivable form of human industry. The chance that had brought me into the very birth chamber of this new time—it was an epoch, no less—was one of those chances that come once in a thousand years. The thing unrolled, it expanded and expanded.

The facts in the case seem to be these: By careful experimentation it has been found that the absorption of terrestrial gravitation by a sheet of lead five centimeters in thickness, if any, is less than two parts in a hundred billion. If the effect had been at all appreciable we should long since have observed it, for the screening effect of the

---

[21]Page 18.

earth upon the gravitational pull of the moon would have made itself evident in the tides on that side of the earth opposite to the moon.

## 4. Mechanical Theories of Gravitation.

The question long ago forced itself upon scientists: Why should gravitation exhibit these negative characteristics? Why should gravitation be wholly inert to experiment except as the one important property of attraction is invoked?

Many theories have been propounded in the past to explain gravitation and like those which we reviewed for the ether they are all based upon material models. That desire of the human reason for analogy and rational explanation is at its highest in the history of these numerous attempts.

It will suffice for the purpose of this volume to mention only two, one by Newton and the other by Georges-Louis Lesage (1724-1803), a France-Swiss physicist and mathematician. The story of the attempt to give a material explanation to the force of gravitation is similar to that of the heroic struggle to endow the ether with substantial properties. There is, however, one striking difference. There finally emerged out of the efforts of the investigators of the ether a magnificent theory of light in terms of electro-magnetic forces; from it we acquire the boon of wireless communication and a tool of great power in exploring the mysteries of energy. The attempts to endow gravitation with a material explanation have been sadly sterile. We have acquired no music of the spheres; we have gained no insight into the relationships between useful quantities. Gravitation stands alone in the universe, a strange and perplexing entity. Nothing connects it with electricity, magnetism, or light. It is constant and unchanging, a sphinx, whose riddle cannot be answered by the delicate balances of the laboratory. Its extreme minuteness baffles experiment; it acts in one direction only and does not exhibit the phenomenon of repulsion common to the two apparently similar entities of electricity and magnetism.

We have already quoted the famous passage of a letter written by Newton to Rev. Richard Bentley in which he expresses the opinion that "it is inconceivable that inanimate brute matter should, without the mediation of something else which is not material, operate upon and affect other matter, without mutual contact." This matter evidently recurred often to him as we see in allusions scattered through his writing, but twenty-five years after the letter to Bentley we find that he has reached a tentative explanation. In an appendix to the second edition of his "Optics," published in 1717, he reflects upon the nature of the all-pervading ether with which he thought space endowed, and states his postulates as follows:

Is not this medium much rarer within the dense bodies of the sun, stars, planets, and comets, than in the empty celestial spaces between them? And in passing from them to greater distances, doth it not grow denser and denser perpetually, and thereby cause the gravity of those great bodies toward one another, and of their parts towards bodies; every body endeavoring to go from the denser parts of the medium toward the rarer? . . . And though this increase of density may at great distances be exceedingly slow, yet if the elastic force of this medium be exceedingly great, it may suffice to impel bodies from the denser part of the medium toward the rarer, with all that power which we call gravity.

This statement of Newton is a curious exhibit of the desire of the mind for material explanation. We must remember that Newton's age marked the first genuine swing away from the occult mysticism and the vague, nebulous speculation of the esoteric philosophy of the middle ages. The tenet of philosophy had been that to have the appearance of wisdom one must be obscure. It reminds one of the story of "The Emperor's New Clothes" as related by Hans Christian Andersen. Two rogues disguised as tailors entered the monarch's domain and commenced the task of weaving new robes for the emperor. They caused the statement to be circulated that the new garments would appear invisible to anyone who was unfit to hold his office or who was incorrigibly stupid. Those who were called in to view the imaginary fabrics upon the looms exclaimed how beautiful their texture was and admired the details of workmanship. Finally the day came for the emperor to parade before his people in his new splendor; the imaginary garments were placed upon him, and he exhibited himself upon the streets. "What beautiful robes," cried the people, until a little child exclaimed, "Why the king hasn't any clothes on!" and the spell was broken.

One likes to turn to the other view of Newton, expressed at the conclusion of the third book of the Principia, where he says: "Hitherto I have not been able to discover the cause of those properties of gravity from phenomena, and I frame no hypothesis; for whatever is not deduced from the phenomena is to be called an hypothesis. . . . To us it is enough that gravity does really exist and act according to the laws which we have explained."

One of the most ingenious theories advanced to give a mechanical explanation of gravity was that due to Lesage who constructed his hypothesis in 1747 when he was only twenty-three years of age. He is said to have been so elated over the idea that he wrote to his father: "Eureka! Eureka! Never have I felt such satisfaction as at this moment, in which I have just succeeded in explaining completely, by the simple laws of rectilinear movement, the principle of *universal gravitation.*"[22]

The theory advanced by Lesage was that space was filled with a huge swarm of "ultramundane corpuscles" of very minute size moving rapidly in all directions. An object placed in such a sea of particles would naturally remain at rest because as many corpuscles would strike it on one side as upon the other and there would be no pressure differential to create motion. It would be otherwise, however, with two bodies immersed in such a "gravitational fluid," because each would screen off some of the corpuscles from the other and the difference in pressure that would thus result would tend to drive the two objects together. Moreover, it is possible to show that the impelling force would vary inversely as the square of the distance between the two bodies.

This theory of Lesage appealed to the philosophers of the nineteenth century because of its simplicity and ingenuity. To be sure it substituted for an incomprehensible attraction, acting at a distance, a metaphysical swarm of ethereal corpuscles, but the picture seemed easier to grasp and accorded more closely with material models. Even Poincaré devotes several pages of his philosophy to a consideration of the consequences of the mechanical problem thus presented.[23]

The weakness of the theory was found to be precisely the weakness of the elastic solid theory of the ether. As soon as one tried to investigate the elasticity of the corpuscles or the material density of the medium which their swarm created, the old dilemmas reappear. If, for example, the particles were perfectly elastic there would be no momentum given to the bodies immersed in them and hence no attraction. Furthermore, the law of inverse squares is not derivable exactly from the Lesage picture unless the corpuscles are completely inelastic, and this leads to difficulties with the astronomical observa-

---

[22]In its completed form it appeared in the transactions of the Royal Academy of Berlin in 1782 under the title: "Lucrece Newtonien." For an historical account see W. B. Taylor: Kinetic Theories of Gravitation, Smithsonian Inst. Report for 1876, pp. 205-282.

[23]Foundations of Science, pp. 517-522.

tion that the planets move about the sun without encountering any resistance from the space medium. To escape this difficulty it is necessary to assume that these ultramundane corpuscles must have a velocity at least $24 \times 10^{17}$ times that of light, but if this be granted then the heat generated by the impact of the particles upon such an object as the earth would be enough to raise the temperature $10^{26}$ degrees a second. The heat necessary to maintain such a gradient may be calculated to be $10^{20}$ times the total output of the sun's radiation. Alas for the double eureka of the imaginative Lesage![24]

## 5.  Space, Time, and Gravitation.

In this, as in the case of the ether, mechanical analogies and material concepts fail us. On the one hand we have the fact of attraction, and one would be mad to deny the evidence of the delicate balances of Cavandish; on the other we have the fact of the transport of energy, and we should be equally mad to deny the evidence of diffraction. But when we try to postulate a transcendental fluid and endow it with material properties of any kind we are faced with contradictions. One who in the enthusiasm of youth wishes to try the old problem again and to enter the lists with the lance of imagination, must be very cautious how he exults over the apparent demise of his metaphysical enemy. The only permanent conquest is likely to be found in the mystical symbols of a mathematical formula which is capable of transformation into conclusions in accord with laboratory experiment.

We turn finally to a consideration of a recent great explanation of gravitation. That it is the true picture may be doubted. That it meets the criteria just laid down, first of formulization in terms of equations and second of reaching conclusions vindicated by experiment is a point not to be controverted. Einstein, following the traditions of Mach and under the stimulus of the success of his special theory of relativity, fell to musing upon the negative characteristics of the gravitational field. Suddenly he was struck by the following question: Is not gravitation, itself, an attribute of space and time rather than an attribute of matter? In other words, perhaps the negative character of these propositions with regard to gravitation may be explained by the assumption that we are experimenting with space and time rather than with matter itself.

---

[24]See "Considerations on Gravitation" by H. A. Lorentz, Proceedings of the Royal Academy of Amsterdam, vol. 2 (1900), pp. 559-574. The theory has recently been revived in a non-mathematical form with radiation pressure replacing the impact of the Lesagian particles in James Mackaye's: The Dynamic Universe (1931).

This potent reflection was destined to bear great fruit. In the view of Einstein it should be possible to shut off gravitation, not by the interposition of a screen of matter, but by changing the character of space. The force of this point is illustrated in a story which seems destined to become as classic as Newton's apple. Einstein seeing a laborer fall from a building rushed up to the man, who was fortunately unhurt, and asked him if he felt anything pulling upon him. The man's reply in the negative corresponded exactly with Einstein's musings.

The idea of course goes back years before the savant's experience just related, for we find the following illuminating passage in the treatise of Lewis Carroll.

The rabbit-hole went straight on like a tunnel for some way, and then dipped suddenly down, so suddenly that Alice had not a moment to think about stopping herself before she found herself falling down what seemed to be a very deep well.

Either the well was very deep, or she fell very slowly, for she had plenty of time as she went down to look about her, and to wonder what was going to happen next. First, she tried to look down and make out what she was coming to, but it was too dark to see anything: then she looked at the sides of the well, and noticed that they were filled with cupboards and book-shelves: here and there she saw maps and pictures hung upon pegs. She took down a jar from one of the shelves as she passed: it was labeled "ORANGE MARMALADE," but to her great disappointment it was empty: she did not like to drop the jar, for fear of killing somebody underneath, so managed to put it into one of the cupboards as she fell past it.

"Well!" thought Alice to herself. "After such a fall as this, I shall think nothing of tumbling down-stairs! How brave they'll all think me at home! Why, I wouldn't say anything about it, even if I fell off the top of the house." (Which was very likely true).

Absurd most of you will think. Not at all says Einstein, who, perhaps, derived his inspiration from this source rather than from the thoughts of Mach. It is the easiest thing in the world to destroy a gravitational field. Just start to fall. The gravitational field immediately disappears. Take your watch out of your pocket and place it in the air at your side. It will float there without support. The only difficulty will be found if you should encounter some other object such as the surface of the earth which is falling in the opposite direction. The explanation of the adventure related by Mr. Carroll was that the hole into which Alice tumbled was itself in motion with an acceleration that partly destroyed the field of gravitation.

To put the matter a little more scientifically let us consider an illustration used by Einstein himself. Suppose that we are riding in an elevator and have no knowledge whatsoever of the world outside. We set out to examine the laws of nature as we find them and we set up a pendulum or a gyroscope or some other device whose behaviour depends upon the gravitational field in which it is placed. If the elevator is at rest with respect to the earth everything will take place inside the elevator according to the same laws of matter that we find in our ordinary text books of mechanics. But suppose that the elevator is moving upward with a uniform acceleration. Not knowing anything about the universe outside we should be under the impression that we are living in a universe with a tremendous field of gravitation. If the elevator moved fast enough we might duplicate the gravitational field of the planet Jupiter, where the only pleasant thing to do is to rest.

On the other hand if the elevator moved with an acceleration of thirty-two feet per second, which is equal to that of the field of the earth, all gravitation would completely disappear. We should not need tables, because table cloths could be spread out on the air and dinner served upon them without the slightest chance of an accident. There would be some difficulties, of course, such as the pouring of tea which would have to be transformed into the pumping of tea, since no force of gravitation would be there to perform the necessary act of pouring. There would be neither up nor down, and space would be exactly the same in all directions. The only forces to be overcome would be those due to the inertia of matter. Commodities such as sugar and flour would no longer be sold by the pound weight, but by the pound inertia. There is an interesting story in point in the tragedy of two miners who found a large quantity of gold near the Arctic circle. This they carefully weighed on a spring balance and shipped to San Francisco for mutual division. But when the gold was re-weighed at the California city a certain amount of it was found to have disappeared. The loss of something like three pounds in a thousand was due to the variation in gravity (the difference between the gravitational pull of the earth and the opposite centrifugal force created by the rotation of the earth). An unhappy tragedy attendant upon the discovery of this loss in the gold would have been avoided had the original measurements been made according to inertial mass.

It is also possible to invert gravitation completely. Suppose that the acceleration of the elevator be increased beyond thirty-two feet.

Our table cloth would now no longer float in the air but would fall upwards toward the ceiling. The whole situation would be that of Topsy Turvey land. You have probably read the adventures of the redoubtable Baron Munchausen, who enjoys the unique distinction of being the greatest liar in the history of the human race. It is not now so difficult to explain the following incident in his career:

On another occasion I wished to jump across a lake. When I was in the middle of it, I found that it was much larger than I had imagined at first. So I at once turned back in the middle of my leap, and returned to the bank I had just left, to take a stronger spring. The second time, however, I again took off badly, and fell up to my neck. I should, beyond any doubt, have come to an untimely end, had I not, by the force of my own unaided arm, lifted myself up by my pig-tail, together with my horse, whom I gripped tightly with my knees.

The explanation of this passage is probably that the Baron had encountered a place upon the surface of the earth where the gravitational field had been reversed by some such process as has been outlined above.

## 6. *Einstein's Theory of Gravitation.*

What then is Einstein's theory of gravitation? Gravitation, according to Einstein, is an intimate property of the space-time continuum, because it is clear that we can do away with it by a proper choice of the space-time with which we are to experiment. To be sure this may not always be desirable in practical affairs, because none of us would care to live very long in a falling elevator, but one can see from the illustration that it is possible to reverse gravitation and otherwise to change it by the device suggested.

Let us see what conclusion can be drawn from this point of view.

First, it explains why gravitation has for so many years given negative results to our experiments. Second, it explains the equivalence of inert mass and weight. Of course a property of space-time could not be screened away by the interposal of matter, nor should it be effected by means of such a material agent as temperature.

These remarks may at first sight appear as metaphysical as those of the old sophists, but here is the marvel. Einstein actually derived an equation for space-time in the neighborhood of gravitating matter. The technical machinery by means of which he reached this interesting equation is very difficult mathematical reading and has led to the remark that only a dozen or so mathematicians are able to understand relativity. While the mathematics is difficult, the point of view and the conclusions are not necessarily so, provided one has had sufficient practice in the art of believing impossible things.

The actual words used by Einstein in explaining his novel concept, while not entirely free from technical nomenclature, will yield their gem of thought if they are carefully scrutinized. The following significant passages are quoted from Einstein's lectures given at Princeton University in May 1921 :[25]

In the first place, it is contrary to the mode of thinking in science to conceive of a thing (the space-time continuum) which acts itself, but which cannot be acted upon. This is the reason why E. Mach was led to make the attempt to eliminate space as an active cause in the system of mechanics. According to him, a material particle does not move in an unaccelerated motion relatively to space, but relatively to the center of all the other masses in the universe; in this way the series of causes of mechanical phenomena was closed, in contrast to the mechanics of Newton and Galileo. In order to develop this idea within the limits of the modern theory of action through a medium, the properties of the space-time continuum which determine inertia must be regarded as field properties of space, analogous to the electro-magnetic field. The concepts of classical mechanics afford no way of expressing this. For this reason Mach's attempt at a solution failed for the time being. . . . In the second place, classical mechanics indicates a limitation which directly demands an extension of the principle of relativity to spaces of reference which are not in uniform motion relatively to each other. The ratio of the masses of two bodies is defined in mechanics in two ways which differ from each other fundamentally; in the first place, as the reciprocal ratio of the acceleration which the same motional force imparts to them (inert mass), and in the second place, as the ratio of the forces which act upon them in the same gravitational field (gravitational mass). The equality of these two masses, so differently defined, is a fact which is confirmed by experiments of very high accuracy (experiments of Eötvös), and classical mechanics offers no explanation for this equality. It is, however, clear that science is fully justified in assigning such a numerical equality only after this numerical equality is reduced to an equality of the real nature of the two concepts.

That this object may actually be attained by an extension of the principle of relativity, follows from the following consideration. A little reflection will show that the theorem of the equality of the inert and the gravitational mass is equivalent to the theorem that the acceleration imparted to a body by a gravitational field is inde-

[25]The Meaning of Relativity (1923), Princeton University Press, pp. 62-65.

pendent of the nature of the body. For Newton's equation of motion in a gravitational field, written out in full, is

(Inert mass) . (Acceleration) = (Intensity of the gravitational field) . (Gravitational mass).

It is only when there is numerical equality between the inert and gravitational mass that the acceleration is independent of the nature of the body. Let now K be an inertial system. Masses which are sufficiently far from each other and from other bodies are then, with respect to K, free from acceleration. We shall also refer these masses to a system of co-ordinates K′, uniformly accelerated with respect to K. Relatively to K′ all the masses have equal and parallel accelerations; with respect to K′ they behave just as if a gravitational field were present and K′ were unaccelerated. Overlooking for the present the question as to the "cause" of such a gravitational field, which will occupy us later, there is nothing to prevent our conceiving this gravitational field as real, that is, the conception that K′ is "at rest" and a gravitational field is present we may consider as equivalent to the conception that only K is an "allowable" system of co-ordinates and no gravitational field is present. The assumption of the complete physical equivalence of the systems of coördinates, K and K′, we call the "principle of equivalence"; this principle is evidently intimately connected with the theorem of the equality between the inert and the gravitational mass, and signifies an extension of the principle of relativity to coördinate systems which are in non-uniform motion relative to each other. In fact, through this conception we arrive at the unity of the nature of inertia and gravitation. For according to our way of looking at it, the same masses may appear to be either under the action of inertia alone (with respect to K) or under the combined action of inertia and gravitation (with respect to K′). The possibility of explaining the numerical equality of inertia and gravitation by the unity of their nature gives to the general theory of relativity, according to my conviction, such a superiority over the conceptions of classical mechanics, that all the difficulties encountered in development must be considered as small in comparison.

What justifies us in dispensing with the preference for inertial systems over all other coördinate systems, a preference that seems so securely established by experiment based upon the principle of inertia? The weakness of the principle of inertia lies in this, that it involves an argument in a circle: the mass moves without acceleration if it is sufficiently far from other bodies; we know that it is sufficiently far from other bodies only by the fact that it moves without acceleration. Are there, in general, any inertial systems for very extended portions of the space-time continuum, or, indeed, for the whole universe? We may look upon the principle of inertia as established to a high degree of approximation, for the space of our planetary system, provided that we neglect the perturbations due to the sun and planets. Stated more exactly, there are finite regions, where, with respect to a suitably chosen space of reference, material particles move freely without acceleration, and in which the laws of the special theory of relativity . . . hold with remarkable accuracy. Such regions we shall call "Galilean regions." We shall proceed from the consideration of such regions as a special case of known properties.

We can summarize these conclusions of Einstein in the following way. Let us assume that gravitation is an aspect of geometry and as such can be made to reveal the secret of the kind of space-time in which we dwell. You will recall from previous explanations in the book that there are three subjective geometries. One of these, due to Lobachevski and Bolyai, assumes that the sum of the angles of a triangle is less than 180 degrees; a second, due to Euclid, assumes that the angle sum is exactly equal to two right angles; the third, to which the name of Riemann is attached, postulates that the sum of the angles exceeds 180 degrees. What then is the geometry of space-time in which a gravitational force reveals itself?

If the gravitational force found always in the presence of material things is to be regarded as evidence of a warp in space-time, this should be capable of mathematical expression. This idea of a warp in space is found, curiously enough, in a short document by W. K. Clifford (1845-1879) published in 1876. This brilliant young mathematician postulated: "(1) That small portions of space *are* in fact of a nature analogous to little hills on a surface which is on the average flat; namely, that the ordinary laws of geometry are not valid in them. (2) That this property of being curved or distorted is continually being passed on from one portion of space to another after the manner of a wave. (3) That this variation of the curvature of space is what really happens in that phenomenon which we call the *motion of matter,* whether ponderable or ethereal. (4) That in the physical world nothing else takes place but this variation, subject (possibly) to the law of continuity." Einstein, following the ordinary procedure of geometers, first set down a very general mathematical formula, which he defined as the metric of space-time. In this formula there occurred ten coefficients, which were to be chosen in such a manner that two fundamental criteria were to be satisfied. The first of these criteria was the very natural one that the geometry, or in other words, the space-time metric, was to be independent of the mathematical coördinates used. To put this otherwise, what does nature care for the language man uses to describe her laws? The second criterion merely assumed that the coefficients of the space-time metric were to be so chosen that space-time was "flat" at distances remote from gravitating matter. In one way this statement is equivalent to the special theory of relativity, which may be regarded as a statement of the invariance of "flat" space-time. It is difficult, if not impossible, to describe the new theory more adequately without invoking the aid of mathematics. Einstein, employing the absolute differential calculus, an abstract mathematical theory developed from the fundamental work of Riemann and Christoffel by G. Ricci and T. Levi-Civita, solved his problem and found an explicit evaluation for his ten gravitational coefficients. The space-time metric of the objective universe was revealed to his view. The problem of gravitation was now merged in the problem of space-time. Some of the more speculative consequences of the new metric will be postponed to the next chapter, and we shall turn to a review of the three crucial experiments which vindicated the new theory.

## 7. *The Vindicating Experiments.*

The first of these experiments concerns the bending of light rays in the vicinity of a gravitation body. Newton had previously held the view that gravitation would influence the path of a ray of light, but for a very different reason. Light in his hypothesis was composed of a swarm of material particles and hence like any other body should suffer deviation in the neighborhood of a large material body like the sun. The deflection of light passing close to the limb of our sun would, on the basis of the corpuscular theory, amount to an angle equal to .87 of a second. But the space-time metric of Einstein gave a different answer. Space-time in the neighborhood of the sun, due to the gravitational field, would vary from the space-time of Euclid's geometry by an amount sufficient to deflect a ray of light by an angle twice that predicted by Newtonian theory or 1.74. This bending is not to be attributed directly to gravitational pull, you will understand, but is due to the *warped nature of space-time* in the vicinity of the gravitating body.

Is there experimental evidence for this belief? When Einstein made his spectacular announcement it immediately became the goal of several eclipse expeditions to verify or disprove the statement. When the shadow of the moon covers the surface of the sun, the stars in the immediate neighborhood of the shadow may be seen. Their light is caught upon a photographic plate and a comparison can then be made between their apparent and real positions as computed for the time of the eclipse. Figure 6 shows what was actually found in the plate obtained by the Crocker Eclipse Expedition to Wallai, Western Australia, 1922. The dots represent stars and the dashes attached to them measure the displacements. It will be evident that on the average the stars near the limb of the sun suffer a greater displacement than those further away. A somewhat more vivid picture of the agreement between theory and experiment is found in the diagram in figure 7, the broken line being the average value of the position of the stars. This is regarded generally as a

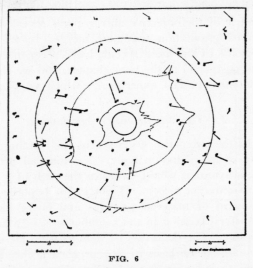

FIG. 6

The actual displacement of stars observed during an eclipse of the sun at Wallai, Western Australia, 1922. The irregular figure about the sun is the outline of the corona. (From Lick Observatory Bulletin, No. 346.)

very satisfactory agreement when all the sources of experimental error are taken into account.[26]

A second triumph for the theory of the space-time view of gravitation has been found in the explanation afforded of the one outstanding discrepancy between Newton's theory of gravitation and actual observation. Mercury, the tiny planet that lies so close to the sun that it can be seen with the naked eye only a few times a year, has never behaved according to Newton's law of gravitation. The perihelion of its elliptic orbit is swinging about in space at the rapid rate of 43 seconds of arc per century. This tiny discrepancy has long puzzled astronomers, and until it has been explained away no

[26]From the Lick Observatory Bulletin, No. 346.

one will feel that the law of gravitation as stated by Newton is absolutely correct. As a matter of fact it may be the key that unlocks new mysteries of space and time. One should remark in passing, however, that the tiny variation which we have mentioned comes out of a tremendous distillation of mathematical equations. Urbain Jean Joseph Leverrier (1811-1877), the great French astronomer who shares with Adams the glory of having discovered Neptune, and Simon Newcomb (1835-1909), father of the American ephemerides, both agree that after the long equations determining the perturbations of the planets have been distilled and redistilled there remains a small residual error which can be accounted for by introducing the perihelion shift already noted. That there may exist other neglected facts in this very difficult problem is a possibility not wholly to be

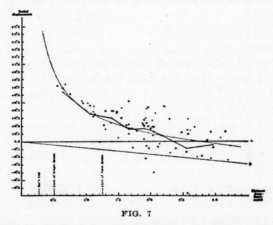

FIG. 7

Diagram showing the displacement of the stars the light from which passes close to the sun. The smooth line is Einstein's prediction; the broken line is the average displacement. (From Lick Observatory Bulletin, No. 346.)

discarded, and the transits of the tiny Mercury across the great disk of the sun are watched with interest by the astronomers.

The thing significant in the present instance is the fact that the theory of gravitation as announced by Einstein exactly accounts for this perihelion discrepancy. Space-time in the neighborhood of the huge gravitating sun has been sufficiently changed so that Mercury, the baby of the planets, exhibits a slight variation in its orbit. One would not care to state that this single triumph is justification for belief in Einstein's theory, but there is another experiment of similar character which adds new luster to the victory.

In another chapter it will be pointed out that some hold to the belief that matter radiates heat, light, wireless waves, etc., because the tiny constituent electrons are constrained to move in elliptical orbits with dimensions depending upon the frequency of the radiation. The radiation is thoroughly characterized by the lines of its spectrum, so we should expect to find some evidence for or against the postulates of relativity in the velocity of the electrons. That this is a tenable hypothesis has been pointed out in the spectrum of hydrogen. As most of you know, hydrogen is the simplest of the gases and according to theory consists of a single electronic planet revolving at high speed around a single proton nucleus. Should not the high velocity of the electron make a difference in the space-time in its immediate neighborhood? According to A. Sommerfeld this is actually the case and the effect to be looked for is a precession of its perihelion exactly like that of the planet Mercury although much more rapid. If such an advance of perihelion actually exists it should make itself known by a fine division of the spectral lines of hydrogen known as *the fine structure* of the lines. The fine structure thus predicted has been found experimentally. According to Sommerfeld this beautiful fact furnishes "ocular evidence not only of the actual occurrence of the elliptic orbits but also of the variability of the electronic mass."[27]

Another triumph of even more spectacular character has come about through the third prediction of Einstein. "Time," said he, "changes in heavy gravitational fields so that the time on the sun is different from our time on the earth." A very good clock to use in testing this conclusion is the vibration of radiating atoms. These vibrations we know with very great precision through a study of the lines of the spectrum. How, then, shall we decide whether time is the same on the sun as on the earth? The answer is to compare the lines in the spectrum of an element on the sun with lines created by heating the same element in a laboratory on the earth. If the lines in the solar spectrum are shifted toward the red end we can interpret this difference to be due to the slower vibration of the

---

[27]From Atomic Structure, Eng. translation (1923), chap. 8. It must be confessed, however, that this relativity explanation has not proved competent to explain all the phenomena of fine-structure. To it there has been added the concept of an *electron spin* which connects the phenomena with electronic magnetism. The brilliant work of P. A. M. Dirac, however, has been able to unite the two theories of the origin of fine-structure by showing that the electron spin is a direct consequence of the relativity principle when the latter is applied to the equations of the wave mechanics (See chapter X). Employing these results Sommerfeld has been led to conclude that electron magnetism is itself relativistic in origin. "Instead of an incomprehensible accident we see here the manifestation of a deep-seated identity which must ultimately lead to a solution of the problem of the electron itself, which includes such questions as: Why do negative and positive electricity occur in elementary quanta, why is their mass unequal, what is their structure, why do they hold together?" Wave Mechanics. English edition (1930), p. 118.

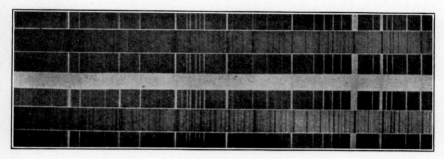

PLATE VII

The central spectrum in each series is that of the spectroscopic binary Mu Orionis. The dark lines are compared with the corresponding lines of titanium and show the Doppler shift toward the red end of the spectrum. This is interpreted as due to a recessive velocity. The lower spectrum indicates a velocity of twelve miles per second. (Yerkes Observatory.)

atom in the sun. In other words clocks on the sun will thus be proved to be slower than on the earth. To be sure there is another interpretation given to the shifting of spectrum lines, which is known to astronomers as the Doppler effect. Just as the pitch of a train's whistle rises as the train approaches and lowers when it recedes, so the spectrum lines move toward the violet as the star approaches and toward the red as it recedes from us. In the accompanying picture (plate VII) we see this Doppler shift clearly in the lower spectrum obtained from the light of Mu Orionis. The lines of the star's spectrum show a displacement corresponding to a recessive velocity of twelve miles per second. Hence conclusions formed on the basis of a spectrum shift become a little doubtful. Shall the shift be attributed to recessive velocity or to the structure of time? This question has to be decided from other contributory evidence.

After prolonged experimentation on these exceedingly delicate differences between earth-time and sun-time, C. E. St. John of the Mount Wilson observatory finally committed himself as follows:[28]

The conclusion is that three major causes are producing the differences between solar and terrestrial wave-lengths, and that it is possible to disentangle their effects. The causes appear to be the slowing up of the atomic clock in the sun to an amount predicted by the theory of generalized relativity, radial velocities of moderate cosmic magnitude and in probable directions, and differential scattering in the longer paths traversed through the solar atmosphere by light coming from the limb of the sun.

But here is the most surprising part of the story. Astronomers were not quite satisfied with the conclusions reached in the investigation of the difference between sun time and earth time; they looked about in the sky for another object where there might be unmistakable differences in space-time due to the gravitational difference. Fortunately there is a remarkable object in the heavens, the tiny white dwarf companion of Sirius, the Dog star. This tiny object is only of the 8.5 magnitude, which means that it is beyond naked-eye visibility. By calculations too technical to give here[29] it has been ascertained that this star has about two-fifths the mass of the brilliant Sirius and from an examination of its spectrum it is estimated that its surface temperature is greater than that of our own

---

[28]On Gravitation Displacement of Solar Lines, Monthly Notices of Royal Astro. Soc., vol. 84 (1923), pp. 93-96. See also Proc. of National Academy of Sciences, vol. 12 (1926), pp. 65-68.

[29]See Eddington: Monthly Notices of Royal Astro. Soc., vol. 84 (1924), p. 308; also, A Debate on Relativity, Chicago (1927), pp. 102-104.

sun. In order to reconcile these facts thrust upon us by a hot, heavy star that is beyond naked-eye visibility, it has been necessary to assume that the density of this amazing object reaches the unbelievable limit of 50,000 times that of water, approximately one ton per cubic inch.

Some astronomers find this density difficult to believe. They ask whether you want to admit that a glass of water could weigh twenty-five tons and then quote Mark Twain upon evidence: "Even the clearest and most perfect circumstantial evidence is likely to be at fault, after all, and therefore ought to be received with great caution. Take the case of any pencil, sharpened by any woman: If you have witnesses, you will find she did it with a knife; but if you take simply the aspect of the pencil, you will say she did it with her teeth."

However, assuming that the white dwarf has this amazing density is there evidence that space-time is changed in its vicinity? Convincingly so! The actual measured shift is nearly forty times the corresponding shift for our sun, which shows that time upon this star is a very sluggish thing, indeed.[30] The relativists claim that this is one of the greatest victories for the Einstein theory; those who oppose it believe that human credulity can go a long ways but not that far.

### 8. *The Music of the Spheres.*

In the mystical pseudo-science of Aristotle we find attributed to Pythagoras the idea of the music of the spheres. "Some authorities," says Aristotle,[31] "maintain that large revolving bodies must cause sound, since bodies on our earth, which are smaller and move with less speed do so. Inevitable, they say, there must be a terrific noise caused by the sun, moon, and other large heavenly bodies moving at such speed. Assuming this and assuming that their velocities and the intervals between them are harmonious, they declare that the revolving stars have a musical sound. They say that the reason why we do not hear this sound—a thing which seems unreasonable—is that it has been part of our experience from birth and is not distinguishable from silence. For sound and silence are only distinguishable with reference to each other. It is similar to the case of coppersmiths, who on account of their regular habit think nothing of the sounds made by their own tools. In the same way mankind generally does not notice the sound of the revolving heavenly bodies, As I have already said, there is much elegance and beauty in this

---

[30]The shift is actually .3 of an Angstrom unit as compared with .008 for the sun. An Angstrom unit is 10-8 cm.

[31]From De Caelo, II, 9. Translation made by Dr. R. H. Coon.

theory, but it cannot be true." The slower and near bodies radiate deep notes and the swifter and further bodies give out the higher notes which blend into a celestial or cosmic octave.

Is there any truth to this mystic science, in spite of the adverse opinion of Aristotle? In 1918 Einstein discussed the existence of gravitational waves[32] on the basis of his relativity theory and reached the interesting conclusion that "every change in the distribution of matter produces a gravitational effect which is propagated in space with the velocity of light." This idea is not a wholly modern one since the possibility of finite propagation of gravitation has been discussed by various mathematicians and astronomers in the past. We find Laplace investigating the velocity on the basis that gravitation is an evidence of fluid pressure. In order to reconcile the fact that the planets move without appreciable loss of energy due to resistance encountered from the space-filling entity, the eminent astronomer was led to the conclusion that the velocity of propagation of attraction could not be less than six million times that of light. F. Zöllner,[33] years later, making use of a formula originally due to H. Weber, suggested a modification of the simple law of Newton, in which terms were introduced containing a velocity factor. If this velocity were chosen equal to that of light the modification caused in the orbit of Mercury would be a precession of the perihelion equivalent to 14.52 seconds, which is, of course, significantly inferior to the one agreed upon by Leverrier and Newcomb. In order to attain the precession of 38 seconds, found by Leverrier and later increased to 43 seconds by Newcomb, a velocity of propagation equal to three-fifths that of light would be required. Similar modifications by Riemann, Gauss, Clausius, Seeliger, and others failed to identify in any natural way the velocity of the propagation of gravitation with the velocity of light so that the perihelion shift could be satisfactorily accounted for.[34] Only P. Gerber in 1898 in a clever paper on the subject succeeded where the others failed, but his law of gravitation has never received the attention that it has perhaps deserved.[35]

The new approach of Einstein has yielded the answer that appeals as a reasonable one and its derivation is a natural consequence of

[32]See: Über Gravitationswellen, Sitzungsberichte der Preuss. Akad. der Wissenschaften. (1918), pp. 154-167; also H. Weyl: Raum, Zeit, Materie. Eng. trans. (1921), pp. 248-252.
[33]Principien einer electrodynamischen Theorie der Materie, Leipzig (1876).
[34]For an account of these researches see F. Tisserand: Traité de Mécanique Céleste, vol. 4, Paris (1896), chap. 28.
[35]Die räumliche und zeitliche Ausbreitung der Gravitation. Zeitschrift für Math. und Phys., vol. 43 (1898), pp. 669-670.

the law of gravitation which takes its structure from the character of the space-time metric. Verification experimentally has naturally been impossible to attain because of the infinitesimal differences involved. If all this is true, however, there is meaning, perhaps, to the music of the spheres. If we could only devise an Eötvös balance sensitive enough we might be able to catch these ethereal vibrations and turn them into sound as we now do with the waves of the radio. Is it too wild a dream to hope that someday we may hear the soft vibrations of the planet Mars or the orchestral symphony of the moons of Jupiter?

Perhaps the following quotation from Through the Looking Glass is the most appropriate response to the question:

"When you say 'hill,' " the Queen interrupted, "*I* could show you hills, in comparison with which you'd call that a valley."

"No, I shouldn't," said Alice, surprised into contradicting her at last: "a hill *can't* be a valley, you know. That would be nonsense——"

The Red Queen shook her head. "You may call it 'nonsense' if you like," she said, "but *I've* heard nonsense, compared with which that would be as sensible as a dictionary!"

## 9.   *What is Gravitation?*

And what are our conclusions about the mysterious action at a distance, with which we started in the first chapter? We have traced its history from the laws of Kepler, through the magnificent postulates of Newton, to the new revelation of Einstein. We have seen it start with the metaphysical assumption that objects are influenced by a force which acts through the vacuum of space; we have reviewed its struggle to gain objective reality by the postulate of an ethereal fluid composed of rapidly moving "ultramundane corpuscles"; we have traced the attempts of careful experimenters to discover some objective characteristic of gravitation other than that of attraction; we have finally witnessed the overwhelming of these objective pictures in the subjective equations of Einstein, in which space-time becomes the reality. Here at last we are able to gain new experimental evidence where all previous efforts had been in vain.

And what conclusion shall we draw from the history of this noble conquest? Will it not be similar to that derived from the struggle of science to endow the ether with rational existence. Both concepts lose their identity in the reality of space-time; all other objective existence is denied them. Their objectivity is replaced by sets of equations, which for the one determine the paths of the planets with marvelous precision, predict the deflection of rays of light in the neighborhood of matter and the shifting of spectrum lines in heavy stars; and for the other, tell the story of the transfer of radiant energy through the emptiness of space, explain diffraction patterns, and predict the experimental behaviour of light.

Do these conclusions satisfy us or is there still that desire of the reason to see further into these perplexing things, to make them more tangible in the sense of making them more akin to sensuous experience? Are we talking metaphysics or are we now seeing a new vision of the meaning of reality?

# CHAPTER VII.

## IS NATURE FINITE?

### 1. *Voltaire and the Infinities of Newton.*

FRANÇOIS-MARIE AROUET, (1694-1778) better known as Voltaire, was one philosopher at least who led a busy life. His days were not all spent in the seclusion of his closet meditating upon the problems of metaphysics. At an early age ideas began to get him into trouble, not ideas perhaps so much as his desire to tell them to other people. His first escapade at the age of 23 involved him with the regent who governed France during the childhood of Louis XV, and he had the good fortune to gain needed leisure by being imprisoned in the Bastile for a period of eleven months. Nine years later Voltaire's mental activities again involved him in a quarrel, this time with the Chevalier de Rohan, and in order to escape a second imprisonment he was forced into exile in England. During this period (1726-1729) Voltaire learned much about the activities of that island and in particular became acquainted with the ideas of Newton. They took fire in his imagination, and when he returned to France he published a series of essays entitled "Letters on the English," which served among other things to introduce the thoughts of the English scientist to the French people. In one of these (XVII) he makes the following comments upon the philosophy of the new mathematics:

The labyrinth and abyss of infinity is also a new course Sir Isaac Newton has gone through, and we are obliged to him for the clue, by whose assistance we are enabled to trace its various windings.

Descartes got the start of him also in this astonishing invention. He advanced with mighty steps in his geometry, and was arrived at the very border of infinity, but went no farther. Dr. Wallis, about the middle of the last century, was the first who reduced a fraction by a perpetual division to an infinite series.

The Lord Brouncker employed this series to rectify the hyperbola.

Mercator published a demonstration of this quadrature; at about which time Sir Isaac Newton, being then twenty-three years of age, had invented a general method, to perform on all geometrical curves what had just before been tried on the hyperbola.

174

It is to this method of subjecting everywhere infinity in algebraical calculations, that the name is given of differential calculations or of fluxions and integral calculation. It is the art of numbering and measuring exactly a thing whose existence can not be conceived.

And, indeed, would you not imagine that a man laughed at you who should declare that there are lines infinitely great which form an angle infinitely little?

That a right line, which is a right line so long as it is finite, by changing infinitely little its direction, becomes an infinite curve; and that a curve may become infinitely less than another curve?

That there are infinite squares, infinite cubes, and infinities of infinities, all greater than one another, and the last but one of which is nothing in comparison with the last?

All these things, which at first appear to be the utmost excess of frenzy, are in reality an effort of the subtlety and extent of the human mind, and the art of finding truths which till then had been unknown.

This naive statement of Voltaire is historically important since it served to introduce the mathematics of Newton into France. Today it interests us because it reflects our still puzzled ideas concerning the notion of infinity.

Whence came this concept into our minds? Is it an *a priori* judgment of the rational intuition? Is it of necessity a part of reason to postulate the existence of the infinitely great and the infinitely little?

Before turning to a consideration of infinity in objective nature, let us examine the logical foundations of this belief.

## 2. *Logical Origins of the Infinity Concept.*

The idea of infinity occasionally appears in the thoughts of children. One cannot maintain that it is an artificial creation engendered by too much learning. It has perhaps been one of your childhood experiences to enter a game with a friend to see which could name the largest number. "One hundred," you say. "A million," counters your opponent. "A billion," you reply. "A trillion," he names. "A vigintillion," you exclaim and expect victory. There is a pause in the battle. "One more than that," says your opponent. You are overwhelmed by the boldness of the idea, until a thought occurs and you turn the tables. "One more than any number that you can name," you cry. Surely the battle is at an end. For a long time your enemy reflects. He sighs, breathes hard, clenches his fist in desperation. Suddenly his face lights up with inspiration and he mutters through clenched teeth: "Infinity." What judge would have the boldness to settle such a controversy!

When we are asked to explain the term infinity we often write the sequence 1, 2, 3, 4, . . . and state that infinity is its limit. It will be readily apprehended that this naive point of view may lead to paradoxes and so it does. One of these is formulated in the statement that there are as many even numbers as there are odd and even together. Reasoning from analogy with the enumeration of material particles where we always make a one-to-one correspondence of the particles with the natural numbers, this correspondence is stated in the following sequences:

| 1 | 2 | 3 | 4 | 5 | 6 | . . . . |
|---|---|---|---|---|---|---------|
| 2 | 4 | 6 | 8 | 10 | 12 | . . . . |

Since to each number in the first row there corresponds a number in the second row there must be as many items in the second as in the first. This is of course essentially the same paradox that was exhibited in section 6 of Chapter 5 when the sequence of rational points between 0 and 1 was found to be identifiable with the sequence of the integers.

The perplexing paradoxes of Zeno are examples of the same kind and derive their puzzles from the nature of infinity. Achilles seeks to catch the tortoise by passing over a set of intervals infinite in number. The problem of the continuum is thus thrust sharply to the front, and as has been exhibited in Chapter 5, we are forced to the conclusion that the points in it cannot be counted by the totality of integers. The problem of the childish game already referred to, now becomes a categorical necessity of reason. Infinity plus one is no longer a fiction, but a number in such excellent standing that it has been given a name. Aleph-zero is an honored child in the household of mathematical logicians. It should be a matter that moves us strongly to reflect that this number of Georg Cantor (1845-1918), the transfinite cardinal which measures the totality of rational points, is from one point of view identifiable with the denominate number which measures the velocity of light. The transfinite cardinal augmented by an infinite integer or by itself remains unchanged. Is this not precisely the fundamental property of the velocity of light as it was explained in section 9 of Chapter 5? If a match be struck, then two opposite fronts of the spherical wave, though advancing in opposite directions with the speed of light, are themselves separating only with the speed of light. Does this logical frenzy give us insight into the nature of the number of points of the continuum, or conversely, does the existence of the continuum give us insight into the nature of infinity?

Let us approach the problem from two newer points of view, one advanced by the Dutch philosopher and mathematician, L. E. J. Brouwer, the other by David Hilbert, one of the most penetrating mathematicians of our time.[1]

The fundamental proposition in the *intuitional* philosophy of Brouwer is that a thing exists only after it has been explicitly exhibited; that a thing logically conceived of by human intelligence does not exist by virtue of this logic alone, especially when an infinite process of construction is involved. The most novel aspect of the intuitional philosophy is found in its denial of the universal application of the so-called "law of the excluded middle."

As is well known the foundations of Aristotelean logic proceed from three postulates:

1. The postulate of identity; namely, "A is A."
2. The postulate of contradiction: "A is B" and "A is not B" cannot hold simultaneously.
3. The postulate of the excluded middle: of the two propositions "A is B" and "A is not B" one must always hold irrespective of what A and B may be.

There is no denial of the universal application of these principles in all finite processes of thought. The main contention of Brouwer and his school applies to the transfinite case: that when the proof of a proposition rests upon an infinite construction, such as for example the method of mathematical induction, then one cannot assert the universality of the third Aristotelean postulate.

This statement may be clarified by an example due to the Dutch mathematician. Let us think of the number $\pi = 3.14159 \ldots$ developed as a decimal fraction and let us denote by $d$ the n-th integer after the decimal point. Now construct the number $N = (-1/2)^m$, where m is the position of $d$ when $d$ equals 0 and the next nine values are the integers 1, 2, 3, 4, 5, 6, 7, 8, 9. We

[1] See A. Dresden: Brouwer's Contribution to the Foundations of Mathematics, Bulletin of the American Math. Soc., vol. 30 (1924), pp. 31-40; Some Philosophical Aspects of Mathematics, *ibid.*, vol. 34 (1928), pp. 438-452; Mathematical Certainty. Scientia (1929), pp. 369-376. D. Hilbert and W. Ackermann: Grundzüge der Theoretische Logik, Berlin (1928). For the general problem of mathematical existence the reader is referred to J. Pierpont: Mathematical Rigor. Bulletin of the American Math. Soc., vol. 34 (1928), pp. 23-53; O. Becker: Mathematische Existenz, Halle (1927); H. T. Davis: A Survey of the Problem of Mathematical Truth (Introduction to H. von Helmholtz: Counting and Measuring, trans. by Charlotte L. Bryan), New York (1930).

readily perceive that N is a real number which equals zero if there is no such sequence in the decimal development of $\pi$, but which is either greater or less than zero if such a sequence actually exists and $m$ is, in the first case, an even or, in the second case, an odd number. Logically the number N exists since we have given a construction for it, and it is in one of the three catagories according to Aristotelean canons.    But this is denied by Brouwer since the tremendous calculations which would have to be made to settle the question forever bar an answer to the intelligence of man.    The number N exists by construction, but since this construction involves an infinite sequence of operations the law of the excluded middle is not valid.

This looks like a very sane and comfortable point of view.    When we are confronted by a logical situation, which requires an infinite sequence of operations to determine it, we deny the validity of the law of the excluded middle.    The introduction of infinite operations into thought except in certain kinds of attainable limits is thus the creation of a daring but mistaken intelligence.

Let us not bother about the continuum over which Achilles passed in the Zeno problem.    The fact that he caught the tortoise is convincing proof of the answer.    Points without dimensions filling up a continuum create a perplexing concept to which the dictum "either it is true" or "it is not true" does not apply.

Hilbert, however, focuses attention upon another aspect of the question and in what is known as the *formalist* theory shifts the point of view from the third postulate of Aristotle to the affirmation of a transfinite axiom which may be added to the axioms of the domain of finite ideas so that the system thus augmented remains free from contradictions.

A great freedom results from this enlargement of the domain of logical principles.    In that uncertain realm beyond the finite we are privileged to make such postulates as we may desire provided only that they do not contradict the postulates of finite logic.    The quarrel between the intuitionalists and the formalists is really over the proposition whether such a freedom from contradiction can be attained without the denial of the law of the excluded middle.    The struggle is waged about certain paradoxes which have been so very troublesome that Bertrand Russell was led to his famous aphorism: "mathematics is the science in which we never know what we are talking about, nor whether what we say is true."[2]

---

[2] For further elucidation of this proposition the reader is referred to B. Russell: Introduction to Mathematical Philosophy (1919).

It will not be profitable for us to proceed further in the investigation of these subtle questions. The primary purpose of this book is to investigate the nature of the principles upon which natural philosophy has erected its structure. We are therefore seeking those postulates which by empirical discovery in the laboratory we have found to be *isomorphic,* that is to say, *in correspondence,* with the facts of nature. This is a point that is very fundamental and has recently been investigated by R. D. Carmichael in an attempt to discover how man makes his discoveries.[3] Logic is a subjective creation; we can invent its infinity and its infinitesimal and from them construct massive edifices of thought. But does this fact convince us that there is necessarily the slightest connection between them and objective nature? This is the problem. The continuity of the ether and the atomicity of matter inevitably force the concept of infinity upon us. Is this concept a necessity of nature? "As in the days of Newton and Leibnitz so now the notion of infinity is our greatest friend; it is also the greatest enemy of our peace of mind," says J. Pierpont. "We may compare it to a great water-way bearing the traffic of the world, a waterway however which from time to time breaks its bounds and spreads devastation along its banks."[4]

The purpose of this chapter is to investigate an interesting question, to which laboratory science is beginning to indicate an answer. This question may be stated as follows: Will the denial of an infinitely great element or an infinitely small element accord with discoveries in the objective world to which these subjective considerations must finally be applied?

The logical difficulty associated with the infinitesimal in nature is clearly defined in the following reflections of Alice:

"What a curious feeling!" said Alice. "I must be shutting up like a telescope!"

. . . she waited for a few minutes to see if she was going to shrink any further: she felt a little nervous about this; "for it might end, you know," said Alice to herself, "in my going out altogether, like a candle. I wonder what I should be like then?" And she tried to fancy what the flame of a candle looks like after the candle is blown out, for she could not remember ever having seen such a thing.

---

[3]The Logic of Discovery. Chicago (1930).
[4]Mathematical Rigor. (loc. cit.). p. 47.

### 3. How Does An Electron Know How Large To Be?

The point at issue with Alice was: What does it feel like to be an infinitesimal? There is a curious proposition in this which is not wholly foolish. A. E. Eddington, the eminent English astronomer and exponent of the theory of relativity, asks the question: How does an electron know how large to be? As he picturesquely states:[5] "An electron could never decide how large it ought to be unless there existed some length independent of itself for it to compare itself with." The adventures of Gulliver among the tiny Lilliputians and again among the lofty Brobdingnagians force the matter to our attention. "Undoubtedly philosophers are in the right," says Gulliver, "when they tell us that nothing is great or little otherwise than by comparison." Micromegas, the giant traveller from a satellite of the great Sirius, according to the record of Voltaire, once established communication with some philosophers on the earth. Marvelling at the insignificance of their size and the greatness of their wisdom he remarked: "I am now more than ever convinced that we ought to judge nothing by its external magnitude. O God! who hast bestowed understanding upon such seemingly contemptible substances, Thou canst with equal ease produce that which is infinitely small, as that which is incredibly great; and if it be possible that among thy works there are beings still more diminutive than these, they may, nevertheless, be endued with understanding superior to the intelligence of those stupendous animals I have seen in heaven, a single foot of whom is larger than this whole globe on which I have alighted." The observation of Micromegas faces us with the question of subjective imagination versus objective magnitude.

This brings us then to the point of our present theme. Is the universe finite? Is the relationship between space-time and matter of such a character that it is meaningless to talk of boundlessness in nature? If the answer to these questions be affirmative, we have broken definitely with the mathematicians. There is a delightful essay in point in the stimulating volume "The Human Worth of Rigorous Thinking" by C. J. Keyser who, almost alone in the mathematical world, dares to assert that infinity is undemonstrable.[6]

And now to my final thesis I venture to invite the reader's special attention, and beg to be held with utmost strictness accountable for my words. The question is, whether it is possible, by means of the

---

[5]Mathematical Theory of Relativity. Cambridge (1923), p. 154.
[6]The Axiom of Infinity, p. 157.

new concept, to demonstrate the existence of the infinite; whether, in other words, it can be proved that there are infinite systems. That such demonstration is possible is affirmed by Bolzano, by Dedekind, by Professor Royce, by Mr. Russell, and in fact by a large and swelling chorus of authoritative utterance, scarcely relieved by a dissenting voice. After no little pondering of the matter, I have been forced, and that, too, I must own, against my hope and will, to the opposite conviction. Candour, then compels me to assert, as I have elsewhere briefly done, not only that the arguments which have been actually adduced are all of them vitiated by circularity, but that, in the very nature of conception and inference, by the most certain standards of logic itself, every potential argument, every possible attempt to prove the proposition, is foredoomed to failure, destined before its birth to take the fatal figure of the wheel.

One is always safest when he is explaining something that no one else knows anything about. Perhaps this accounts for the many pages in philosophy devoted to infinity. There would undoubtedly be more were it not so difficult to attach concrete attributes to the idea. After the paradoxes have been exhibited the question is sterile, for there are no answers. Nowhere in physical nature do these concepts intrude. To be sure we sometimes speak of creating the Newtonian potential function by bringing matter together from infinite dispersion, but that is rather a figure of speech. A very great distance would do fully as well. W. Nernst, the chemist, reflecting upon the problem of what would happen to entropy if the reciprocal of the absolute temperature became infinite was led to his third law of thermodynamics, denying this possibility.[7] There is no need for infinity or the infinitesimal in objective nature since the subjective postulate affirming the contrary apparently can always be dispensed with.

This is a bold idea, but it seems to be a deduction from the discoveries in modern physics. The one difficulty in the path is the fact that the chemistry of our minds has in some way made us Euclidean. We want to believe that the ordinary concept of parallel lines as taught in Euclidean geometry is the true one; that the sum of the angles of a triangle equals 180 degrees; that space is infinite. We feel with Lucretius, as previously quoted, that "The existing universe is bounded in none of its dimensions; for then it must have an outside."

Of course it is possible for a thing to be finite yet boundless, which may afford a partial reply to the argument advanced by

---

[7] The New Heat Theorem, London (1926).

Lucretius. Consider, for example, the surface of a sphere. Enlarge it to such tremendous dimensions that its curvature cannot be detected by our most accurate scientific instruments; clearly the surface would be finite though boundless. Upon it there would be no end point from which the spear of Lucretius could be hurled past the uttermost boundary of the surface. We are not playing with words as might appear. By *finite* we mean that the area of the surface is limited, and by *boundless* that there is no point or line of points beyond which we shall find no more of the spherical surface.

### 4. *Space-Time and Infinity.*

Let us now apply this idea to the four-dimensional manifold which Einstein has linked together into the concept of space-time. To some this invoking of the fourth dimension may seem mystical and unreal. But that such is the fact is far from being the case. By the most accurate scientific experimentation a true physical validity has been given to the underlying framework of events. This we now call space-time instead of the more metaphysical concept of the ether. Can there not be a finite quantity, volume, so to speak, of the four-dimensional framework, without a bound existing to it?

Reflect a little longer on the case of the surface of the sphere. Here we are dealing with a surface which has all the appearance of reality to us because it is immersed in a three-dimensional manifold which our human intellect thinks it comprehends. But how mysterious the notion of finite yet boundless would be to a being endowed with faculties that appreciated only two dimensions! Similarly the difficulty of carrying the projected analogy over into the four-dimensional manifold is inherent in our chemical structure which holds as rational only that which has length, breadth, and thickness, and as transcendental that which involves higher dimensions. Of a being endowed with a five-dimensional intellect the problem of a four-dimensional surface requires no greater mental agility than the case of the surface requires of us. But there is a minor difficulty in the way. Who cares to postulate the existence of a five-dimensional intelligence! Even those who look upon the ether as a reality might hesitate at such a step.

In order not to appear too mystical we shall abjure such speculation and return to a safer point of view. Let us regard the equations of the Einstein law of gravitation as possessing objective existence and confine our attention to the conclusions which can be drawn by mathematical deductions from them. In this way we shall keep our feet solidly upon experimental data, while we reach for the secret of the clouds.

It will be recalled that Einstein was able to calculate, on very reasonable and essentially simple assumptions, the form of the space-time metric. This calculation involved the density of matter which acted upon space-time in the capacity of a distorting or twisting agent. This distortion made itself manifest in the three crucial experiments, one of which concerned the perihelion of Mercury, the second the behaviour of rays of light, and the third the shifting of star spectra. If these experimental observations seem confirmatory evidence of sufficient magnitude to make us adopt the Einstein philosophy, we may essay the bold adventure of exploring the structure of the four-dimensional manifold of reality.

At the very outset we are met by a profound question about which we must make a hypothesis. What causes the motion of the Foucault pendulum? Why is it that cyclones in the northern hemisphere turn in one direction and those in the southern hemisphere in the opposite direction? Why does the earth bulge at the equator and flatten at the poles? In other words, why is there an absolute rotation of the earth independent of the framework of the fixed stars?

To this puzzling question we can give at least two answers. The first of these assumes that inertia, which is at the bottom of the problem, is derived from the presence of all the other matter in the universe. The second leads to the de Sitter universe, which we shall consider later. In the first we postulate that a single particle of matter in an otherwise empty universe would have no inertial mass. To invoke Newton's laws of motion in such a vacuum would be wholly meaningless because we ask: With respect to what could such a particle change its direction of motion? To put it otherwise, if the sun and all the stars and the galaxies were removed to infinite distances from us so that their influence were completely annihilated, then the Foucault pendulum would cease to behave as it does. There would be no absolute rotation of the earth, the polar caps would not flatten nor the equator bulge. This suggestive thought, as we have stated in chapter two, goes back to Mach, who saw much that Einstein later formulated and who exerted a large influence upon the latter's views. At the conclusion of his Princeton lectures upon relativity Einstein makes the following exposition of his position:[8]

---

[8]The Meaning of Relativity, Princeton (1923), p. 119.

The idea that Mach expressed, that inertia depends upon the mutual action of bodies, is contained, to a first approximation, in the equations of the theory of relativity; it follows from these equations that inertia depends, at least in part, upon mutual actions between masses. As it is an unsatisfactory assumption to make that inertia depends in part upon mutual actions, and in part upon an independent property of space, Mach's idea gains in probability. But this idea of Mach's corresponds only to a finite universe, bounded in space, and not to a quasi-Euclidean, infinite universe. From the standpoint of epistemology it is more satisfying to have the mechanical properties of space completely determined by matter, and this is the case only in a space-bounded universe. An infinite universe is possible only if the mean density of matter in the universe vanished. Although such an assumption is logically possible, it is less probable than the assumption that there is a finite mean density of matter in the universe.

The cat is now out of the bag. Einstein's answer to the ancient problem of the extent of space and time is that the question of the limitation of the space-time metric of reality is inextricably united to the question of the limitation of matter. The essential postulates that are to be made are these:

1. The fundamental metric which throws the cause of the gravitation of ponderable bodies back upon the character of space-time is the substratum of reality.

2. Inertia is a cosmic phenomenon which depends wholly upon the totality of matter in the universe.

It must be realized that in making postulates about things whose nature is little known one has great leeway. We should never be wholly unmindful of the sarcasm of Voltaire who advanced the proposition that Aristotle's discussion on the soul should be quoted in the Greek language, since "it is but reasonable we should quote what we do not comprehend in a language we do not understand."[9] The scrutiny we should apply to such hypotheses depends wholly upon such experimental evidence as may be brought to bear either directly upon the basic assertions or upon the conclusions to be derived from them.

In the case of the first hypothesis Einstein gained overwhelming prestige by his bold prediction of phenomena at the time undiscovered. That there would be adherents for such a theory was inevitable. One must, however, settle the question of his own belief in the new science by weighing the probability that such predictions

---

[9]Micromegas, chap. 6.

could be wholly fortuitous against his own intuition that such propositions can actually represent the facts of nature. Scientific feeling today seems to be in favor of adopting the new point of view while waiting patiently for the accumulation of new data.

The second assumption of Einstein rests upon a far less secure basis. We have the one solitary fact of inertia—baffling, isolated, mysterious. The earth turns in space both on the evidence of the fixed stars and on the evidence of the pendulum swinging within the walls of the laboratory. What is its cause? Does it reside in the totality of matter in the universe or is it independent of other bodies? If all the material which fills proximate space were slowly withdrawn from our neighborhood would the Foucault pendulum gradually cease turning and finally come to rest as the earth approaches isolation? Is this the source of the kinetic energy which we assume the earth to have? Are its billions of potential horse power derived wholly from the presence of other matter in the universe? Those who wish to make the positive reply with Mach and Einstein travel in great company; those who wish to seek the explanation in another direction have as yet no large body of experimental facts to reconcile with any hypothesis that they might wish to make.

## 5. Einstein's Cosmology.—The "Ghost Star" Theory.

It is entertaining at least to explore the cosmology of Einstein which results from his postulates.

First, the time ordinate of space-time is infinite in both directions and is not curved. We pass on from event to event along the world lines of experience and never return again to the point from which we started. Time, to be sure, has no longer the old meaning in Newtonian mechanics, but it shares with Newtonian thought an infinite past and an infinite future.

In the second place, however, the affair is different in the case of the space coördinates. Space has a curvature and a straight line prolonged far enough will ultimately return to the space-point from which it started. This idea has led to the poetical theory of "ghost stars," which has received considerable comment in popular accounts of Einstein's theory. Simply stated it is this. If space has a curvature then rays of light should finally return from their journey around the universe and should converge at the point from whence they started, to form ghostly images of the material parent stars. Thus we have a stellar universe peopled with the images of countless

suns.  The point of light that we call Polaris may be but the light
from an empty spectre, the real star having long since lost itself
among the constellations of the Milky Way.

Of course you may wonder where the image of our own sun is.
It is probable that light in its long path around the universe would
gradually be absorbed or scattered by matter diffused in space or it
might perhaps be deflected by gravitational fields so that the focus
would be blurred and dim.  Someone has advanced the suggestion
that the mysterious Gegenschein, which can be seen occasionally at
sunset 180 degrees removed from the sun and in the place where the
sun's ghost should appear, might be evidence of this long trip of the
sun's light around the universe.  It is much more probable, of course,
that the Gegenschein is caused by reflected light from quantities of
cosmic dust.  Analysis made by the spectroscope shows that the light
is partially polarized and identical with sunlight that has been reflected from very small particles or molecules of gas.  However, the
other possibility remains.  Fantastic as these ideas may seem to you
they are alive with the poetry of astronomy, and no apology need be
made in bringing them to your attention.

Some scientists have been curious to know what limitations are
put upon this finite universe.  The fascinating aspect of the theory is
the enunciation of the belief that the amount of space-time depends
upon the amount of matter.  Create a single electron and you have
created with it a little quantity of space-time; create two electrons
and more of the substratum of reality has appeared; create the stars
and the spiral nebulae and you have brought into existence the sum
total of the space-time metric which reveals its existence and its
actual extent by the behaviour of the Foucault pendulum through
the inertia of matter.  This concept has been put paradoxically in
the statement: "The more matter there is, the more room there is
for it to exist in."

One of the principal arguments first urged against the Einstein
cosmology was that it posited the existence of vast quantities of
matter which had not yet been discovered.  This objection to the
Einstein theory, however, has proved to be one of its most convincing
arguments.  The cosmological speculations of the father of relativity
preceded the interpretation of the spirals as new galaxies of stars
and hence the deficiency of world stuff which faced the theory in
1920 has acted as a stimulus to the discovery of undreamed treasures
of cosmic matter in the ensuing decade.  We shall enlarge upon these
matters in the next section.

## 6. *Astronomical Space.*

Let us turn from this speculation for a moment to review the story, never old and always stirring, of the extent of visible space. You will recall in Mark Twain's, "Captain Stormfield's Visit To Heaven," the great difficulty encountered by the captain in explaining to the keeper of the celestial gates whence he had come. "Finally he came down," reports the captain, "and said he thought he had found that solar system, but it might be fly-specks. So he got a microscope and went back. It turned out better than he feared. He had rousted out our system, sure enough. He got me to describe our planet and its distance from the sun, and then he says to his chief—'Oh, I know the one he means, now sir. It is on the map. It is called the Wart.' " To most people this is all that one needs to know and perhaps can ever know about cosmology. However, the astronomers labor ceaselessly pushing back the boundaries of space. The great 100 inch reflecting telescope on the top of Mount Wilson in California has contributed greatly to this expanding knowledge.

Let us turn to a few figures of common knowledge and see what modern investigation has to say about the nature of matter in visible space. Let us start with the earth and its nearest neighbor, the moon. The earth has a diameter of approximately 8,000 miles and the moon a diameter approximately 3/11ths of this. The latter is on the average about 239,000 miles away from us. The earth and the moon belong to the solar system which consists of the sun, its planets, the planetoids, a little cosmic dust and a few comets. If the sun were represented by a circle an inch in diameter the earth could scarcely be seen at all by the naked eye and Jupiter, the largest, would appear as a tiny speck one tenth of an inch across. It is difficult to appreciate cosmic distances, and yet, in order to comprehend space and time, some numerical knowledge is necessary. It does not mean a great deal, to be sure, to know that the earth is ninety-three million miles from the sun, and that Neptune, the outer planet, is 2,800 million miles away, but relative distances are better understood if, as above, we represent the sun's diameter by an inch. Then the earth, in terms of these magnitudes, will be about nine feet from the sun and Neptune approximately 269 feet away.

As soon as we leave the solar system, space increases in a terrific manner. No longer is the distance from the earth to the sun or even the diameter of the solar system itself large enough to use as a measuring rod. We must employ light-years—the distance that light will travel in 365 days. In terms of this "yard stick" the distance from the earth to the sun is only a few seconds over eight minutes and the distance to Neptune is approximately four hours and ten minutes. Alpha Centauri, our nearest neighbor among the stars is between three and four light years away. In the scale adopted above, an inch for the diameter of the sun, this would put our closest stellar companion between three hundred and four hundred miles distant. Astronomers have found the light year an inconvenient unit to use and they more often employ the distance known as the *parsec*. The parsec by definition is the distance at which a star would have a parallax of one second of arc which is equivalent to 3.258 light-years or more than 19 trillion miles.

How vast the universe and how trivial these figures make us feel! Will increasing knowledge tend to reduce man to utter insignificance, a cosmic infinitesimal, or is there some meaning behind the fact that he is able to open up for himself these tremendous vistas? Perhaps this insignificance is only an apparent one.

### 7.  Is Matter Uniformly Dense Throughout Space?

Before considering the possibility of there being a structure to the universe of stars, let us first reflect upon the following problem: Is there a uniform density of matter in the universe? That is to say, do the stars recede indefinitely from us and does each cubic parsec of space contain approximately the same number as every other cubic parsec?

The astronomers have been bold enough to give a negative answer to this question. For all of the blaze of glory in the clear evening sky, the uncountable multitude of stars, "which stand as thick as dew drops on the fields of heaven," there appears to be evidence that the density is not uniform.

Certainly it appears true that the density of the luminous matter in the sky is not the same in every part of visible space. The first argument that can be advanced is that there is not a proper increase in the number of the stars of higher numerical magnitude over those of lower numerical magnitude. To make this statement clearer let us assume that all the stars in the sky are of the same intrinsic brightness. This, of course, is not true, but the variations in actual luminosity among the stars is not on the average too great to vitiate the following argument made upon such an assumption. On this hypothesis then there would be four times as many stars of the

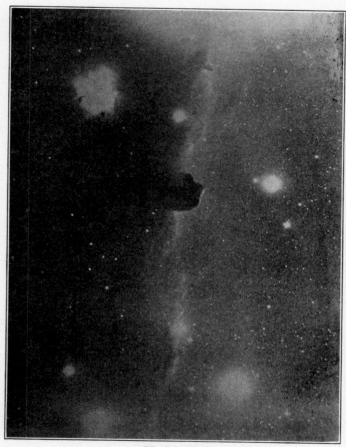

PLATE VIII

This photograph of the region south of zeta Orionis gives evidence of the existence of dark masses in the sky stretching with shadowy arms across the canopy of stars.

second magnitude as of the first, four times as many of the third as of the second, etc. As a matter of experimental fact the actual ratio of increase is slightly less than three for the stars visible to the naked eye and sinks to slightly less than two for those of twentieth magnitude. Matter thins out with distance apparently, and while stars may exist to the utmost conceivable limits of space their distribution seems to be something like that of prime numbers, which gradually diminish in density as we get into numerical reaches far from the integer *one*.

Of course it may be argued on reasonable ground that this apparent scarcity of stars at remote distances from us is due to occulting matter or the absorption of light travelling over so long a path. The accompanying picture (Plate VIII), one of the most magnificent in the gallery of astronomy, gives evidence of the existence of dark masses in the sky, great black nebulae perhaps, reaching with shadowy arms across the canopy of stars. It is equally certain, however, that these regions of obscuration are comparatively rare, and that there is not in general loss of light from distant sources, even though they may be as remote as 100,000,000 light years from us.

A very beautiful argument, the conclusions of which are in agreement with those just advanced upon the evidence of the luminosity of the stars, was first made by Lord Kelvin.[10] This argument starts with the hypothesis that the stars are uniformly distributed in space within the configuration of some geometrical figure and are moving under their mutual gravitational attractions.

Let us examine carefully the admissions which this involves. The first proposition is the one which we wish to controvert and the second comprises an assumption to which no reasonable objection can be raised, since it is merely that of universal gravitation. For simplicity let the geometrical figure of this cosmic gas be that of a sphere, and let us assume that the density of the stellar distribution is one star of mass equal to that of our sun within a volume equal to a sphere one parsec in radius. Under these hypotheses it can be shown that the period of revolution of a star on the outside of this gravitating cloud of stellar bodies would be 93,000,000 years, no matter what the radius of the sphere might be. It is not a serious mathematical problem to show that any star near the center of the sphere, in order to escape from this vast stellar cloud, must have a velocity 1.73 times that of the star revolving on the outside. For a

[10]On Ether and Gravitational Matter Through Infinite Space, Phil. Mag., vol. 2, sec. 6 (1901), pp. 161-177, in particular p. 168 et seq.

sphere of radius 1,000 parsecs this velocity of escape must be 112 kilometers per second; for a sphere ten times this, 1,120 kilometers per second, etc. With increasing radius the escape velocity enormously increases, and for a sphere of nearly infinite dimensions it is beyond calculation.

Now the velocities of the stars in the regions visible from the earth are not remarkably great, being for the most part less than 50 kilometers per second, although there are a few notable exceptions, in which the velocity exceeds three hundred kilometers. It is thus clear that if the stars are distributed with the assumed density of one per cubic parsec in a sphere as large as 10,000 parsecs radius none of the stars whose proper motions are now known could ever escape from the gravitational influence of the stellar gas. Hence those stars which are at a greater distance must be assumed to be moving in paths which will never bring them close to our part of the universe. If on the contrary we assume that the stellar gas ball has a radius inferior to 1,000 parsecs, the faster stars are escaping and will sometime disappear into the depths of space, exactly as the atmosphere of the moon is believed to have escaped from the weak gravitational field of that body. Neither of those conclusions seems to be a satisfactory hypothesis. We must either deny the original hypothesis of uniform density or modify our ideas about the universality of gravitation. The former seems the easier to disbelieve.

What a magnificent conclusion from such slender data. To be sure we have made the tacit assumption that the stars of the Milky Way are arranged in a globe, whereas the most likely figure is that of a thin disk; but the general argument and its conclusions are in no wise invalidated by this postulate. The mathematics is only slightly more complicated and dynamical considerations are involved in the possible rotation of the entire mass.

## 8.  The Galaxy and the Spirals.

Let us return from such engrossing speculations to a more specific consideration of our galaxy, or as it is usually referred to, the Milky Way. It is now commonly held that all of the billion or more stars in the heavens belong to the galaxy. The reason why we see stars in all directions from us is that we ourselves are close to its center. To judge from the distribution of the stars and the apparent increasing density which we find in the plane of the Milky Way as compared with the density toward the galactic poles, the galaxy is shaped like a lens, and its thickness is about one sixth of its diameter. Estimates of its diameter vary from 60,000 to 300,000 light years, the latter being the estimate of Harlow Shapley. This distinguished astronomer has located the center of our huge system about 52,000 light-years from the sun in the densely populated region near Sagittarius.[11]

The objects in our galaxy may be arbitrarily classified into four different types. The first of these are the stars, of which probably more than a billion are within the reach of the great 100 inch reflecting telescope at Mount Wilson. As has been mentioned before, the velocities of most of these great suns are less than 50 kilometers per second with respect to our solar system. The second objects of interest are the globular star clusters. There are more than a hundred to be seen in the heavens. They contain from ten thousand to a hundred thousand stars, and some have the comparatively large relative velocity of 300 kilometers per second. A third class of objects, the subject of much investigation, are the diffuse nebulae. These are enormous tenuous cloud-like masses, which are moving with very low velocities. There are probably ten thousand such nebulae in the sky. Finally the planetary nebulae are small round objects which generally have a central star as nucleus. Their spectra seem to indicate a gaseous condition of at least a part of their material. There are more than one hundred fifty such objects in the heavens, and they are moving on the average with velocities slightly less than a hundred kilometers per second.

Close to a million spiral nebulae are estimated to be within reach of our telescopes. Curiously enough the spirals are to be found in that part of the sky where the stars are fewest, that is to say, they tend to accumulate in the neighborhood of the galactic poles, about 400,000 on one side of the Milky Way, and 300,000 on the other. They are evidently not a part of the galaxy, but lie beyond it. One of their most peculiar features is found in the fact that they have on the average a truly enormous radial velocity (velocity in the line of sight) some of them attaining a speed of 1,200 kilometers per second, and this *velocity is recessive*. To put this significant fact in other language this means that these tremendous masses of world stuff are all moving away from our solar system with velocities that are truly enormous compared with the average speed of the stars and other cosmic bodies of our own galaxy. Surely such a

---

[11]Star Clusters, New York (1930), p. 177.

fact must have some profound significance, since the theory of probability is here wholly violated if the motions of the celestial objects are to be regarded as random,—a very reasonable proposition.

What the secret of the spiral nebulae is nobody knows, but there are daring spirits among the astronomers who are willing to believe that they are great "island universes," to use the picturesque expression of von Humbolt, like our galaxy, perhaps, and that each contains within its boundaries another billion stars. Their distances vary from perhaps a half million to a million light-years from us, although these figures are but guesses. This would mean that, in the scale we have been using of one inch for the diameter of the sun, the great spiral of Andromeda would be a distance from us a little less than our distance from the sun. There are some who whisper that perhaps our own galactic system is itself but one of these huge spirals, although it has been aptly put by Shapley that "if we call them islands, the galaxy is a continent," so much more extensive does the latter appear to be. One of the arguments used in trying to establish this position is the fact that the spirals seem to be the most numerous in the regions of the galactic poles. The explanation is offered that this is due, perhaps, to a large quantity of occulting matter in the galactic plane which hides those we should otherwise see, through the dense star swarms of the Milky Way. Such dark bands are found in spirals which are seen edgewise by us. The lens-like shape of our galaxy and the discovery of definite streaming among the stars, from the great researches of J. C. Kapteyn (1851-1922) who established this fact as far as statistical analysis of our knowledge of stellar proper motions would allow, give some evidence in favor of the proposition that we live within a spiral nebula.[12]

If there is any lesson to be learned from the history of astronomy it is preeminently this,—one must at all times hold an open mind and never attach himself uncompromisingly to any theory. His agility must be that of one who is willing to believe again in the geocentric theory of the universe if evidence once more should point to this conclusion. Certainly in surveying the vast cosmology opened up by the "bigger and better" telescopes of modern astronomy we must be very cautious in forming any kind of dogmatic conclusions.

We are certainly much like the infinitesimal intelligence which may reside upon an electron in the planetary system of an oxygen

[12]See W. W. Campbell: Stellar Motions, New Haven (1913), chap. 6.

atom within the center of a flat wafer-like stone on the surface of the earth. What would this diminutive being be able to conclude from the confines of his prison? Neighboring rocks would be spiral nebulae perhaps; the earth an assemblage of stars beyond the bounds of comprehension, the stars of our cosmology—well, who has an imagination that cares to go so far? Man lives between two worlds—a macro-universe of apparently measureless extent, and a micro-universe so small that its dimensions stagger our imagination. In one of them distance expands and increases like the wildest of De Quincey's dreams, but time slows up and velocities become comparatively small; in the other distances shrink and shrivel up, while time and velocities are marvelously accelerated. The forces upon us the old problem: What is the factor that determines size? How do we know how large to be? Why are we creatures between the macrocosmos and the microcosmos? Do these universes extend indefinitely in both directions from us? Is the statement of W. D. MacMillan that "the sequence of physical units is infinite both ways" the categorical imperative of rational belief?

### 9. De Sitter's Cosmology—The "Wall of Time" Theory.

We turn to another concept of the universe which is in some striking ways superior to that of Einstein. This concept is derived from the work of the great Dutch physicist, W. de Sitter, who differs from Einstein and Mach in their assumption that inertia is an inherent phenomenon of the totality of matter and that the Foucault pendulum would cease to rotate if all the other matter in the universe were removed. De Sitter points out that the Einstein postulate gives too great reality to matter, and in order to have substantiation, must posit the existence of vast quantities of world matter. His theory perhaps presents too much the aspect of going back to material models and makes the reality of inertia too substantial. In a way de Sitter's position is a curious example of the desire, found increasingly in modern science, to swing as far away as possible from the material concepts; to regard with distrust explanations that have their roots too firmly fixed in solid matter or in analogies drawn from sensuous models. Maxwell's answer to the puzzle of the ether rests in a set of equations; modern atoms are real only in the symbols that represent their activities; gravitation vanishes in a metric of space-time. Are we not reactionary when we try to explain the inertia of matter in terms of matter, even though this be thought of merely as the sum of all the particles throughout space?

The naive point of view of de Sitter is this. Let us look at infinity and try to find out the fundamental character of the metric of space-time from speculations based upon our own intuitive feelings with regard to the four-dimensional geometry of that remote region. What a glorious freedom for the new physics! What a declaration of independence is found in the following dictum of the eminent astronomer:[13] "How they (gravitational potentials) are in those portions of space and time of which our observations have not yet penetrated, we do not know, and how they are at infinity (of space or of time) we shall never know. All assumptions regarding the value of them (gravitational potentials) at infinity are therefore extrapolations which we are free to choose in accordance with theoretical or philosophical requirements."

Galileo would have us choose these gravitational potentials at infinity so that space-time would be flat or Euclidean; Einstein made his selection so that all were zero except the one involving time, which placed a logical blemish upon his theory because the set of values thus assumed was not wholly invariant for mathematical transformations. De Sitter, turning his back upon the material consideration that led Einstein to his cosmology, made his "philosophical requirement" the invariance of the potentials, and calmly set them all equal to zero in that remote and inaccessible region of infinity. The consequences of the de Sitter postulate agree spatially with those of Einstein but differ for the variable of time. The radius of the universe, spatially speaking, is the same as that of the German savant, but the time concept differs in this interesting conclusion that a ray of light could never make the complete circuit and return again to form a ghostly image of its former self. Thus the fantastic "ghost star" theory must be abandoned by those who go with de Sitter, but it is replaced by the equally poetical one which we may call the postulate of the "wall of time."

In order to prepare for this new concept let us turn again to the philosophy of Lewis Carroll, to the passage in which he meditates on time.

"If you knew time as well as I do," said the Hatter, "you wouldn't talk about wasting *it*. It's *him*."

"I don't know what you mean," said Alice.

"Of course you don't!" the Hatter said, tossing his head contemptuously. "I dare say you never even spoke to Time!"

---

[13]On Einstein's Theory of Gravitation and its Astronomical Consequences. Monthly Notices of the Royal Astronomical Association, vol. 78, p. 3, November, 1917.

"Perhaps not," Alice cautiously replied, "but I know I have to beat time when I learn music."

"Ah! That accounts for it," said the Hatter. "He won't stand beating. Now, if you only kept on good terms with him, he'd do almost anything you like with the clock. For instance, suppose it were nine o'clock in the morning, just time to begin lessons: you'd only have to whisper a hint to Time, and round goes the clock in a twinkling! Halfpast one, time for dinner! . . ."

"That would be grand, certainly," said Alice thoughtfully; "But then—I shouldn't be hungry for it, you know."

"Not at first, perhaps," said the Hatter: "but you could keep it to half-past one as long as you liked."

"Is that the way *you* manage?" Alice asked.

The Hatter shook his head mournfully. "Not I!" he replied. "We quarreled last March—. . . .

"Well, I'd hardly finished the first verse" (of a song at the great concert given by the Queen of Hearts), said the Hatter, "when the Queen bawled out 'He's murdering the time! Off with his head!' "

"How dreadfully savage!" exclaimed Alice.

"And ever since that," the Hatter went on in a mournful tone, "he won't do a thing I ask! It's always six o'clock now."

A bright idea came into Alice's head. "Is that the reason so many tea-things are put out here?" she asked.

"Yes, that's it," said the Hatter with a sigh: "it's always tea-time, and we've no time to wash the things between whiles."

"Then you keep moving around, I suppose?" said Alice.

"Exactly so," said the Hatter: "as the things get used up."

"But what happens when you come to the beginning again?" Alice ventured to ask.

"Suppose we change the subject," the March Hare interrupted, yawning. "I'm getting tired of this. . . ."

The picture that de Sitter wishes to convey to us is that of a great wall of time barring the path of anything such as a ray of light which wants to make the circuit. As we look deep into space, at the spiral nebulae perhaps, time appears to slow up until at very remote distances from us it is always six o'clock. We have used the phrase "appears to slow up" which is the de Sitter concept. If we should actually travel out to this remote part of space we should find that the hands of our watches still moved with their ordinary velocity, but if we looked back at the earth that we had left, time would seem to have slowed up on that planet. In other words time, in regions remote from our own, flows less swiftly from our point of view, so that a ray of light, as it recedes from us, would seem to lose velocity, until in the neighborhood of the great wall of time it would cease to move altogether.

Is there experimental evidence for this strange concept? Most assuredly so and evidence of a remarkable kind. Every luminous body like the sun or like a star carries its own clock in the form of atomic vibrations. These vibrations we can measure in terms of spectral lines and compare them with the same vibrations on the earth. In other words we can measure a star's time with earth time by the most perfect mechanisms in the world.

If the spectral lines of a star shift toward the red end of the spectrum when compared with our own, this shift can be due to at least two causes as we have previously explained.

First, the star may be receding from us. This is known as the Doppler principle and is analogous to the change in pitch of a locomotive whistle as the engine moves away from us. Second, it may measure a genuine difference between star-time and earth-time. This difference, you will recall, was actually measured in the case of the heavy white dwarf which we knew was not receding from us with any great velocity, since it was the companion of Sirius.

We have already commented upon the fact that the spiral nebulae are apparently, on the average, receding from us with almost incredible velocities, some of these being in the neighborhood of 1,000 kilometers per second, and one at least nearly twice this figure. Recent investigations by Shapley at Harvard amply confirm this strange fact. Are all, or nearly all, of the spirals, on the evidence of their Doppler shift, receding from us at high rates of speed? And if so, why?

De Sitter believes that this curious discovery of modern astronomy furnishes experimental evidence for his concept of space-time. Time, in the remote regions where the spirals exist, is slowing down a bit and the atomic watches of these remote masses are revealing this in the Doppler shift. The spirals are not all receding from us with those huge velocities, as we have thought. They are merely nearer the wall of time and their atomic clocks in consequence move more slowly.

A recent speculation has been made by G. Lemaître which attempts to preserve the best features of both the Einstein and the de Sitter universes. One posited the existence of great masses of world matter which have since been discovered; the other has explained the recessive velocities of the spiral nebulae. Hence Lemaître has assumed that we are in a state of transition from the static universe of Einstein to the static universe of de Sitter, in other words, that the radius of the universe is not a constant, but that it grows with time. How far have we progressed? Lemaître assuming with de Sitter that there exists a distance such that the light from bodies beyond this limit is thrown into the invisible region of the infra red, estimates that this *horizon of knowledge* is approximately ten times the range of the great telescope of Mount Wilson. Already our penetration into space is so great that the shift of light toward the red end of the spectrum corresponds to a Doppler velocity of 3,000 kilometers per second.[14]

## 10.  *Is Nature Finite?*

What a vast distance we have come from the philosophy of Kant. The subjective, *a priori* intuitions of the philosopher now merge into a single substratum of reality.  "The business of geometry," said J. J. Sylvester, the mathematician, "is with the evolution of the properties of space, or of bodies viewed as existing in space."[15]  The laboratory of the sky evidently can contribute profoundly to this evolution.

We return finally to the main theme of our chapter: Is nature finite?  It is a strange and startling fact that science, timidly perhaps, but seriously in certain quarters, is trying to set bounds upon all those phenomena with which material things are concerned.  The discussion which follows must, however, be understood to be largely speculative and entirely tentative.  The new philosophical position is not yet grounded in the tenets of science, but where men's daring thoughts may go there is always interest in exploring the trails.

We have already mentioned in a previous chapter the establishing of an absolute temperature scale for matter and the location of its zero 490 degrees Fahrenheit below the freezing point of water. This material bound represents the state of matter when all its thermal energy has been pumped away.  What matter, thus emptied of its activating entity, may then become we do not clearly know, nor is it our concern at this time.  The interesting fact is that tempera-

[14]"Un universe homogène de mass constante et de rayon croissant, rendant compte de la vitesse radiale des nébuleuses extra-galactiques.  Annales Société sc. Bruxelles, vol. 47 (1927) (A), pp. 49-59.

[15]Collected Mathematical Papers, vol. 2, p. 5.

ture is bounded at one end.  Is it also bounded at the other?  There have been recent speculations in this direction likewise, and one venturesome spirit has made the tentative guess of $1.1 \times 10^{13}$ degrees, which is hot enough even for those modern exponents who delight in making us shudder at their estimates of the central heat of the stars.[16]

We have already commented at great length in Chapter 5 upon the maximum relative velocity of material quantities, that is to say, the speed of light, and upon the significance of this maximum in the new geometry.  We shall merely recall it here as other evidence of the existence of natural limits.

Passing from these problems we inquire into the old problem of the finiteness of space.  We have already related the agreement between de Sitter and Einstein that space-time may be bounded in its spatial elements.  What that really means, if its meaning can be divorced from the mathematical symbols of the metric, is that the geometry of space is not the geometry of Euclid, which we have taught so many years in our schools.  It is rather the geometry of Riemann, which is founded upon fully as logical concepts as the other, however novel it may appear to ordinary intuition.  The nature of this geometry, you will recall, is exhibited by the postulate that through a point exterior to a straight line no other line can be drawn so as to be parallel to the first.  That is to say, by a simple deduction, the sum of the angles of a triangle in such a space is greater than two right angles.  Riemann's space is spherical in character and hence is finite, however difficult such words may be to explain to the layman in plain language.  These glorious theorists, with the help of the astronomers who have kindly furnished them an estimate of the density of matter in cosmic space, have actually agreed, tentatively to be sure and with the possibility of error of enormous magnitude, that the radius of the Einstein universe is $2.7 \times 10^{10}$ parsecs.  To put it slightly more intelligibly, it would take light perhaps one hundred billion years to make the circuit of space.[17]

Thus we reach one answer to the old question which you probably asked your teacher many years ago: Where would a cannon ball go if it were shot off the earth in such a direction as never to hit a star?  What a fascinating speculation this is and how strange the story of

---

[16]See for example S. Suzuki: The Existence of the Upper Limit of Temperature and a New Radiation Formula.  Proceedings of the Physico-Mathematical Society of Japan, vol. 8, 3rd ser. (1928), pp. 175-179.

[17]This estimate is due to E. Hubble, Extra-galactic Nebula.  Astrophysical Journal, vol. 64 (1926), pp. 321-369, in particular p. 369.

its evolution through the merging of mathematical geometries, with the quest of the elusive ether and the conquest of the heavens. Is there a more intriguing story in the annals of man than this? Extremely slender though the probability of its correctness may be, nevertheless the probability is not zero, but has some finite value derived from the physical experiments from which the estimate is derived.

We turn finally to another speculation of similar character though of inverse magnitude and inquire whether or not it is possible that inferior limits are also to be found for natural dimensions. If there be an upper limit to space-time is it not possible that this value bears a fundamental relation to the smallest unit of space? In other words, as Eddington picturesquely asks, "How does an electron know how large to be?"

Eddington himself essays to answer this question and makes the following striking remark:[18]

There is strong ground then for anticipating that the solution of the unknown equations (of the electron) will be radius of electron in any direction = numerical constant $\times$ radius of curvature of space-time in that direction.

This concept of nature leads at once to the full atomistic philosophy. The problem of Zeno no longer exists, since we deny the existence of the continuum wherein the paradox resides. If there be a smallest object then there must also exist a finite number of them between any two other objects, and any partitioning of the interval below this smallest unit is as impossible as the attainment of a velocity exceeding that of light.

One can not help but speculate as to the final rôle of number in this vast but finite universe. What happens to the sequence 1, 2, 3, 4, . . ., which we wrote down at the beginning of the chapter? Far be it from us even to suggest the possibility that this celebrated sequence of the mathematicians should have a bound. Eddington, courageous dreamer, daringly estimates the total number of electrons in the universe to be of the order of the square of $3 \times 10^{42}$. Could the mathematicians, whether it be in the practical application of their great science or in the far reaches of their logical speculations, be wholly satisfied with a number of this magnitude? Or not to seem to be lacking in generous spirit, we might even increase this tentative number so as to include all the possible combinations of these

---
[18]The Mathematical Theory of Relativity, Cambridge University Press (1923), p. 154.

electrons? In this connection the following remark made by Eddington is certainly not deficient in imaginative qualities :[19]

. . . . among the constants of nature there is one which is
a very large pure number; this is typified by the ratio of the radius
of an electron to its gravitational mass $= 3 \times 10^{42}$. It is difficult
to account for the occurrence of a pure number (of order greatly different from unity) in the scheme of things; but this difficulty would
be removed if we could connect it with the number of particles in the
world—a number presumably decided by pure accident. There-is an
attractiveness in the idea that the total number of the particles may
play a part in determining the constants of the laws of nature; we
can more readily admit that the laws of the actual world are specialized by the accidental circumstances of a particular number of
particles occurring in it, than that they are specialized by the same
number occurring as a mysterious ratio in the fine-grained structure
of the continuum.

Our conclusion must be like that of all who tilt with the concept
of infinity. We can say nothing with certainty. However, it becomes increasingly apparent from the writings of the wise that
modern scientists, the mathematicians and the physicists, are not
wholly loathe to assume the following postulates:

1. A thing does not exist by virtue of its logical conception
alone. There may be doubt where the canons of Aristotle's logic
involve the use of infinite operations; or if one prefers to regard the
problem in another way, we are limited in the realm of transfinite
consideration only by the postulate of consistency with finite special-
ization. (Modern mathematical rigor).

2. The physical universe in its material elements is finite.
(Modern physics).

By these postulates we may perhaps reorder the structure of the
universe in such a way that the mysteries of the continuum of Zeno
and Cantor disappear in an atomic concept of all properties associated
with matter.

---

[19]The Mathematical Theory of Relativity, loc. cit., p. 167.

# CHAPTER VIII.

## THE ATOM CONCEPT.

### 1. *Continuity versus Atomism.*

WE COME now to the strangest story ever related by the romancers of our race. And in making such a statement well do we remember the adventures of the heroic Odysseus who thought that :[1]

> . . . all experience is an arch wherethro'
> Gleams that untravell'd world, whose margin fades
> For ever and for ever when I move!

But even Homer, for all those stirring moments related in the moving music of the Greeks, can scarcely match the modern tale of the conquest of the atom. This great adventure is unfortunately not available to many who might otherwise be thrilled by its stirring drama, because most of the action goes on behind the heavy curtain of mathematical formulas and in the technical apparatus of the laboratory. It is the purpose of the present chapter to trace in as simple terms as possible some of the romantic passages of the tale.

The first chapter opened in the third and fourth centuries B. C., when Democritus, following the ideas of earlier writers, enunciated the belief that matter is not indefinitely divisible, but that all substances are formed of indivisible particles or atoms which are eternal and unchangeable, that the atoms are separated from one another by void, and that a combination of these atoms constitutes what we call matter.[2]

We have discussed previously some of the characteristics of the atomistic views of Democritus, but it is now time to reflect more philosophically upon this strange doctrine. By the assumption just stated we give up the notion of continuity, which is certainly one of our most treasured intuitional concepts.

The atomists would have us believe that there is a smallest physical unit, from which all larger objects are constructed; the position of the continuists is wittily put in the well known verse of Dean Swift :[3]

---

[1] A. Tennyson: Ulysses.
[2] See E. Zeller: Pre-Socratic Philosophy (1881), London, vol. 2, p. 207.
[3] From "On Poetry: A Rhapsody."

So, Nat'ralists observe, a Flea
Hath smaller Fleas that on him prey.
And these have smaller Fleas to bite 'em,
And so proceed *ad infinitum*.

All modern mathematics with its infinitesimals and its infinity, its point-sets and its continuum, is based upon the assumption of continuity. To be sure some strange results have emerged from this assumption. One of the most remarkable of these is the curve of the German mathematician, Karl Weierstrass (1815-1897), which has the extraordinary property of being everwhere continuous but nowhere possessing a tangent. The existence of such a curve makes us pause and scrutinize again the concept of continuity, which Poincaré characterizes as "a belief which it would be difficult to justify by apodeictic reasoning, but without which all science would be impossible."[4] Complete atomistic philosophy applied to the logic of mathematics would surely be fatal to certain branches of it. On the other hand the postulation of complete continuity in natural phenomena would appear to be equally disastrous since even to account for so common a thing as the high compressibility of gas would impose a superhuman agility upon the imaginations of the continuists.

The most celebrated atomist of antiquity was the Latin poet Lucretius, whose philosophy of space, infinity, and the atom has already been commented upon earlier in the book. "De Rerum Natura," in which the poet states his reflections upon the nature of the physical universe, has some remarkable passages dealing with the atomic theory of matter. The following quotation is wholly typical of the depth of his ideas, which are interesting and instructive in showing how far an intellect, unaided by laboratory instruments, can see into the difficult problem:[5]

Again things which look to us hard and dense must consist of particles more hooked together, and be held in union because welded all through with branch-like elements. In this case first of all diamond stones stand in foremost line inured to despise blows, and stout blocks of basalt and the strength of hard iron and brass bolts which scream out as they hold fast to their staples. Those things which are liquid and of fluid body ought to consist more of smooth and round elements; for the several drops have no mutual cohesion and their onward course too has a ready flow downwards. All things lastly

[4]Foundations of Science, p. 173.
[5]From Munro's translation: Book 2, lines 444-477.

which you see disperse themselves in an instant, as smoke mists and
flames, if they do not consist entirely of smooth and round, must yet
not be held fast by closely tangled elements, so that they may be
able to pierce the body and enter it with biting power, yet not stick
together : thus you may easily know, that whatever we see the senses
have been able to allay, consists not of tangled but of pointed elements.  Do not however hold it to be wonderful that some things
which are fluid you see to be likewise bitter, for instance the sea's
moisture : because it is fluid it consists of smooth and round particles, and many rough bodies mixed up with these produce pains ;
and yet they must not be hooked so as to hold together ; you are to
know that though rough, they are yet spherical, so that while they
roll freely on, they may at the same time hurt the senses.  And that
you may more readily believe that with smooth are mixed rough first-
beginnings from which Neptune's body is made bitter, there is a way
of separating these, and of seeing how the fresh water, when it is
often filtered through the earth, flows by itself into a trench and
sweetens ; for it leaves above the first-beginnings of the nauseous
saltness, inasmuch as the rough particles can more readily stay behind
in the earth.

The significance to be attached to this crude picture is the evidence
which it affords of the necessity of postulating primary units whose
combinations make up the structure of various states of matter.
Those who believe in the continuity of universal substance tend to
draw their picture in terms of a fluid ; those who postulate atoms
ask how, otherwise, the structure of a gas with its enormous powers
of condensation and rarefaction, can be rationally explained.  It is a
curious fact that those who deal with phenomena by means of
differential equations, the nature of which is grounded in considerations of continuity, speak of the tubes of electromagnetic forces as
moving through a continuous fluid medium filling all space and
permeating all material bodies ; only Mendeléeff, the chemist, speaks
of the ethereal atom.  The point at issue is, indeed, one of vital
importance.  It is a battle as old as human thought.  The issue
today is nearly as obscure as it was in the early dawn when Democritus and Lucretius began to translate crude experience into hypotheses.  We find Poincaré in his stimulating article on "The
Quantum Hypothesis" making this significant observation :[6]

Is discontinuity destined to reign over the physical universe, and
will its triumph be final?  Or will it finally be recognized that this
discontinuity is only apparent, and a disguise for a series of continuous processes.  The first observer of a collision thought he was

---

[6]Dernières Pensées; chap. 6, sect. 8, Flammarion, Paris (1913), p. 192.

witnessing a discontinuous process, but we know today that what he saw was the result of changes which, although very rapid, were continuous. Any attempt at present to give a judgment on these questions would be a waste of paper and ink.

The weight of the authority of Aristotle was thrown in favor of the continuity concept; Newton, on the other hand held the contrary view. In discussing the structure of solid bodies he expressed his belief[7] "that the smallest particles of matter may cohere by the strongest attractions, and compose bigger particles of weaker virtue; and many of these may cohere and compose bigger particles whose virtue is still weaker; and so on for divers successions, until the progression ends in the biggest particles, on which the operations in chemistry, and the colours of natural bodies, depend, and which, by adhering, compose bodies of a sensible magnitude. If the body is compact, and bends or yields inward to pression, without any sliding of its parts, it is hard and elastic, returning to its figure with a force rising from the mutual attraction of its parts. If the parts slide upon one another, the body is malleable or soft. If they slip easily, and are of a fit size to be agitated by heat, and the heat is big enough to keep them in agitation, the body is fluid; and if it be apt to stick to things, it is humid; and the drops of every fluid affect a round figure, by the mutual attraction of their parts, as the globe of the earth and sea affects a round figure, by the mutual attraction of its parts by gravity."

## 2. An Atomic Picture of Matter.

Let the reader reflect upon his own conception of matter. It may be illuminating in the sequel, if the guesses of these modern days have not fully penetrated to his thought, to speculate upon the structure of a piece of stone. Suppose that he has eyes of high resolving power, supplemented, perhaps, by the diamond lens of the redoubtable Roland Cleeve of Frank R. Stockton's romance, so that he can look beyond the surface of the solid matter. What does he believe that he would see? That which our crude sense of touch thought was solid is now found to be incredibly porous, mostly void, but with a vast number of tiny particles in tremendous agitation moving through it. The appearance of solidity is merely a statistical illusion due to the mobility of the particles, which permits them to be many places at almost the same time. To those to whom this picture seems

---

[7] See Sir David Brewster: Life of Sir Isaac Newton, chap. 17, 2nd ed., p. 270.

bizarre the consideration of a single base-ball in a large room is rec-
ommended. If the ball rests upon the floor the room will appear to
be almost entirely empty. But let the ball acquire some speed and
bounce several times per second off of the walls. The emptiness of
the room to the visitor is now no longer so evident as it was. But
let the ball attain the velocity of light and he will affirm that the space
is entirely filled with flying particles so ubiquitous is the ball from the
incredible number of reflections which it has from the walls. Time
and velocity, you see, are not inconsiderable items in the illusion of
solidity.[8]

Are we then to regard atoms, where we use the word in its
genetic sense to mean the indivisible unit, as small, hard balls moving
with ceaseless activity from place to place and producing to our crude
sense of touch the illusion of solidity? If this is, indeed, our picture
and it probably conforms to the mental image of the average man,
then we might ask why we could not conceive of such an atom divided
into two parts? The answer to this question is simple. We could so
think of the divided atom, but the two parts, in consequence of our
hypothesis, would lose their identity as things. The point that we are
making is due originally to Clerk Maxwell whose view is an attrac-
tively modern one. He says in his Theory of Heat (page 285):

We do not assert that there is an absolute limit to the divisibility
of matter: what we assert is, that after we have divided a body into
a certain finite number of constituent parts called molecules, then
any further division of these molecules will deprive them of the
properties which give rise to the phenomena observed in the substance.

There is a vast amount of room for division between the smallest
atom ever conceived and the largest mathematical point. We are not
imposing insuperable logical difficulties when we ask the question:
Divide the atom and what then? The answer of Maxwell asserts
that we shall mean merely that a divided atom loses its material identity and whatever else its constituent parts may be they are not
material entities.

### 3. The Hypothesis of Avogadro.

Historically, so far as modern science is concerned, the atomic
theory started with the work of John Dalton (1766-1844), who con-

---

[8]P. W. Bridgman has discussed this problem for a single molecule traveling in a
horizontal line. Proc. of the American Academy of Arts and Sciences, vol. 49, No. 1, p.
105 et seq.

ceived of atoms as small, indivisible constituents of matter which combined in various proportions to make the substances of the world. In his theory the atoms of any given substance are identical, but atoms of different elements are different and have different weights. For example if a gram of water be divided electrolytically into its components it will be found to consist of eight times as much oxygen, by weight, as hydrogen. Hence, according to Dalton, the water particle is made up of two atoms, one of hydrogen and the other of oxygen, the latter being eight times as heavy as the former.

When further insight into chemical processes was gained, however, it was found that a better hypothesis could be substituted for the purely atomic one. Amadeo Avogadro (1776-1856) in 1811 advanced the proposition that equal volumes of different gases contain equal numbers of *molecules,* that is to say, groups of atoms in combination. This law must be recognized to be merely a convenient agreement, much like the astronomical agreement to regard the sun as the center of the solar system rather than the earth. Equal *volumes* of gases instead of equal *weights* were made the basis for defining the relative size of atoms. One can readily appreciate the convenience of this hypothesis. For example, it is found that equal volumes of hydrogen and chlorine will completely combine to form hydrochloric acid. Hence we say that hydrochloric acid is composed of one atom of hydrogen and one of chlorine, the latter atom being thirty-five times as heavy as the former. Similarly one part of oxygen, speaking volumetrically, will combine with two parts of hydrogen to form water, so we assume that the molecule of this common fluid consists of two atoms of hydrogen in combination with one of oxygen, the latter being sixteen times as heavy instead of eight, as in the Dalton theory.

We should mention in this connection the suggestion made in 1815 by William Prout (1785-1850) that the "first stuff" postulated by the ancient philosophers is realized in hydrogen.[9] His theory, truer than anyone then thought, was essentially the assumption of a basic atom from which by processes of alchemy all the other forms of matter could be constructed.

### 4. *The Atom of Boscovich.*

"It is remarkable that involuntarily we always read as superior beings," says Emerson in his essay on History. With what pity,

---

[9] In an anonymous paper in the Annals of Philosophy (1815).

then, we look upon the masters of the past as they struggled with these weighty matters. How far down seems the foot of the mountain to one who has toiled laboriously up the slope. We must pause a moment to survey the guesses of our predecessors, as those who follow us will survey our own attempts to probe to the ultimate in nature.

The first of those belonging to the modern age of science who tried to give a material picture of the atom was Ruggiero Giuseppe Boscovich (1711-1787), an Italian natural philosopher, born at Ragusa in Dalmatia. His concept began with the traditional one of the indivisible particle, merging into the monadism of Leibnitz, since he failed to endow his atom with finite size. This primary substance was able to move continuously in a line and could occupy only one place at a given time. It possessed mass and could be changed from its straight-line propagation only by the impressing of force. The chief characteristic of the Boscovich atom, however, was its varying spheres of action. For a given distance, a small fraction of an inch, perhaps, atoms were attracted to one another by a force varying inversely as the square of the distance between them. But within a second sphere of influence the attractive force was changed to one of repulsion. More than one such sphere might probably be conceived of, but the final domain of activity was necessarily one in which repulsive forces held. This led to the second fundamental assumption of the Boscovich atom, which asserted that no two atoms could ever coincide since the ultimate repulsive forces would always increase as the two approached one another, until any conceivable force could be exceeded. Clerk Maxwell makes the following comment upon this hypothesis:[10]

But this seems an unwarrantable concession to the vulgar opinion that two bodies cannot coexist in the same place. This opinion is deduced from our experience of the behaviour of bodies of sensible size, but we have no experimental evidence that two atoms may not sometimes coincide. For instance, if oxygen and hydrogen combine to form water, we have no experimental evidence that the molecule of oxygen is not in the very same place with the two molecules of hydrogen. Many persons cannot get rid of the opinion that all matter is extended in length, breadth and depth.

Although the concept of the Boscovich atom continued to interest a number of scientists, including Lord Kelvin, for many years, it may finally be regarded as furnishing merely another model for the his-

---

[10]From Maxwell's article on the Atom. Encyclopedia Britannica, 9th ed.

toric gallery. Some day perhaps some philanthropist will endow a museum for these magnificent theories of the past, with bottles for the various ethers and plaster models of all the atoms that have been conceived. The atom of Boscovich has one feature of peculiar interest to our speculation: it substitutes for the substantive particle of Democritus and Lucretius a pure theory of action at a distance. The atom was of infinitesimal dimension, wholly replacing the property of finite size by the more elusive property of repulsion and attraction. This was a fine idea and we turn from it with certain regrets.

### 5.  *The Vortex-ring Theory of the Atom.*

Another famous concept of the atom was due to Lord Kelvin, and it has already been mentioned briefly in another place under the name of the vortex-ring theory. The basic idea was a very simple one, being merely the generalization of smoke rings. In 1858 Helmholtz published a short paper of extraordinary power entitled, "On the integrals of the hydrodynamic equations which express vortex-motion." This remarkable paper was translated for the Philosophical Magazine in 1867, and thence came to the attention of Lord Kelvin, then William Thomson. This scientist, with his passion for seeing physical interpretations in everything, suddenly had the inspiration that here was a model for the atom. Vortex-rings in the ether might be the solution of the ancient problem. His ideas are vividly told in the following quotation from a letter written by him to Helmholtz on the event of his conception of this atom.[11]

Take one side (or the lid) off a box (any old packing-box will serve) and cut a large hole in the opposite side. Stop the open side AB loosely with a piece of cloth, and strike the middle of the cloth with your hand. If you leave anything smoking in the box, you will see a magnificent ring shot out by every blow. A piece of burning phosphorous gives very good smoke for the purpose; but I think nitric acid with pieces of zinc thrown into it, in the bottom of the box, and cloth wet with ammonia, or a large open dish of ammonia beside it, will answer better. The nitrite of ammonia makes fine white clouds in the air, which, I think, will be less pungent and disagreeable than the smoke from phosphorous. We sometimes can make one ring shoot through another, illustrating perfectly your description; when one ring passes near another, each is much disturbed, and is seen to be in a state of violent vibration for a few seconds, till it settles again into its circular form. The accuracy of the circular form of the whole ring, and the fineness and roundness of the sec-

---

[11]Thompson's Life of Lord Kelvin (loc. cit.), vol. I, pp. 513-514.

tion, are beautifully seen. If you try it, you will easily make rings of a foot in diameter and an inch or so in section, and be able to follow them and see the constituent rotary motion. The vibrations make a beautiful subject for mathematical work. The solution for the longitudinal vibration of a straight vortex column comes out easily enough. The absolute permanence of the rotation, and the unchangeable relation you have proved between it and the portion of the fluid once acquiring such motion in a perfect fluid, shows that if there is a perfect fluid all through space, constituting the substance of all matter, a vortex-ring would be as permanent as the solid hard atoms assumed by Lucretius and his followers (and predecessors) to account for the permanent properties of bodies (as gold, lead, etc.) and the difference of their characters. Thus, if two vortex-rings were once created in a perfect fluid, passing through one another like links of a chain, they never could come into collision, or break one another; they would form an indestructible atom; every variety of combinations might exist. Thus a long chain of vortex-rings, or three rings, each running through each of the others, would give each very characteristic reactions upon other such kinetic atoms. I am, as yet, a good deal puzzled as to what two vortex-rings through one another would do (how each would move, and how its shape would be influenced by the other). By experiment I find that a single vortex-ring is immediately broken up and destroyed in air by enclosing it in a ring made of one's fingers and cutting it through. But a single finger held before it as it approaches very often does not cut it and break it up, but merely causes an indentation as it passes the obstacle, and a few vibrations after it is clear.

An interesting question to be considered in connection with the vortex-theory is this: If the atoms are indestructible, once they are set up in the ether, how were they created in the first place? But perhaps this is too metaphysical to be considered a legitimate question. The vortex theory finally met destruction in the same way as all other theories which rely in any essential manner upon material properties of the ether. The theory, on the basis of mathematical consideration, required a finite density for the ether, and, as we have shown in previous chapters, this assumption is untenable.

## 6. The Ether-Squirt Atom.

We must not forget that the main objective of this volume is to exhibit the metaphysical character of the fundamental assumptions upon which the structure of modern physics is built. That this metaphysical aspect of reality is not a sudden reversal of scientific attitude nor a violent overthrow of previous belief is another thesis just as important as the first. Great philosophical currents join with a stream of thought built upon careful laboratory experience to show us that that which was physical is now metaphysical and that the metaphysical problems are now the problems of reality.

An interesting example of this merging of the two ideas is to be found in a powerful paper written by that universal genius, Karl Pearson, under the alluring title: "Ether Squirts, Being an attempt to specialize the form of ether motion which forms an atom in a theory propounded in former papers." This paper was not published, as its title might indicate, in the magazine section of a Sunday newspaper, but appeared in 1891 in the conservative American Journal of Mathematics.[12] It runs to fifty pages bristling with equations. To be sure Pearson quotes the following statement of Fitzgerald, which is highly mindful of the modern trend of physical literature: "It has become the fashion to indulge in quaint cosmical theories and to dilate upon them before learned societies and in learned journals. I would suggest, as one who has been bogged in this quagmire, that a successor in this chair might well devote himself to a review of the cosmical theories propounded within the last few years. The opportunities for piquant criticism would be splendid."

The theory of Pearson starts with the assumption "that an atom or the ultimate element of ponderable matter is an ether squirt"; the definition of squirt is due to W. K. Clifford, who says:[13] "Suppose that the lines of flow are straight lines diverging from a fixed point, so that the fluid is everywhere streaming from this point; that there is no spin anywhere, and no expansion except at the fixed point."

A layman might be curious to know why such a strange concept of the atom should have occurred to Pearson. He might feel as envious as the White King who remarked to Alice:

". . . And I haven't sent the two Messengers, either. They're both gone to town. Just look along the road, and tell me if you can see either of them."

"I see nobody on the road," said Alice.

"I only wish I had such eyes," the King remarked in a fretful tone. "To be able to see Nobody! And at that distance, too! Why, it's as much as I can do to see real people, by this light!"

The answer to the question raised is that mathematical assumptions underlying the concept of the squirt led to this picture of the atom, just as the mathematical postulates associated with moving tubes of force led to the structure of Clerk Maxwell's ether.

---

[12]Vol. 13, pp. 309-362.
[13]W. K. Clifford, Elements of Dynamics, London (1878), p. 212.

Obvious difficulties which underlay the vortex-atom made a radical change in point of view necessary. Pearson conceived of the atom as being in some way a change in the structure of the ethereal fluid. One way to account for such a change, or rather one way of looking at this change in mathematical language, was to assume that it was created by a streaming of something into or out of the point in space where the atom resided. To be sure this raised the question: What was streaming and whence did it come? Pearson's answer to the first was that the streaming was the ethereal fluid, and to the second that it didn't concern a physical theory to make such explanation. "From whence the ether flows and why its flow resists variations are problems which, as they fall outside the range of physics, I leave to the metaphysicians to settle."[14] Later, however, in his delightfully stimulating "Grammar of Science," he does offer the explanation that the ether squirt may be a flow of ether into our three-dimensional manifold of existence from a four-dimensional space transcending our sensations. He concludes his speculations with the interesting remark:[15] "Should a time ever come, which may, perhaps be doubted, when a happy conception as to the structure of the prime-atom is discovered to be a *perceptual* fact, then if such a conception involves the existence of four-dimensioned space, our friends will have done yeoman service in preparing a way for a scientific theory of the supersensuous—*out through the doorway of matter!*"

The ether-squirt theory of the atom, if one is willing to admit the metaphysical structure upon which it rests, does avoid many of the difficulties of other ethereal concepts. By defining the mass of the atom to be the mean rate at which ether is squirting into space at the point in question, the law of inverse-square attraction can be derived. Other phenomena, such as chemical attraction, properties of light and electromagnetism, cohesion, etc., are amenable to treatment by the strange theory.

The possibility of ether sinks also occurs as soon as we admit ether sources, and these would behave like atoms of negative mass. Since no such phenomena are observed in nature we must conclude that the repulsion exerted by one upon the other has finally driven the ether-sink atoms out of the universe of our perceptions. Such is the magic and mysticism with which this delightful romance is clothed.

---

[14]Amer. Journal of Mathematics (loc. cit.), p. 309.
[15]The Grammar of Science, Second ed., London (1900), p. 270.

### 7. Crookes' Fourth State of Matter.

Abandoning now these pre-radioactive atoms, we turn at last to the modern picture. We are now no longer primarily interested in trying to explain gravitational attraction by our atomic models, but we have turned to the great question of radiation. Let us put the matter as picturesquely as we can: Consider a ball of iron at ordinary room temperature. Now to it apply a source of heat. At first the material sphere will remain dark, but from it there is nevertheless emanating a peculiar thing. Our hand, held near it, becomes warm; invisible radiations are conveying energy to our flesh across the medium separating us from the iron. Apply the heat a little more and the phenomenon becomes ocular. The iron begins to glow, at first a dark red, merging into scarlet, and finally into a white glowing ball difficult to look upon. There is between us and the iron a radiant bond just as real and just as mysterious as the bond of gravitation. What is its explanation?

Another phenomenon, which we must recall in order to set the stage for the modern exploration of the structure of the atom, is that of X-ray radiation. This remarkable radiation was discovered in 1895 by William Konrad Röntgen (1845-1923) while experimenting with a Crookes' tube.

Many years previous several investigators, notably Julius Plücker (1801-1868), J. G. Hittorf (1824-1903), and William Crookes (1832-1919), had commenced to study the discharge of electricity through tubes in various stages of evacuation. When the poles of an electrical generator are connected to two metal electrodes fused into the ends of a glass tube several inches in length, and the air is gradually withdrawn by a vacuum pump, a series of interesting phenomena is observed. At first the electricity has great difficulty in getting through the tube, due to the large resistance offered by the air, but as the pressure is gradually reduced irregular streamers of pink light appear, which finally broaden until almost the entire tube is filled with a pink glow. While this transformation is taking place a luminous tuft of violet light appears at the cathode, or negative electrode, and as the pressure is further diminished, this grows until it entirely surrounds the metal target. Between the two glows appears a darker region known as the *Faraday dark-space*. With greater rarefaction another vivid glow appears, this time at the anode, or positive electrode, and the pink light breaks up into thin fluctuating disks or striae. As the pressure is continually reduced these laminar glows thicken, the Faraday dark-space enlarges, the cathode glow increases in brightness and volume, and a beautiful green fluorescence appears on the walls of the tube. As the tube is further exhausted the cathode glow breaks away and moves further into the tube, while a second violet glow takes its place. Between these two violet lights appears a dark region known as the *Crookes,* or *cathode dark-space.* Still reducing the pressure this dark-space gradually increases, the negative glow slowly fades until all trace of luminosity has disappeared, and finally the dark-space fills the entire tube. As this phenomenon is taking place the tube begins to shine in the region of the cathode and finally throughout with a brilliant green fluorescence characteristic of X-ray vacua. If the pressure (now less than one fiftieth of a millimeter) is further reduced the resistance of the tube increases until the electricity will no longer pass through the tube.

Surely here was mystery enough to keep a generation of scientists at work. Attention was soon centered upon the last strange fluorescence of the tube, and it was attributed to rays originating from the cathode, now known as cathode rays. At first violent disagreement arose as to their nature, but when it was found that they were capable of deflection by magnetic forces those who would characterize them as rays similar to light were soon vanquished. Crookes himself, in a moment of inspired intuition suggested that they might represent a fourth state of matter. At the end of a brilliant article published in the Philosophical Transactions for 1879 he makes the following observation:[16]

The modern idea of the gaseous state of matter is based upon the supposition that a given space of, say a cubic centimeter, contains millions of millions of molecules in rapid motion in all directions, each having millions of encounters in a second. In such a case the length of the mean free path of the molecules is excessively small as compared with the dimensions of the vessel, and properties are observed which constitute the ordinary gaseous state of matter, and which depend upon constant collisions. But by great rarefaction the free path may be made so long that the hits in a given time are negligible in comparison to the misses, in which case the average molecule is allowed to obey its own motions or laws without interference; and if the mean free path is comparable to the dimensions of the vessel, the properties which constitute gaseity are reduced to a minimum, and the matter becomes exalted to an ultra-gaseous or mole-

[16]The Bakerian Lecture: On the Illumination of Lines of Molecular Pressure, and the Trajectory of Molecules, Trans. Royal Phil. Soc. of London, vol. 170 (1879), pp. 135-164. In particular pp. 163-164.

cular state, in which the very decided, but hitherto masked properties now under investigation come into play.

The phenomena in these exhausted tubes reveal to physical science a new world—a world where matter may exist in a fourth state, where the corpuscular theory of light may be true, and where light does not always move in straight lines, but where we can never enter, and with which we must be content to observe and experiment from the outside.

What is the secret of cathode radiation? The answer to this question is that we have been describing the birth of the electron, a particle far smaller in size than the atom and moving with a tremendous velocity. The old concept of Lucretius has been reduced a step further and the atom has been subdivided into units incredibly smaller than the indivisible units of the older theory.

## 8.   X-Rays and Radio-activity.

It seems rather curious that the investigations of Crookes did not lead earlier to the discovery of X-rays, but the facts are that these radiations were not described until 1895, as has already been related. X-rays are formed when the electrons of the Crookes tube impinge upon a metal target, or, as a matter of fact, upon any matter. The discovery of Röntgen was made quite by accident, as many such discoveries are. He had been working on the problem of invisible light rays and during his investigation turned on a low pressure tube which was concealed under a covering of heavy black paper. To his surprise he noticed that a fluorescent screen some distance away from the apparatus commenced to shine. Then by interposing matter between it and the tube so as to cast shadows upon the screen, he was able to trace the invisible radiation to the Crookes tube. Another dramatic moment was at hand in the annals of man's quest of the unknown. X-rays had been discovered.

Investigation by many men who were instantly attracted to this discovery revealed after much ingenious and penetrating labor the nature of the new radiation. The cathode rays were tiny particles possessing mass and a charge of negative electricity; X-rays were radiations similar to light although of very much smaller wave length and with a corresponding ability to penetrate opaque matter.

The next great discovery in these closing years of the nineteenth century was that of radio-activity by Antoine Henri Becquerel (1852-1908) in 1896. Like his predecessor in the discovery of activities in nature which would penetrate opaque objects Becquerel was investigating the possible existence of invisible radiations. His experiments proceeded from phosphorescent substances, which he placed upon a photographic plate wrapped in black paper. By rare good fortune the phosphorescent substance chosen for the investigation was a preparation of uranium, and when the plate was developed it was found to have been darkened. Further study of this interesting phenomenon soon revealed the fact that phosphorescence had nothing to do with the matter, but that uranium itself possessed a hitherto unsuspected property of emanating something that would penetrate opaque substances.

Soon after this there appeared the epoch-making work of Pierre (1859-1906) and Marie Curie, who discovered radium. This remarkable element, similar in many ways to uranium and other radioactive substances, though possessing these powers in much higher degree, is now known to give off three types of radiation which are called by the first three letters of the Greek alphabet, Alpha, Beta, and Gamma rays. The first two rays differ in a very fundamental way from the third, since they exhibit the characteristics of corpuscles or particles while the last is an undulatory phenomenon. The alpha rays are much more sluggish than the beta particles, traveling with velocities of a few thousand miles per second, while the latter approach the ultimate velocity itself. The alpha particles are also more massive and carry a positive charge of electricity. Their mass can be measured by deflections created in their path by a magnetic field and is found to be equal to the mass of the helium nucleus. Other tests that can be applied confirm the identification of these two. Beta-rays, on the other hand, are as light as they are swift. They can also be weighed by deflections caused in their path by a magnetic field, and this mass is found to identify them with the electron, when proper correction is made for the change in mass predicted by the relativity theory. The gamma radiation, on the other hand, is a true wave motion, similar in character to that of light, but very much more penetrating. Gamma rays are not corpuscular in character as many experiments show. Magnetic fields, for example, will not affect their propagation, nor will they leave a positive or negative charge upon matter on which they fall. Their velocity, subject to experimental error, is approximately that of light itself.

We must pause a moment and reflect upon this remarkable proposition. Here the human race stumbles by accident upon a phenomenon in which three types of things are involved. The first two are corpuscular in character. They possess some of the properties of matter; they have finite mass and velocities smaller than that of light; they can be deflected by magnetic fields, they possess charges of electricity, and otherwise behave like quantities for which we have definite objective feeling. But look at the mysterious gamma ray. Here is a new property of the ether; this ray behaves like a vibrating entity similar to light but with incredible powers of penetrating matter. It resembles the X-ray, with the one difference that it has a smaller wave length. Oh curious word! How can we think of wave length when there is no substance of material quality for it to undulate in? For the electron we have intuitive feeling; for the mysterious radiation in the evanescent ether we have none. Here suddenly a new world of rays and minute quantities are opened to the speculation of man before he has had time to coordinate his ideas about the sub-stratum of reality in which these phenomena are taking place. This discussion is interpolated here so that the sequel will be more vivid.

### 9.   *Radium and the New Alchemy.*

The mystery of radium and uranium and of the forty or more other radio-active substances found since the great discovery is explained by saying that we are witnessing in these remarkable substances the destruction of atoms. The dream of alchemy, "that art without art, which has its beginning in falsehood, its middle in toil, and its end in poverty," has at last become a reality. To be sure the decay of atoms is in general a very slow process and, as yet, one whose secret has not yielded to the persistent search of man. Uranium, for example, suffers transmutation of half of its atoms in 4,500 million years. The first product resulting from this disintegration has a short life, half decaying in twenty-four days, and yielding a substance of the most ephemeral character, since it has a period of approximately sixty-nine seconds. The second product from uranium has an uncertain length of life, estimated by Sommerfeld at two million years. The intricate relationships between these heavy elements have been traced by Sir Ernest Rutherford, the English physicist, and many others, step by step from the massive uranium, through radium with its inert emanation (niton) of period equal to four days, to the final product, lead, which results after two thousand years of disintegration. What a wonderful picture of the creation of the elements is this! But the old question persists, just as it does in the problem of energy: Where did uranium come from? Why in the lapse of countless geologic ages has the decay not persisted until all the radio-active elements have broken down into their final structure?

The absorbing story of the ingenuity spent in finding out these facts about the ultimate nature of matter can not be related in detail here because of its technical difficulties. The point that is sufficient for us in philosophical speculation is now easily apprehended. Radium and cathode radiation show that there is an atomic nature both to matter and to electricity. Even as late as 1897 Lord Kelvin was still discussing the possibility of a fluid structure of electricity, but these new discoveries were already pointing out the proof of the existence of an atomic nature of electricity as well as of matter.

## 10. Sub-Atomic Exploration.

The dramatic incidents in the birth of the electron have been related above. To do this theme justice, however, would require the art of Laurence Sterne, that noted English wit, who devotes the major portion of the four large volumes on "The Life and Opinions of Tristram Shandy," to the details incident to the birth of his hero. His piquant volumes start with the following philosophical observation: "The HOMUNCULUS, Sir, in however low and ludicrous a light he may appear, in this age of levity, to the eye of folly or prejudice, to the eye of reason in scientific research, he stands confessed—a Being guarded and circumscribed with rights." Change homunculus to electron and we should have a proper prologue for our theme.

With the birth of the electron and the verification that a fourth state of matter actually existed within the Crookes tube, the age of sub-atomic exploration was at hand. The name "electron" is due to G. Johnstone Stoney who in 1891 used it as a designation for the "natural unit of electricity."[17] This term is frequently specialized to denote the actual charge on the particles of the Crookes tube, and the word "corpuscle" is reserved for the material quantity by which the charge is carried. In this volume we shall adopt the definition of Lorentz, who characterizes electrons as "extremely small particles, charged with electricity, which are present in immense numbers in all ponderable bodies, and by whose distribution and motions we en-

[17]Scientific Trans. of the Royal Soc. of Dublin (11), vol. 4 (1891), p. 563.

deavor to explain all electric and optical phenomena that are not confined to the free ether."[18]

At once some important questions arise which might be enumerated as follows: (1) How large is the charge of electricity carried by the electron? (2) What is the mass of the electron? (3) How fast does it move? (4) Can a volume be assigned to it? (5) Are there sub-electrons, that is to say particles smaller than the particles of the Crookes tube?

Very many ingenious methods have been devised to answer these important questions, but it will be impossible to review them adequately here, since they are technical in nature. A general idea of the attack made, however, is both instructive and interesting and can be set forth as follows:

We have already stated that the fundamental "particular" character of the electrons was demonstrated by the deflections which they suffered while passing through magnetic and electric fields of force. It is easily deduced from the equations of mechanics, which, though they originally applied to the large ponderable masses dealt with in the ordinary affairs of the world, may be assumed to hold also for the tiny electron, that a relationship between the velocity of the electrons and the ratio of charge ($e$) and mass ($m$) can be derived from the size of the deflections caused by a known magnetic field. But the question can not be so easily answered as to which is the value of the ratio $e/m$ and which the velocity.

The velocity of the particles in a Crookes tube was determined independently in 1897 by Sir J. J. Thomson[19] and E. Wiechert.[20] The latter by means of a tube containing two magnetizing coils was able to control the deflections of the cathode beam falling upon a fluorescent screen, in such a way as to be able to measure the velocity of the particles. These he found attained the not inconsiderable speed of $5 \times 10^9$ centimeters per second, or one-sixth that of light. Hence, knowing the velocity, the ratio $e/m$ could then be easily calculated. Sir J. J. Thomson in his method deflected the electrons by means of a magnetic field into a hollow vessel where their aggregate electrical charge could be measured by an electrometer and where their total kinetic energy was determined by means of a delicate thermo-electric couple in terms of units of heat. From these two values, together with the strength of the deflecting field, and the

[18]Theory of Electrons (loc. cit.), p. 8.
[19]Phil. Mag. (5), vol. 44 (1897), pp. 293-316.
[20]Verb. der phys.-ökon. Ges. zu Königsberg (1897).

radius of the path taken by the electrons, he was able to compute the average value of the velocities of the particles and hence the desired ratio.

The ratio of $e$ to $m$ was thus found to be a large number. This indicated either that $e$ was a comparatively large unit, or that the mass of an electron was exceedingly minute. If $e$ was of the same order of magnitude of the electrical charge on the hydrogen ion in solutions, the mass of the electron was only 1/1800th of the mass of the hydrogen atom. This latter possibility has the exciting consequence that if it be the correct interpretation, we shall have subdivided the atom and can peer into depths never before seen by man. The atom will then have structure and be composed of much smaller units than had previously been postulated. To be sure, this possibility merely means that what was once considered the smallest divisible unit will have yielded to a smaller one, the sequence now being molecules, atoms, and electrons. The smallest unit has merely changed its name.

### 11.  *Weighing the Electron.*

Speculation next centered around the problem of how the value of the electric charge and the mass of the electron could be independently determined. Human ingenuity reaches one of its highest levels in the beautiful chain of experiments which culminated in the very accurate determination for which R. A. Millikan was awarded the Nobel prize in 1923. The fundamental idea goes back to J. S. Townsend, C. T. R. Wilson and others who saw in the formation of clouds the possibility of weighing the electron.[21] The basic assumption is that water vapor must have nuclei around which to condense if clouds are to be formed and these nuclei are ions.

Any one who has had the privilege of sitting upon a high peak and watching clouds form below him will always remember the event. The wind, laden with moisture, sweeps up the valley and strikes against the cold wall of the mountain. Puff! Out of nothing suddenly appears the cloud. Where a moment before the sun shone clearly through, there is now a weaving mist which scuds rapidly away to make room for the next. And what is the nature of this phenomenon? You will read in books on meteorology that the moisture laden wind sweeps up the valley and the water is condensed by contact with the cold cliff. But there is more than that

---

[21]Proc. of the Cambridge Phil. Soc., vol. 9 (1897), pp. 244 and 345.

in this interesting phenomenon. Suddenly a brilliant glare flashes across the valley, and one is aware that there are dynamic forces in the clouds. The water vapor was not merely condensed by the cold air of the mountain, but carried within itself a charge of electricity. Each droplet contained as its core at least one elementary charge of this mysterious element, which first terrified the human race as an evidence of celestial wrath and now is harnessed to do the myriad tasks of mankind.

To put the matter somewhat more scientifically the following assumptions were made:

First, that each drop of condensed water vapor had one charge of electricity as its nucleus, so that the total number of ions, or charge bearers, was equal to the total number of drops.

Second, that the average weight of the water droplets making the cloud could be determined by watching their rate of fall and computing their radii from a theoretical law derived by G. G. Stokes.[22]

Admitting these two propositions the matter was theoretically a simple one. Townsend in his experiment determined the electrical charge per cubic centimeter of the cloud by means of a quadrant electrometer, weighed the total amount of water composing the fog and divided it by the number of droplets to get the total number of ions per cubic centimeter. The total electrical charge divided by the number of ions was the charge per ion.

While this is the crude outline of the experiment both of Townsend and of those who followed him, it is obvious that many sources of error are present. First the assumption of the equivalence between ions and drops may be doubted. Stokes' law had not been experimentally tested; the drops were not necessarily uniform in size; the obvious assumption that evaporation would take place had been neglected; convection currents certainly would play a part in the movement of the cloud particles.

The subsequent efforts of Sir J. J. Thomson, C. T. R. Wilson, H. A. Wilson, and R. A. Millikan, who made the fundamental contribution to physical science of computing accurate values for $e$ and $m$, were devoted wholly to overcoming the difficulties cited above.[23] The latter, whose values are generally regarded as being the most accurate, developed a very fine experiment by means of which he could actually study the movements of an individual drop with its nuclear charge which he desired to measure. The following

---

[22]Cambridge Phil. Trans., vol. 9 (1850).
[23]For an admirable account of the matters treated in this chapter the reader is referred to Millikan's book: The Electron, Chicago (1917).

quotation shows the elegance which characterized the investigation of the "star" upon whose motions so much of the modern work in atomic physics was to rest.[24]

My original plan for eliminating the evaporation error was to obtain, if possible, an electric field strong enough exactly to balance the force of gravity upon the cloud and then by means of a sliding contact to vary the strength of this field so as to hold the cloud balanced throughout its entire life. In this way it was thought that the whole evaporation-history of the cloud might be recorded, and that suitable allowances might then be made in the observations on the rate of fall to eliminate entirely the error due to evaporation. It was not found possible to balance the cloud, as had been originally planned, but it was found possible to do something much better: namely, to hold individual charged drops suspended by the field for periods varying from 30 to 60 seconds. . . . The drops which it was found possible to balance by an electrical field always carried multiple charges, and the difficulty experienced in balancing such drops was less than had been anticipated.

The procedure is simply to form a cloud and throw on the field immediately thereafter. The drops which have charges of the same sign as that of the upper plate or too weak charges of the opposite sign rapidly fall, while those which are charged with too many multiples of the sign opposite to that of the upper plate are jerked up against gravity to this plate. The result is that after a lapse of 7 or 8 seconds the field of view has become quite clear save for a relatively small number of drops which have just the right ratio of charge to mass to be held suspended by the electric field. These appear as perfectly distinct bright points. (The apparatus is illuminated by light from both sides.) I have on several occasions obtained but one single such "star" in the whole field and held it there for nearly a minute.

Is there not poetry in this measurement of these "stars" and the weighing of that infinitesimal particle so many magnitudes below our visibility? There is drama in the movements of the tiny speck, the adjusting of the field to hold it in suspension, the weighing of that infinitely small particle, from whose myriad swarms come the phenomena of ponderable bodies. The value of the mass is wholly beyond our comprehension because of its minuteness, but is of the order of $9 \times 10^{-28}$ of a gram.

What mental picture can we form of this tiny quantity from which the structure of things is made? Is it spherical like a marble after the concepts of the Lucretian atom? Does it have size, or is it

---

[24]A new Modification of the Cloud Method of Determining the Elementary Charge and the most Probable Value of that Charge, Phil. Mag. (6), vol. 19 (1910), p. 209. See also: The Electron, p. 57.

merely a strain in the metaphysical ether? One man's guess is as good as another's. The tentative agreement among scientists, for want of better hypothesis, has been to regard the electron as a spherical entity, whose mass is wholly derived from its electrical charge. This model is due to Sir J. J. Thomson who demonstrated that the apparent inertial mass of a sphere in motion is slightly increased if it be charged, and he showed how to calculate the total mass of such a body. Applying his formula to the electron and assuming that the whole mass is electrical the approximate size of the electron is $2 \times 10^{-13}$ centimeters, or in slightly more understandable language, if ten trillion such bodies were placed in a row one just touching the other their total length would not exceed an inch and a half.

We have already indicated above the fact that the electron, since its discovery in the Crookes tube, has been found throughout nature. It attains its most majestic place in the high speed beta rays of radium; these particles have been completely identified with their slower brethren. There has recently been evidence to show that artificial beta rays may be created in the laboratory. W. D. Coolidge has invented a tube in which streams of electrons can be generated with high velocities.[25] This tube is an evacuated bulb with two long extensions. At one end, called the cathode, a copious supply of electrons are emitted from the heated filament of tungsten, but these electrons are not like those emitted from radium because of their comparatively low velocities. In order to accelerate them the second part of the apparatus, which consists of a long copper tube, is given a voltage somewhere in the neighborhood of 250,000 or 300,000 volts. Under the influence of this potential the electrons speed up and are discharged at the end of the tube through a thin nickel window. The velocities thus obtained, however, are much lower than those of radium rays so Coolidge devised a scheme for increasing their speed. This was done by making the end of the first tube a new cathode for a second Coolidge tube, into which the electrons now poured with their already high velocities. So far three tubes with an effective voltage of 900,000 have been used, and it is estimated that a little over three times this will be sufficient to produce beta rays of radium.

So far in our story we have said nothing about the proton or positive particle which is found to be the constituent entity in the

---

[25]Production of High-Voltage Kathode Rays Outside the Generating Tube, Journ. Franklin Inst., vol. 202 (1926), pp. 693-721. See also: Science, vol. 62 (1925), pp. 441-442.

alpha rays of radium. A great deal of ingenious work has been done in exploring the properties of these curious elementary substances, but most attention of recent physics in this regard has been directed to their swifter companions. In structure they are similar to the electron, although very much more massive, which accounts for their more sluggish movements. They are not all of the same size, but differ for different substances, and are probably very much smaller than the electron, in spite of their greater mass. Measurements indicate that their mass is never less than that of the hydrogen atom or $1.65 \times 10^{-24}$ grams, and their radius is probably 1/2000th that of the electron.

### 12.  Do Macrocosmic Laws Hold in the Microcosm?

If we are willing to believe the evidence that has been accumulated in the laboratory concerning these exceedingly small particles moving with their enormous velocities, the structure of the microcosmos may not be wholly discordant with the universe of man's activities. We have made assumptions that the laws of mechanics applicable to the large ponderable bodies apply also in the movements of these tiny particles ; we have assigned an inertia to their movements identical with the mysterious inertia of our greater systems. This raises the speculation whether, if Mach and Einstein be correct, these tiny bodies are also inextricably connected with all the other matter in the macrocosm. We have regarded them as spheres of ponderable stuff with minute charges of electricity wholly conceivable and in accord with rational belief. We have merely replaced the crude atom of Lucretius by smaller particles with measurable properties and attributes consonant with experiment. The picture does not surprise us. We look with a certain feeling of confidence upon Bohr's image of the atom, a little solar system with a protonic nucleus and the electrons moving in elliptical orbits about it. Perhaps, we say, the clue to the structure of matter is to be found in astronomy ; we apply to one the same dynamical equations used in investigating the other ; the laws of Kepler for the planets are the laws for the hydrogen atom. That superb unity in natural law, long dreamed of by those who followed the trail of the great Newton, seems about to be revealed to us. The microcosm and the macrocosm are identical, and physical science can do nothing better than to accumulate more and more evidence to show this cosmic harmony. It is a beautiful picture ; but, alas, the story is not yet told !

### 13.  *The Photo-Electric Effect.*

We turn next to a remarkable fact, which is essentially the basis of the strange dilemma with which modern physics is now confronted. This fact is technically known as the *photo-electric* effect and can be described far easier than it can be explained.

When light is allowed to fall upon a metal plate we discover that electrons are given off and the quantity increases with the intensity of the incident beam. One feels in this statement the approach of trouble. With these words we connect the electron with the great mystery of radiation. We have already prepared the way by citing the phenomenon of the hot material body throwing off its streams of radiant energy. All about us in every conceivable activity of nature we find evidence of a union between matter and radiation. There is an undiscovered bond between the activities of the electrons in ponderable bodies and the elusive entity which conveys the evidence of their activity. It is the ancient metaphysical problem of matter and its relation to the substratum of reality. Just as we were wholly baffled in our attempts to give a rational explanation to the motion of ponderable bodies through the medium which conveyed radiation, so we should expect a similar difficulty when we try to trace the relationship between the motion of the electrons and the radiation that results from their activity.

But what is so mysterious in the photo-electric effect? That electrons should be cast out of a metal plate by the bombardment (technically spoken of as absorption) of light is not unreasonable. But here is the strange fact. The stream of photo-electrons is made up of electrons whose velocity can never exceed a value determined by the frequency of the incident light. Increase the intensity of the radiation and more electrons, but not more rapidly moving ones, are cast out of the metal. The greater the energy the greater the number, but not the greater their kinetic energy. Further investigation of the phenomena led to the conclusion that, allowing for a certain amount of energy necessary to detach the electron from the metal plate, the kinetic energy of the electrons was proportional to the frequency of the incident light, in which the factor of proportionality was a universal number called Planck's constant and equal in c. g. s. units (erg second) to $6.56 \times 10^{-27}$.

Does the peculiarity of the phenomenon now make itself apparent? If not, reflect upon the waves of the sea. Suppose one were standing upon the beach on a stormy day watching the water roll the pebbles upon the sand. And suppose the wind increased in violence and the waves came in with higher crests and greater volume. Would you not consider it a strange phenomenon if the pebbles which you had been watching were thrown no higher upon the beach, but merely that more of them were affected by the waves? And would it not seem stranger still if investigation showed that waves of a certain frequency, no matter how large their size, always moved their pebbles a certain distance and no farther? This analogy which is frequently used in explaining the new difficulties of physics is picturesque and accurate. The waves of light falling upon the metal plate may increase in intensity, but this intensity serves only to eject more electrons from the surface and not to give them greater energy.

### 14. *The Ether and Natural Law.*

With this brief description of an epoch making phenomenon we shall bring the present chapter to a close. We started out auspiciously to study the atomic structure of matter, and beyond our highest hopes, were able to demonstrate the existence of primary units, which seemed to combine the mystery of matter with the mystery of electricity. The last fortress of the continuists, so far as objective nature was concerned, was taken. Nature was atomic: the fluid concept of electricity was to be replaced by a corpuscular theory, in which swarms of tiny particles bearing their charges of negative or positive electricity were to yield to the analysis of the mathematical theorems of the kinetic theory of gases.

But a remarkable aspect of the problem has been revealed. The ether, that strange necessity of thought, inaccessible to sensuous experience, baffling and mysterious has intruded upon the picture. Not content with overthrowing our *a priori* concepts of space, time, and gravitation, the ether has again encroached upon the cherished principles of Newtonian mechanics. One can not forbear to quote the Ancient Mariner.

> When looking westward, I beheld
> A something in the sky.
> At first it seemed a little speck,
> And then it seemed a mist,
> It moved and moved, and took at last
> A certain shape I wist.

As we have traced step by step the history of philosophical speculation in its relation to the problems of the world of matter this strange spectre has been with us. Its wraith-like form intertwines with every theory. We start out hopefully with a material model and with postulates firmly grounded in sensuous experience and upon rational intuitions. At some turn in the road the spectre waits. Our theories lose their reality, and the metaphysical finally replaces the physical in a set of equations which tell the story but leave us sadly puzzled. To be sure, we have not yet gone far enough in the present romance to be able to draw this conclusion with conviction, but the quantum theory and its resulting wave mechanics will prove to be an even more remarkable substantiation of our theme than the perplexities of the space-time manifold, the history of which we have completed in previous chapters.

# CHAPTER IX.

## THE LAWS OF CHANCE.

### 1. *Probability and the Discontinuity of Nature.*

IN THE last chapter we traced the history of the atomic concept of matter from its beginning in the vague outline of Democritus and Lucretius to the brilliant experiments which demonstrated the existence of the tiny corpuscles of the Crookes tube. We saw science postulate an atomic structure for electricity and matter, giving shape, size, inertia, and electric charge to these basic units of objective nature. The model was simple and satisfactory. It was easy to visualize and strained credulity only to the extent of imposing upon thought a discontinuous structure for the universe instead of a continuous one. Moreover this strain upon belief is apparent rather than real, for the latter view, if it be thoughtfully considered, will appear fully as difficult to conceive as the former. One we derive from considerations of a fluid, the other from the compressibility of a gas.

But after these satisfactory conclusions had been attained a grave difficulty appeared. Matter radiates the troublesome undulations whose history we have traced earlier in connection with theories of the ether. And these radiations are ubiquitous. Wheresoever matter is, there we find them, and where matter is not, they are also present. Radiant energy is the most common phenomenon of nature; in every cubic centimeter of space it is to be found. Its density varies from its tremendous value near the surface of the stars to its infinitesimal value in the dark cold reaches of interstellar space. It is the most important phenomenon in nature. Matter is either in equilibrium with it or seeks perpetually to attain this equilibrium. The mystery of its source and the mystery of its laws are the puzzles of modern physical science.

It may seem strange to some that a chapter upon the laws of chance should be interpolated between chapters on the atomic concept and the metaphysics of the quantum theory, but the mystery of radiation forces the issue upon us. What mathematical model shall we employ in its description? Poincaré's comment on the theory of quanta radiation is highly significant: "It is useless to remark how far removed this concept is from our customary ideas, since the

227

laws of physics will no longer be susceptible of being expressed by means of differential equations."[1] We have already witnessed in previous chapters the struggle of those who attempted to fit the ether into a system of differential equations and we have seen in the theory of relativity that the invariance of these equations for transformations in a non-Euclidean geometry was one of the principal concepts of Einstein's theory. Shall the new approach to the mysterious relationship between radiation and matter be taken through these continuous creations of subjective thought?

The answer is that the theory of probability furnishes a more satisfactory mathematical structure upon which to construct an approach to atomic concepts. Its foundations are rooted in the "law of large numbers" which implies by its very name the postulate of discrete quantities. In such an analysis the description of the activities of aggregates of particles, is surely to be found. If nature can be studied through rational models here is the open road.

## 2.  *The Nature of Natural Law.*

The mathematician is often accused of being impractical, a dreamer who spins intricate patterns out of the web of his imagination, who builds theories that have little in common with the practical affairs of life. The story is told of Euclid that a youth who had come to him for instruction, after having learned the first proposition, asked: "But what am I to get out of this?" and Euclid for reply commanded a slave to give him a coin, since he needs must have a gain for all that he learned.[2]

But there is one subject in mathematics which possesses the elegance of those abstract theories that delight the artistic spirit and yet, at the same time, has vital contact with the practical affairs of life. This is the theory of the laws of chance, a theory at once so elusive that one does not find agreement among mathematicians as to the full validity of its laws and yet a theory so sound that millions of dollars have been invested in insurance companies built upon its foundations.

"Yet how dare we speak of the laws of chance? Is not chance the antithesis of all law?" asks Bertrand at the beginning of his "Calcul des probabilités." In commenting upon this question Poincaré says: "But this conception (of phenomena either obeying harmonious law or else rebellious to all law) is not ours today. We have become absolute determinists, and even those who want to reserve the right of human free will, undoubtedly will let determinism reign undividedly in the inorganic world at least. Every phenomenon, however minute, has a cause; and a mind infinitely powerful, infinitely well informed about the laws of nature, could have foreseen it from the beginning of the centuries. If such a mind existed, we could not play with it any game of chance; we should always lose. . . . Chance is only the measure of our ignorance. Fortuitous phenomena are, by definition, those whose laws we do not know.[3]

The calculus of probabilities should be regarded as an attempt to reduce to numbers the uncertainties of life and thus to afford a way of aiding judgment. The universe about us presents a maze of perplexities. We are ignorant of the past and uncertain of the future, but it is by no means true that this uncertainty and ignorance are uniform and homogeneous. We are uncertain whether the sun will rise tomorrow, but we should attach far more value to a guess about it than we should to a guess about our ability to throw a head in a single toss of one coin.

But from where do we derive our greater certainty? Suppose that we saw a sunrise for the first time and we should inquire: What is the chance that this phenomenon will occur again? In the game of matching pennies we observe that the chance of throwing heads is equal to the chance of throwing tails, or numerically stated it is 1/2. Suppose that we attach this probability, because of ignorance, to the phenomenon of the sunrise.

Further we might deduce from our experience of tossing coins that the chance of throwing heads ten times in succession is 1 to 1024; but we observe that the sun rises ten, twenty, or even a hundred times in succession. Hence it would appear highly unlikely that our original assumption of a probability of 1/2 was right. Moreover, if we continue to assign larger and larger fractional values, always leaving something for our uncertainty, to the probability of the rising of the sun and continue to collect data on the phenomenon, we shall eventually find that all our original assumptions are in error because no cases of failure appear.

Thus we are finally led to assign as the probability of the rising of the sun a number which differs from unity, or certainty, by a

[3]Science and Method, chapter 4. Foundations of Science, p. 395.

value indefinitely small. When such a probability exists it may be said to define a law.

By using properly the experience of many men we are acquiring much greater ability to predict the future than did our ancestors with all their magicians and soothsayers. It was once the fashion to consult the "sortes of Virgil" in order to learn the probable success of a venture, but today it is much more the custom to consult a table of statistics.

However, our progress is slow and the pitfalls in the way of chance are many. Richard Harding Davis has an extravaganza relating the experiences of a man who could guess the future. If one of us had the power of infallible prediction, it would not be long before this one would be ruler of the world. To him there would be no calculus of probabilities because all things would be certain. Failing, however, to possess this remarkable gift we must find some yard stick that can measure in a degree the extent of our ignorance and uncertainty. We flip a coin. Will it fall heads or tails? We buy a share of stock. Will it rise or fall? As in O. Henry's story of "The Roads of Destiny" we come to a parting of the ways. Do success and happiness lie along the middle road or along those to the right or left?

There is deep philosophical speculation in these ideas. Are we to regard the events of the universe as wholly fortuitous, guided by blind accident? Is the freedom of the will of man an illusion and are the acts of choice which we think that we perform daily merely predetermined acts for which we are but the vehicles of expression?

Laplace to whose immortal treatise we can trace most of the stimulus acquired by modern students of the laws of chance has stated in a philosophical essay the following rational view which we shall tentatively adopt :[4]

Present events are connected with preceding ones by a tie based upon the evident principle that a thing cannot occur without a cause which produces it. The axiom, known by the name of the *principle of sufficient reason,* extends even to actions which are considered indifferent; the freest will is unable without a determinative motive to give them birth; if we assume two positions with exactly similar circumstances and find that the will is active in the one and inactive in the other, we say that its choice is an effect without a cause. It is then, says Leibnitz, the blind chance of the Epicureans. The con-

[4]Page ii of the Introduction to his "Théorie Analytique des Probabilités," 3d ed., Paris (1820). See English translation of the Introduction by F. W. Truscott and F. L. Emory (1902), p. 3.

trary opinion is an illusion of the mind, which, losing sight of the evasive reasons of the choice of the will in indifferent things, believes that choice is determined of itself and without motives.

We ought then to regard the present state of the universe as the effect of its anterior state and as the cause of the one which is to follow. Given for one instant an intelligence which could comprehend all the forces by which nature is animated and the respective situation of the beings who compose it—an intelligence sufficiently vast to submit these data to analysis—it would embrace in the same formulas the movements of the greatest bodies of the universe and those of the lightest atom; for it, nothing would be uncertain and the future, as the past, would be present to its eyes. The human mind offers, in the perfection which it has been able to give to astronomy, a feeble idea of this intelligence. Its discoveries in mechanics and geometry, added to that of universal gravitation, have enabled it to comprehend in the same analytical expressions the past and future states of the system of the world. Applying the same method to some other objects of its knowledge, it has succeeded in referring to general laws observed phenomena and in foreseeing those which given circumstances ought to produce. All these efforts in the search for truth tend to lead it back continually to the vast intelligence which we have mentioned, but from which it will always remain infinitely removed. This tendency, peculiar to the human race, is that which renders it superior to animals; and their progress in this respect distinguishes nations and ages and constitutes their true glory.

### 3. *The Law of Large Numbers.*

The definition of mathematical probability is usually given as follows: The probability that, among several equally likely events, a given event will happen is the ratio of the number of favorable cases to the total number of possible cases.

There is much tacitly implied in this brief statement, however. In elucidation let us consider a simple example. We throw a die. Any one of the six faces may appear, and one is no more likely than another. Hence we say that the probability of any particular face appearing, for example five, is one-sixth. But this must be properly understood. Does this mean that once and only once the five spot will appear in every six throws of the die? Not at all. It means that on the average, if many throws are made, the five will be found to have appeared approximately one-sixth of the time. This proposition is known in the theory of probability as the *law of large numbers* and is the rock upon which the structure rests. It forces us to distinguish between *a priori* and *a posteriori* probability. The former by definition applies to the probability derived from a study of empirical data. We reflect upon the tossing of a coin and conclude from pure intuition that the chance of throwing heads in a single toss is 1/2; to test this conclusion by experiment would require evidence derived from a large number of actual tosses.

Some definitions of probability include the law of large numbers as an integral part, as for example the statement of the Danish astronomer T. N. Thiele that probability is the name "for the limiting value of the relative frequency of an event, when the number of observations (trials) under which the event happens approaches infinity as a limit."[5]

Let us illustrate this by determining through actual empirical trial the probability that a coin will fall heads. Toss the coin once and compute the *a posteriori* probability of the event on the basis of this single experiment. It will be either certainty (one) or impossibility (zero). But suppose that the experiment be continued to ten thousand tosses. It can be shown that the probability is so large that the difference between the calculated answer and the *a priori* one of one-half will be less than one-one thousandth. If we continue our tosses to a million, two million, three million, etc., the difference will be found continually to diminish until ultimately it may be made smaller than any limit we wish to set.

But whence do we derive this certainty? Does it come from the experience of countless penny tossers or does it have a more fundamental derivation from subjective intuition? It may be proved on intuitional postulates with some rigor and a minimum of assumption that if the *a priori* probability actually exists then the difference between it and the one obtained by experiment may be made as small as we choose. But who would care to state that the *a priori* probability always exists? Suppose we test the validity of the assumption that heads will fall half the time in a series of tosses with a single coin. A million actual trials will probably serve to show merely that one side of the coin is slightly heavier than the other or that some other systematic error exists.

On the other hand there is remarkable objective validity in the law of large numbers and unsuspected problems may be solved by its application. The following celebrated example was first given by George Louis LeClerk, Comte de Buffon (1707-1788) and can be tried with profit by any one who wishes to assure himself that the law is fundamentally applicable to the material universe.[6]

Take a stick of length 2L, say two inches, and from a short

---

[5] Quoted by A. Fisher: Mathematical Theory of Probabilities, New York (1923), p. 84.
[6] This example appeared first in Buffon's "Essai d' Arithmétique Morale (1777), vol. 4 to Supplement à l'Histoire Naturelle, although it was written about 1760.

height drop it upon a table upon which are drawn two lines a distance D, greater than 2L, say four inches apart. Then the stick will either cross one of these two lines or it will not. Suppose that this experiment be tried N times, say 1000, and the observation be made that the stick crosses one of the lines C times. Is it not a beautiful conclusion that the value of $\pi = 3.1416 \ldots$, the ratio of a circumference to its diameter, can be computed with some degree of accuracy from these numbers, namely, $\pi = 4\, N\, L/C\, D$? Augustus De Morgan (1806-1871) had one of his pupils make 600 trials and thus calculated $\pi = 3.137$.[7] In 1864 Captain O. C. Fox made 1120 trials using some precautions to get actual random falls for his stick and obtained $\pi = 3.1419$.[8] To the reflective mind it must be a perpetual wonder that this important number, the center about which revolves a conspicuous part of the mathematical universe, should have its secrets bared by the dropping of sticks upon a table top.

Another example of similar character and one important in the history of the theory of chance is the probability of writing down at random a pair of prime numbers. Thus suppose that N pairs of numbers such as, for example 23 and 96, are written down at random, and account taken of the number, C, that are prime to one another. It is a curious fact that $\pi$ may be approximately calculated from the formula: $\pi = \sqrt{6\,N/C}$.[9]

Those who remember the painful toil necessary to compute the ratio of the circumference to its diameter by the methods of elementary geometry will find in this an interesting reflection. Straight lines defined as rays of light, as we have seen in another place, might lead the paths of geometrical instruction to the laboratory; the law of large numbers assures us that abstract ratios in this same subject may be computed by empirical trials with sticks of wood or pairs of prime numbers. Archimedes, instead of employing subjective methods to calculate the upper and lower bounds within which the value of $\pi$ must lie, might have attained the same limits and with almost the same accuracy by dropping sticks of wood for a sufficient number of times.

It is truly surprising how far the elementary definition of probability will lead. It is in this fact, perhaps, that the charm of this subject lies, namely that one can go so far upon so small a postulate.

---

[7] Budget of Paradoxes, London (1872), pp. 171-172.
[8] On an Experimental Determination of $\pi$ by Asaph Hall. Messenger of Mathematics, vol. 2 (1873), pp. 113-114.
[9] This result is due to the Russian mathematician, P. S. Tschebyscheff. See A. Fisher, loc. cit., pp. 46-48.

Many problems of geometrical nature are amenable to the calculus of chance, although it may seem strange that close connection should exist between branches of mathematics so divergent. Consider for example an interesting episode in Poe's fanciful story of "The Pit and the Pendulum." The hero of the tale is imprisoned in a dungeon of the Spanish Inquisition. He recovers from his first period of unconsciousness to find himself in complete darkness, unable to see the walls of the prison or anything about him. After some meditation he decides to make a circuit of the dungeon, and when this is accomplished he estimates that it has a perimeter of approximately fifty yards. This task completed, he decides to cross the prison from wall to wall, but in the darkness trips and falls upon his face, to find that he is lying upon the edge of a circular pit opened there to accomplish his destruction. An interesting problem in probability is suggested by this tale. Suppose that the circumference of the pit had been L yards in length, what was the probability that the prisoner would have fallen into the pit had he attempted to cross the dungeon in any random direction? It is a surprising result that this mathematical probability, under the single assumption that both pit and dungeon were convex in shape, is merely the ratio of the length of the circumference of the pit to the perimeter of the dungeon, namely $L/50$. Thus if the pit had had a radius of four yards the prisoner would have had an even chance for his life.

Look about you and see the innumerable places where these probabilities occur. Count the letters on an English page and determine the probability of the occurrence of the letter e; you will remember how important this knowledge was in deciphering the mystery of Poe's "Gold Bug." We have already indicated the use of chance in considering cosmic puzzles such as the density of matter in the universe; that a law of some kind was working in the distribution of the asteroids is implied by the discovery of the existence of radial gaps in their orbits, the probability of which, on the assumption of a purely fortuitous distribution, is 1 to 137,438,953,472, according to the figures of Daniel Kirkwood (1814-1895), the astronomer.[10] Death whose certainty is assured but whose time is subject to the whim of fate holds for every age an empirical probability upon which the colossal financial structure of life insurance is erected.

The power of the theory of chance lies in its calm disregard of the causes of the events subject to its analysis, provided only that these causes be sufficiently numerous. We toss a penny and note

---

[10]Distribution of Asteroids. Sidereal Messenger, vol. 4 (1885), p. 259.

that its trajectory is affected by many circumstances. Its ultimate position on the table top is determined by numerous things besides the law of gravitation; its initial position in the hand that throws it, the direction and force with which it starts, the air through which it falls, the elasticity and smoothness of the table top, upon which it drops, combine to form a complexity of causes that would defy the most skillful analyist to untangle. The same point is beautifully illustrated in the numbers in a table of logarithms. It would be folly, for example, to wager with a friend that he could not tell whether the first digit in the logarithm of a number named by you was greater or less than five. It would even be unwise to make the same wager with regard to the second digit for the law of its formation is not essentially complex; but it is perfectly safe to make an even wager upon the last number in a five place table because for it the causes which affect its magnitude have become so numerous that its size is entirely fortuitous. This statement must be properly understood because it is evident that we can at any time calculate the digit in question by the known laws of logarithms. But to one uninstructed in the method the appearance of one number rather than another is a fortuitous event. Poincaré calls this "a first degree of ignorance" in contrast to the second degree of ignorance represented by a complex mechanical situation such as we find in the tossing of a coin. The smoothing process exerted by the complex series of causes in the calculation is shown in the fact that there are as many even numbers as odd in this fifth column of the table; there are as many sevens as there are twos. And if this be the case for a set of quantities subject to mathematical determination how much more we might expect it for those complex events which make up the world-lines of our existence.

### 4. The Laws of Chance.

But the events with which we ordinarily deal are not usually isolated ones. They follow one another and there are numerous independencies of which account must be taken. To the definition of probability, two laws must be adjoined before the foundation of the structure is laid. The first of these has to do with compound probability and may be stated thus: The probability that two *independent events* will happen simultaneously or in succession is the product of the probability of the two events taken singly.

For example, the probability of getting a head in one throw of a single coin is 1/2, and the probability of getting two heads in two throws of one coin or one throw of two coins will be $(1/2) \times (1/2)$ or $1/4$.

This law must be carefully understood because a too hasty application of it may lead to error. For example, the probability of getting a head in one throw of a single coin is $1/2$ and the probability of getting a tail is also $1/2$, but the probability of getting a head and a tail in one throw of two coins is not $1/4$. We might argue as d'Alembert did. There will be three cases:

A. Two heads; B. Two tails; C. One head; one tail.

We thus deduce that the probability is $1/3$, which is again an answer that experience will not justify. The error lies in the fact that A, B, and C are not all equally probable. Thus in case C one coin might come down heads and the other tails or vice versa, while in A and B there is but one possibility. Hence the correct answer would be $1/2$. However, if we throw one coin twice and specify in advance the order, thus one head and one tail, the probability becomes the same as in cases A and B or $1/4$.

The second law of chance has to do with mutually exclusive events and may be stated as follows:

The probability that a given event in a series of mutually exclusive events will happen and all others fail is called *partial probability*. The probability that any event whatever of the series will happen and the others fail is called *total probability* and is equal to the sum of the partial probabilities.

To illustrate, suppose A, B, and C match pennies, odd man to win. What is the probability that either A or B wins? Since only one can win, the winnings by A, B, or C are mutually exclusive events. But A's chance is $1/3$ and B's chance is $1/3$, so the chance of either A or B winning is $2/3$.

Another illustration is contained in the following. Suppose a difficult problem is to be solved and three men whose abilities are known are set to the task. Suppose the estimate of A's chance of working the problem is placed at $1/2$, B's chance at $1/3$, and C's chance at $1/4$. What is the probability that the problem will be solved?

It will be seen that the following are the mutually exclusive events which lead to the solution of the problem, namely A, B, or C solves the problem and the others fail; A and B, A and C, or B and C solve the problem and the other fails; or all three succeed. Consider one of these possibilities, for example the case where A and B solve the problem and C fails. The individual cases are mutually independent so that the probability of the event in question will be $(1/2) \times (1/3) \times (1 - 1/4) = 1/8$.

In a similar way the other probabilities may be computed, and since they all represent mutually exclusive events, in that the occurrence of one precludes the occurrence of any other, their sum, $3/4$, will represent the total probability that the problem will be solved. Another way in which the same answer might have been obtained was by computing the probability that all three would fail to solve the problem, namely, $(1/2) \times (2/3) \times (3/4) = 1/4$, and subtracting this value from unity. Since it is certain that the problem will either be solved or not solved, these two events form a mutually exclusive system.

Many delightful problems arise out of the combination of these laws, but we can not tarry to examine them. Paradoxes are to be expected, but the root of the trouble is usually found in the subtle introduction of infinity into the picture or in obscuring the fact that the events considered are not equally probable. One paradox, in particular, has cast considerable discredit upon certain types of application of the theory of probability. This problem concerns the attaching of monetary value to chance, and the explanation is not wholly satisfactory even at the present time. This paradox is known as the St. Petersburg problem and may be stated as follows:[11] How much money should A give B as a fair price for the following offer? A is to throw a coin until heads appears. If this event happens on the first toss, then A gets \$1; if however, heads do not appear until the second toss, A gets \$2; until the third toss, \$4; until the fourth toss, \$8, etc.

Since the respective probabilities are $1/2$, $1/4$, $1/8$, $1/16$ etc. and the events are mutually exclusive it is clear that the sum of the products of the probabilities by the expected gains is the desired answer. To our astonishment it turns out to be infinity, so that even a million dollars would be inadequate to pay one who would make such a proposition. Casual trial of the problem will soon convince anyone that the answer is absurd. We have combined an infinitesimal probability of winning an infinite fortune in such a way that human credulity is shaken.

Wherein is the flaw in the reasoning? Various answers have been proposed, but none places the paradox in the same point. Daniel

---

[11]This is similar to a problem proposed by N. Bernoulli to P. Montmort. See the latter's "Essai d'analyse sur les jeux de hazard" (1714), p. 402. For an account of the St. Petersburg problems see: I. Todhunter, "History of the Mathematical Theory of Probability," Cambridge (1865), and also A. Fisher (loc. cit.), pp. 51-53.

238      PHILOSOPHY AND MODERN SCIENCE

Bernoulli (1700-1782) gave a clever explanation by introducing the idea of moral hope.[12] Thus, he argues, the pleasure of gaining $1,000 is greater to one who has nothing than to a millionaire, hence the expectation from fortuitous events must be measured in comparison with what we already have. Introducing this idea into the problem he was able to reduce the answer to a reasonable figure. On this assumption Laplace estimated that if A has a capital of only $200 he could not pay B more than $9 for the offer.

Poincaré on the other hand puts the difficulty upon B. The fortune of this man is limited so that A can not hope to win an infinite sum even though he should have the marvellous luck to throw tails indefinitely. By simple analysis Poincaré is able to show that if B's fortune is only $1,000, A could afford to pay $6 per game, but that he could increase this to $16 if his opponent were a billionaire.[13]

Augustus De Morgan on the other hand regards the infinite answer as the sensible one and looks upon the game as B's business.[14] If B should decide to play just a thousand games and then retire, his charge per game would be smaller than if he decided to run his business for a million games. The average loss per game, in other words, increases with the total played, and if the business is to be solvent for several generations a prohibitive price per game would have to be charged.[15]

The subtlety of the subject under consideration is now apparent, but the following example cited by J. M. Keynes in his treatise on probability focuses attention upon this aspect of its philosophy. It is instructive for the reader to reflect what decision he would have reached in the following proposition.[16]

The London "Daily Express" had offered a beauty prize, which, amounting to 400 pounds in value to each winner, was to be competed for on the following basis. Out of 6,000 photographs submitted in the contest, a certain number were to be selected and published in various districts into which the United Kingdom had been divided. The readers in these districts were then to decide by their votes which were the fifty most beautiful pictures. After this selection had been

[12]From, Specimen Theoriae Novae de Mensura Sortis. Commentarii Acad. Petrop., vol. 5 (1730-1731), 1738, pp. 175-192.

[13]Calcul des probabilitiés, Paris (1896), pp. 41-43.

[14]Essay on Probabilities, London (1838), pp. 99-101.

[15]As De Morgan puts it: "A larger net would have caught, not only more fish, but more varieties of fish; and in two millions of nets we might have expected to have seen cases in which heads did not appear until the twentieth throw."

[16]The case is Chaplin vs. Hicks (1911). See J. M. Keynes: A Treatise on Probability, London (1921), p. 25.

made the fifty winners were then to present themselves before a hardy gentleman, who, unmindful of the fate of Paris of Troy, was then to choose the twelve winners. Now it happened that one of the fifty beauties selected in the preliminary contest was not given ample opportunity to display her charms in competition with the others, so she brought suit against the Daily Express for damages since she had been defrauded of her chance to win one of the twelve prizes. The case was carried through two courts and the plaintiff was finally assessed damages computed at 12/50 of the value of a single prize.

### 5. From Effect to Cause.

We turn next to the consideration of another aspect of the theory of chance, about which the storms of controversy have waged for many years. This is the so-called problem of *inverse probability*. In essence it postulates the possibility that one can reason from an event to its cause. If we know the cause of a certain act of nature it is easy to predict the behaviour of an object influenced by the same cause: but is the converse problem always true? If we are in the presence of an event can we then reason back to that which brought it to pass? The answer, in very general terms and subject to exception, is that if the process is a reversible one then the relationship between cause and effect is reciprocal with effect and cause. But alas, nature does not always act in this reversible way.

The problem of inverse probability may be stated thus: We are in the presence of an event which we know has proceeded from one of a complex of mutually exclusive causes whose respective probabilities of producing the event can be numerically expressed. The question is this: What is the probability that the event proceeded from a particular specified cause?

A simple example will clarify this definition. Suppose a black ball has been drawn from one of three bags, the first containing three black balls and seven white, the second five black balls and three white, the third eight black balls and four white. What is the probability that it was drawn from the first bag? This you see is a procedure from effect to cause and there are subtle logical difficulties in the way. To be sure an answer, in the present case 36/191, is easily derived by a formal rule, but the interesting question is the philosophical justification of the rule.

The rule by means of which a numerical probability is attached to such a problem as that just stated is attributed to Thomas Bayes, an

English clergyman, and was first published in the London Philosophical Transactions in 1763, two years after the author's death. It has been vigorously attacked by theory and paradox,[17] one of the most famous of the latter being due to the Danish actuary J. Bing, who shows by one mode of application of the rule that[18] "if, among a large group of equally old people, we have observed no deaths during a full calendar year then another person of the same age outside the group is sure to die inside the calendar year." The point to the controversy seems to be this: To obtain a rigorous answer we must have full information about the actual probabilities associated with the complex of mutually exclusive causes. For example, we may know that an event must proceed from a set of circumstances, but we may have no further information about them. Are we justified in assigning an equal probability to each cause? By no means. Shall we say that the probability of throwing a five in a single toss of one die is one-sixth because the die has six faces and we have no reason to believe that one side will appear more frequently than another? Such assumption on the basis of "insufficient reason" may lead to grave error since the die may be loaded on one side. The only safe principle to follow is what has been called the principle of "cogent reason" by which we assure ourselves that the die, typical of every quantity subject to statistical reason, is symmetric in every particular. On the basis of this knowledge we can assume with assurance that the probability of throwing a five must be one-sixth. The matter has been put admirably in the following statement of Arne Fisher:

. . . we require not alone an exact enumeration of the various complexes from which the observed event may originate, but also an exact and complete information about the structure of such complexes in order to evaluate their various probabilities of existence. If such information is present, we can meet even the most stringent requirements of the general formula, and we will get a correct answer. But in the vast majority of cases, not to say all cases, such information is not at hand, and any attempt to make a computation by means of Bayes' Rule must be regarded as hopeless. We may, however, again remark that very seldom we are in complete ignorance of the conditions of the complexes, which is the same thing as saying that we are not in a position to employ the principle of equal distribution of ignorance in a rigorous manner. From other experiments on the

[17]R. A. Fisher, Proc. Cambridge Phil. Soc., vol. 26 (1930), p. 528, says: "I know only one case (Bayes' rule) in mathematics of a doctrine which has been accepted and developed by the most eminent men of their time, and is now perhaps accepted by men now living, which at the same time has appeared to a succession of sound writers to be fundamentally false and devoid of foundation."

[18]See A. Fisher: loc. cit., pp. 72-76.

same kind of event, or from other sources, we may have attained some partial information, even if insufficient to employ the principle of cogent reason. Is such information now to be completely ignored in an attempt to give a reasonable, although approximate answer? It is but natural that the mathematician should attempt to obtain as much of such information as possible and use it in the evaluation of the various probabilities of existence.[19]

Fisher, in illustration, cites the attempt of the mathematician to evaluate a cargo of 100,000 pieces of fruit valued, if the fruit is untainted, at 10,000 Kroner. Samples of thirty pieces are chosen at random from the cargo and found to be perfect. Making the assumption that it is equally probable that all, half, or none of the remaining individual pieces of fruit are without blemish, Fisher, using Bayes' rule, finds that the value of the cargo might be estimated at 9,687 Kroner. However, if information is at hand to show that, in numerous other shipments of fruit, the probability is between .9 and 1 that the fruit is free from decay, then the valuation of the cargo may be set at 9,726 Kroner.

## 6.   *The Reliability of Testimony.*

An instructive and amusing application of Bayes' rule has been made to the probability of testimony. Most of our information is derived from secondary sources and it must frequently be a question in our minds as to how much reliability should be placed upon certain statements.

Let us suppose for concreteness that a ball has been drawn from an urn known to contain one white and nine black balls. A witness to the drawing assures us that the white ball was drawn. Can we then assume as certain that the white ball was actually drawn? Those who have had experience know that the reliability of the witness is an important factor and in some cases we should be loathe to place even a modicum of belief in the statement that the white ball was the one drawn. Since no mortal is wholly reliable in all events, being subject to human frailties such as faulty memory, faltering attention, and the like, the probability that he has told the truth is never exactly unity. But let us assume from the observation of an individual's characteristics with regard to accuracy, that we have ascertained that the witness tells the truth on the average of five times in six. With this reliability, then, what should be our

---

[19]From "Theory of Probabilities," second edition (1922), p. 78.

measure of belief that the rather improbable event of the drawing of
the single white ball from the ten in the urn actually occurred?
Surely it will be larger than the *a priori* probability of 1/10th, since
that is unaffected by the testimony of the witness. The actual observation of the event and a favorable report upon it should have some
weight. The mathematics by which the answer is obtained can not be
given here, but it is interesting to observe that an application of the
principle of inverse probability yields the answer 5/14, or a little
more than one chance in three. At first sight this comparatively low
probability surprises us, until we reflect that a witness whose reliability is not perfect is reporting on an event which is quite improbable.

An interesting application of this conclusion is to be found in
the general lack of confidence in reports about psychic phenomena.
A number of eminent men, distinguished scientists skilled in careful
scrutiny of laboratory data, have investigated some of these affairs
and reported their belief based upon ocular and instrumental testimony. But do we eagerly accept their faith? The answer is too
well known to require comment. Their testimony so far has merely
served to discredit them rather than to persuade us of the reality of
the phenomena, because their admittedly high scientific accuracy is
applied to reporting upon phenomena whose probability of happening, as far as the normal mind is concerned, is exceedingly small. If
the probability of their being wrong were just equal to the probability
of the reality of the event which they have witnessed, we might then
give them a grudging half measure of belief. But if intuition demands that the probability of the actual reality of the event is a
thousand times as small as the powers of observation of the witness,
then the chance of its being an actual event is one in a thousand.
The conclusion is inevitable. A tremendous volume of expert testimony must be amassed before the world will give even a small
amount of belief to these affairs.

The following comment of Laplace upon the problem of testimony
is well worth the reflection of those who probe into historical events
and believe all that they find there.[20]

The action of time enfeebles, then, without ceasing, the probability of historical facts just as it changes the most durable monuments. One can indeed diminish it by multiplying and conserving
the testimonies and the monuments which support them. Printing
offers for this purpose a great means, unfortunately unknown to the

[20]Introduction to the "Théorie des probabilitiés," p. lxxxii, Eng. translation (loc. cit.),
p. 124.

ancients. In spite of the infinite advantages which it procures, the physical and moral revolutions by which the surface of this globe will always be agitated will end, in conjunction with the inevitable effect of time, by rendering doubtful after thousands of years the historical events regarded today as the most certain.

Craig has tried to submit to calculus the gradual enfeebling of the proofs of the Christian religion; supposing that the world ought to end at the epoch when it will cease to be probable, he finds that this ought to take place 1454 years after the time when he writes. But his analysis is as faulty as his hypothesis upon the duration of the moon is bizarre.

## 7. *The Normal Universe.*

We turn next to another consideration in which resides much of the power of the application of the laws of chance to physical affairs. Applying our definition and the two laws of independent and mutually exclusive events to a heterogeneous swarm of statistical units we encounter what is generally called the "normal scheme."

This can be illustrated by means of a simple machine described by Sir Francis Galton (1822-1911) in his "Natural Inheritance."[21] The apparatus consists of a shallow box, covered on one side with a piece of glass, and containing a large number of pegs irregularly distributed over the surface of the back-board. At the bottom of the machine directly below the pegs a number of long narrow slots are made by equally spaced partitions. If, then, a quantity of small shot be introduced by means of a funnel at the top of the apparatus to a point midway between the compartments and directly above the pegs, an instructive phenomenon will be observed. The shot fall helter-skelter down between the pegs, striking now on this and now on that, bouncing back and forth in irregular courses, first to one side and then to the other, until all are lodged finally in the compartments arranged to receive them. An interesting fact is then to be observed. The final arrangement of the shot in the compartments forms a regular bell-shaped curve, the central slots containing the largest quantity and the end slots the least. Most of the pellets in falling through the pegs were deflected as much to one side as to the other and hence the tendency was for the largest number to accumulate in the central compartment. A few, however, suffering a succession of collisions which threw them constantly to one or the other side, finally landed in the outer slots. These are the statistical exceptions which

---

[21]London (1889), p. 63.

represent the rare events found in all phenomena to which this calculus applies.

In this picture of the scurrying shot we find the model of statistical swarming. Here is the ideal norm to which phenomena must be subjected. Take at random a large group of men and measure them according to height, weight, girth, or any other physical unit. Some are short and some are tall; some are heavy and some are light, but the vast majority tend to accumulate around a definite average value. The deadly mean is found in all statistical populations; the dwarfs and the giants only are objects of curiosity and can capitalize upon their exceptional characteristics; the genius and the criminal are subjects for our interest, the latter, alas, being the more thoroughly scrutinized by popular attention. This observation may be, perhaps, the source of an ancient dictum; "that those things which are bizarre are beautiful."[22]

Science in many fields directs its attention to the discovery of the monsters on the one hand and to the variations in the normal law on the other. We find, for example, two modal points instead of one in a distribution of the characteristics of a certain type of shellfish.[23] This leads us to the conclusion that the apparently homogeneous population is the mixture of two species whose mingling has not served to efface the primary characteristic of the two groups. Variations in the normal law are always to be regarded as evidences of correlations between types of things. The causes that are tending to produce the distribution are not all independent and of the same magnitude. There is evidence of exception to the postulate that the events occurring are wholly random. For example, suppose that we should drop our shot through the machine previously described and suddenly discover that the compartments to the right were distinctly fuller than those to the left; our normal curve would appear skewed to one side. This mysterious exception to statistical expectation must have a cause. Some primary disturbance has been impressing its influence upon the pellets; the paths of the shot can not be due wholly to a complex of uniform causes. We might find upon examination that we were using steel pellets instead of lead and that a magnetic field on the right was exerting an appreciable effect upon them.

The charm of the subject of statistics can only be appreciated

[22]For example see Thomas Browne: Religio Medici, part I, sec. 16: "There is no deformity but in monstrosity; wherein, notwithstanding, there is a kind of Beauty; Nature so ingeniously contriving the irregular parts, as they become sometimes more remarkable than the principal Fabrick."

[23]Karl Pearson: Contributions to the Mathematical Theory of Evolution (III), Phil. Trans. of the Royal Society (A), vol. 185, part 1 (1894), pp. 71-110.

after long contact with the delicate methods and the subtle deductions employed in it. The fundamental assumptions considered in the foregoing description of the theory have been hastily surveyed so that the applications which we contemplate and the conclusions that we shall draw may appear more striking proof of our contentions. The "sweet reasonableness" of the basic postulates appeals to our intuitions. We assume causality in nature, but we posit the impossibility of untangling the complex of causes which underlie the behaviour of individuals in a swarm of statistical units.

## 8.  Probability and the Theory of Gases.

It was very natural then that Clerk Maxwell should have turned to the methods of probability when he undertook to study the motion of the particles of a gas. In the introduction to his historical papers on the dynamical theory of gases, which have been so powerful in the new physics, he makes the following statement of his problem:[24]

So many of the properties of matter, especially when in the gaseous form, can be deduced from the hypothesis that their minute parts are in rapid motion, the velocity increasing with the temperature, that the precise nature of this motion becomes a subject of rational curiosity. Daniel Bernoulli, Herapath, Joule, Krönig, Clausius, etc., have shown that the relations between pressure, temperature, and density in a perfect gas can be explained by supposing the particles to move with uniform velocity in straight lines, striking against the sides of the containing vessel thus producing pressure. It is not necessary to suppose each particle to travel to any great distance in the same straight line; for the effect in producing pressure will be the same if the particles strike against each other; so that the straight line described may be very short. M. Clausius has determined the mean length of path in terms of the average distance of the particles, and the distance between the centers of two particles when collision takes place. We have at present no means of ascertaining either of these distances; but certain phenomena, such as the internal friction of gases, the conduction of heat through a gas, and the diffusion of one gas through another, seem to indicate the possibility of determining accurately the mean length of path which a particle describes between two successive collisions. In order to lay the foundation of such investigations on strict mechanical principles, I shall demonstrate the laws of motion of an indefinite number of small, hard, and perfectly elastic spheres acting on one another only during impact.

[24]Illustration of the Dynamical Theory of Gases. Phil. Mag., vol. 19 (4th ser.) (1860), pp. 19-32; vol. 20 (1860). In particular, p. 19.

The beautiful analysis which Maxwell applies to his swarm of particles is one of the gems of physical literature. From it he and his successors have been able to derive most of the facts of thermodynamics and even the elusive concept of entropy finds a place among the statistical constants.

For the purposes of our discussion, however, we shall direct attention to a single phase of the problem. Let us visualize the swarm of atoms in a cloud of gas according to the picture suggested by normal intuition. The particles move with high velocities within the boundaries of the gas, frequently colliding with one another, shooting off at new angles to their former course, jostling helter-skelter in all directions.

Is it not a postulate founded upon the most secure intuitional belief to assume that the average velocities of the swarm of particles will be the same in every direction and that at any instant there will be approximately as many atoms moving toward the top of the gas container as toward any other side? Many attempts have been made to prove this proposition, but like the parallel postulate of Euclid it defies rigorous demonstration. Instead of seeking a proof we are perhaps more wise merely to assume that this very reasonable state of affairs exists within the swarm of particles and accept as intuitionally evident the following verdict of Maxwell, known in science today as the theory of the equipartition of energy:[25]

It appears . . . that the velocities are distributed among the particles according to the same law as the errors are distributed among the observations in the theory of the "method of least squares." The velocities range from 0 to infinity, but the number of those having great velocities is comparatively small. In addition to these velocities, which are in all directions equally, there may be a general motion of translation of the entire system of particles which must be compounded with the motion of the particles relatively to one another. We may call the one the motion of translation, and the other the motion of agitation.

### 9.  *Probability and the Energy of the Ether.*

We return again to an old question: How does the luminiferous ether fit into the scheme of this rational picture? To put it differently, let us ask whether, if we regard the ether as the seat of energy and the medium for conveying it from place to place, can we build a rational picture of the distribution of this energy by means

---

[25]Loc. cit., pp. 23-24.

of the normal scheme derived from the postulates of the laws of chance?

To be sure we have thus far regarded energy somewhat in the light of a continuous entity and have revealed our inner thoughts by speaking of its flow from place to place. To anticipate a little of the material of the next chapter we shall see that the photo-electric effect has caused a profound change in our point of view. Energy may, in one sense, be regarded as discontinuous. We may think of it as moving about in packages called quanta, swarming hither and thither between material things. Luminous bodies radiate their energy in pellets and absorb it again in discrete quantities. If this, then, is to be regarded as the modern picture, what shall we say about the statistical behaviour of these quanta? Do they come under the same body of laws as the molecules and atoms of the gas? Are they statistical swarms subject to the normal scheme?

The most profound mystery of modern physical science rests in the conclusion that radiant energy is not amenable to study by the laws of chance. The mysterious ether,

> a dagger of the mind, a false creation,
> Proceeding from the heat oppressed brain,

again refuses to reveal its nature by submitting to rational laws. The reason why in this age of physical triumph we dare to speak of the new metaphysics is revealed by this fact more forcibly than by the failure of those who strove in earlier years to endow the ether with material properties. We turn from these speculations to a consideration of some physical facts.

# CHAPTER X.

## THE METAPHYSICS OF THE QUANTUM THEORY AND WAVE MECHANICS.

### 1. *On the Nature of Belief.*

MANY years ago a king whose name has been forgotten dwelt in a kingdom whose history has been effaced by time. This obscure monarch undertook to determine the depth of the sea. The wisest of those who sought to answer this question for the king finally decided that the depth of the sea was but a stone's throw. Those who essay the task of exploring the relationship between the energy of ether and the electrons of ponderable matter seem frequently to phrase their conclusions in language of similar implication. Modern physical theories often sound as oracular as the utterances of Delphi. The current of the stream of speculative thought directed to the problem of the ether and its energy reminds one of the similar mystical stream of Coleridge's immortal dream:

> Five miles meandering with a mazy motion
> Through wood and dale the sacred river ran,
> Then reached the caverns measureless to man,
> And sank in tumult to a lifeless ocean.

In the last two chapters we have discussed the birth of the electron and the basic assumptions of the mathematical theory which has been found, we dare not say most useful, but at least highly so, in the discussion of the activities of these ubiquitous particles. We have also turned our attention to a phenomenon that connected the behaviour of the electronic motions with the vast ocean of ether and its universal radiations. The photo-electric effect was discovered to present questions of strange difficulty and directed attention to another property of the ether more repugnant to reason than the denial of its elasticity, rigidity and density.

But in making our approach to the difficulties which beset modern physical thought we do not want to appear to adopt the point of view of those who believe that all things, to be understandable, must be capable of explanation in terms of mechanical models. To say that

248

only twelve men in the whole world understand relativity does not mean that they belong to some esoteric society to whose members the secrets of nature are revealed in terms of things comprehensible. It means, if it means anything, that these men are familiar with the phenomena upon which the theory rests and the mathematical symbols by which the interpretation of these phenomena may be explored. The final conclusions regarding space-time and the framework of reality is as incomprehensible to their rational intuitions as to ours.

Roger Coates, (1682-1716) who edited the third edition of Newton's Principia, made statements worthy of reflection in discussing the epistemological question: Whether the law of gravitation could be understood. "For causes usually proceed by a continuous binding together from the composite to the simpler. When one has arrived at the simplest cause it is impossible to advance further. Hence no mechanical explanation can be given of the simplest cause; for if this were the case, then this cause is not yet reduced to its lowest terms. Will you then call the simplest causes mystical and order them to be banished? If this be so you will in very truth banish those causes which depend upon the simplest, and those that depended upon the next, and so on until philosophy will at last be freed from any cause whatsoever."[1]

We return again to a consideration of the photo-electric effect described in chapter eight, which may be defined roughly in recapitulation to be the observation that, if monochromatic light be thrown upon a metal plate, electrons will be ejected from its surface with a velocity which depends wholly upon the frequency of the incident beam and not upon its intensity. The latter serves merely to eject more electrons but does not accelerate them. Since we shall have occasion to speak in further detail of the fundamental rôle of the curious property of light known as *frequency* we shall define it simply to be the value which represents the number of crests of a wave passing any given point in unit time. *Wave length,* another fundamental concept in the theory of radiation, is the distance between these crests. With these words we commit ourselves to the undulatory theory of radiation and are compelled to think in terms of some medium, however different it may be from ordinary matter, which conveys the energy from one place to another. From our previous experience with the theory of the ether we are now prepared to admit that metaphysical concepts may be forced upon us as explanations of the realities which we observe in the laboratory.

---

[1]Newton's Principia, Editoris praefatis, 2nd ed., p. xxv.

## 2. *Failure of the Equipartition of Energy.*

It is well to approach our difficulties historically. Suppose that we begin as the discoverers of our present trouble began, by creating some kind of a concept of the method by which energy is generated in a radiating body. Let us suppose that matter, from which ethereal waves are proceeding, is made up of electronic oscillators. We have shown in the phenomenon of the Crookes tube and in the evidence afforded by currents of electricity that there are numerous *free electrons* in the universe which are able to move about under the influence of impulsive forces impressed upon them. But it may readily be conceived, on the evidence of the existence of ponderable bodies, that there are also numerous *bound electrons* which are attached to their constituent atoms by forces the nature of which we but dimly understand. Let us assume that the phenomenon of radiation is an evidence of the activities of these bound electrons and that their oscillations are capable of setting up periodic disturbances in the ether.

What shall our mental picture be of this activity? As in all theories about the phenomena of the physical universe, our minds work better if we can obtain some modelized concept of the cause. Let us assume then that the bound electrons are tiny vibrating particles pictured, perhaps, as knobs upon the ends of a host of elastic rods. If these knobs be affected by a quantity of energy they create waves in the ether; if the waves of the ether beat upon them they are set in oscillation. There is mutual interplay, and the ceaseless flow of energy through the world is but evidence either of their ability to radiate or of their ability to absorb.

Now if a set of such oscillators were immersed in a medium resembling air we should expect something like this to take place. Gusts of wind blow upon them and they commence to weave back and forth like trees in a storm. The violence of the stream of air, which to preserve the analogy of waves must be considered to have regular periods of intermittance and intensity, increases the agitation of the rods and finally one of the knobs breaks loose from its attachment. And if the energy of the gale be conceived to increase still further then more of the knobs will be torn loose and their average energy of translation will grow with the violence of the storm; that is to say they will be hurled through longer and longer distances. But this, we have just observed, is not at all the case with the bound electrons in the stream of light, for these never fly from the security of their atoms with more than a certain velocity determined wholly by the character of the metal and the frequency of the incident beam. Hence our picture of the knobs is not consonant with experiment.

We might, however, look at the other aspect of the problem. Suppose our field of rods and knobs has been put into agitation by the wind and we then enclose it within a building whose walls are perfect reflectors of the waves of air. What should we expect to happen? According to Newtonian mechanics and the principle of the conservation of energy we should observe that, after a while, our waving knobs were losing their power of oscillation. Slowly the viscosity of the air would steal their kinetic energy, and in the course of time all the motion would have disappeared into the internal energy of the medium. But what if the contrary thing were really seen? What if we should observe, after a long period of time, that the field of rods which we had left in oscillation was still in vigorous motion? If we were to state that such was the evidence of our eyes we should certainly be denied a certificate of rationality by any alienist who based his judgments upon the principles of Newtonian mechanics. Is it therefore not surprising and very disturbing to those who want to believe in a rational universe, defined in terms of laws founded upon models comprehensible to our present chemical natures, to learn that electrons oscillate according to the second picture rather than according to the first?

The matter has been admirably put by J. H. Jeans who said after consideration of a picture similar to the one which we have just described :[2]

To put the matter shortly ; in all known media there is a tendency for the energy of any systems moving in the medium to be transferred to the medium and ultimately to be found, when a steady state has been reached, in the shortest vibrations of which the medium is capable. This tendency can be shown to be a direct consequence of the Newtonian laws. This tendency is not observed in the crucial phenomenon of radiation ; the inference is that the radiation phenomenon is determined by laws other than the Newtonian laws.

Let us return for a moment to the picture of the oscillating knobs in the building the walls of which are perfect reflectors of the waves of air. According to the statement of Jeans, derived from comparatively elementary considerations, Newtonian mechanics demands

---

[2]Report on Radiation and the Quantum Theory, 2nd ed. (1924), p. 2.

that after a while the entire energy of the knobs shall be returned to the medium, since, by hypothesis, the confining walls are perfect reflectors. And in what form will this energy then reside? According to Jeans it will exist in the smallest waves of which the medium is capable, which for air may be shown on reasonable grounds to be of the order of $10^{-7}$ centimeters.[3] But for the ether this limit is probably very much lower since, as Jeans remarks, "whatever is regarded as certain or uncertain about the ether, it must be granted as quite certain that it approaches more closely to a continuous medium than to a gas. If it has any grained structure at all the distance between adjacent grains must be enormously less than $10^{-7}$ centimeters assumed for the corresponding distance in the gas. But even if this distance were as great as $10^{-7}$ centimeters, only one-millionth of the total radiant energy ought to be of wave-length as great as $10^{-5}$ centimeters—entirely contrary to what is observed."[4]

### 3. Is a Vacuum Empty?

We must return again to the problem as old as science: What is radiant energy? What is its structure? In what does it reside? How does it get about from place to place? To essay the answer let us examine a small quantity of this illusive stuff with critical eyes. For our present purposes imagine that we have shut in a small quantity of space by means of an enclosure which is perfectly reflecting to radiation and let us examine what we have captured. If we introduce a thermometer into the box we shall find that this particle of space is not empty but contains a vigorous entity whose presence is made manifest by the fact that the thermometer will register a definite temperature. This temperature is highly characteristic of the substance that we seek to investigate, since the total energy per unit volume is proportional to the fourth power of the temperature measured from the zero of the absolute scale or 273 degrees below

---

[3] Report on Radiation and the Quantum Theory (loc. cit.), p. 4.

[4] Jeans' Report, 1st ed. (1914), p. 6. The change in view about the ether in recent times is shown in the following alteration of the statement just quoted as it appears in the second edition of the Report: "Thus, it may be argued, the difference in the cases we have been discussing may perhaps not be one of obedience or disobedience to the classical mechanics, but of the existence or non-existence of a surrounding medium. Our arguments may not prove the breakdown of the classical mechanics, but merely the non-existence of the ether. It is greatly to be wished that the question of the existence or non-existence of the ether could be settled by such simple considerations; unfortunately it cannot. The theory of relativity in effect requires that it shall be impossible to decide as to whether an ether exists or not, either by these or by any other purely mechanical considerations; the equations or radiation and absorption of energy are precisely the same whether the energy is radiated into, and absorbed from, an ether or empty space. The analysis we shall now give will show that the existence or non-existence of an ether is wholly irrelevant to the question, so that if our analogies break down, it is not on the question of the reality of the ether."

zero centigrade. This fact is known as the Stefan-Boltzmann law, J. Stefan (1835-1893) having discovered it empirically, and L. Boltzmann (1844-1906) having developed it from thermo-dynamical considerations.[5]

Further investigation reveals the fact that this empty space of ours also has periodic properties which show that the inmate of our cage may be spoken of in terms of wave lengths, whatever such terminology may mean when used in connection with the metaphysical medium of space. A further beautiful discovery about our captive space was made by W. Wien who found that in radiation of a uniform temperature there is one particular wave length favored above the rest, since more energy is associated with it then with any of the others.[6] In fact if the density of radiation be graphed along

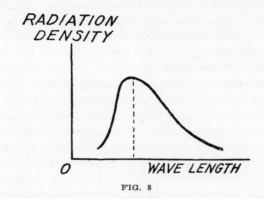

FIG. 8

the vertical axis of a diagram (fig. 8) and wave length along the other we shall discover that the resulting curve is bell shaped and very much resembles the curve of normal distribution discussed in the preceding chapter. This tremendously suggestive discovery is at the basis of the work of Max Planck, to whose initial efforts in the study of black body radiation we owe the present status of the quantum theory.

Energy then may be regarded as a property of space. Whatever its ultimate structure may prove to be and however different it may seem from concepts based upon material models, there is unquestionable certainty in the laws of Stefan-Boltzmann and Wien,

---

[5] Ableitung des Stefan'schen Gesetzes, betreffend die Abhängigkeit der Wärmestrahlung von der Temperatur aus der elektromagnetischen Lichttheorie, Ann. Phys. Chem., vol. 22 (1884), p. 291.

[6] Eine neue Beziehung der Strahlung schwarzer Körper zum zweiten Hauptsatz der Wärmetheorie, Berlin Sitzungsberichte (1893), p. 55.

which connect it functionally with the absolute temperature of the space and with a certain periodic phenomenon which can be measured in terms of a thing, from analogy with waves of sound, called wave length.

This was the situation when Planck began to reflect upon the problem. In 1900 he published the result of a long series of investigations made on the character of radiation inside of a nearly-enclosed cavity maintained at an even temperature.[7] As we have seen, this cavity is filled with an entity which is completely characterized by the temperature of the space and by its periodic properties. The former is uniform by the conditions of the experiment, but with the latter the case is otherwise, since it is distributed over a long range of wave lengths. Such a situation immediately suggests the statistical swarm studied in the previous chapter, because waves of radiation are moving about in all directions with lengths varying between upper and lower limits. Consideration must also be paid to the bound electrons oscillating upon the walls of the cavity, since in this instance it is clear that we could not attain the state of perfect reflection postulated in our first abstract consideration of energy density of space.

The beautiful statistical problem presented by this picture was studied by Planck, and, as has been indicated earlier in our discussion, he found that the postulate that radiation was taking place according to Newtonian mechanics was wholly untenable. He argued that a continuous medium always extracts all the energy from any system of oscillating particles placed in it. If this were the case then no equilibrium between the oscillating particles composing the walls of the cavity and the energy of the intervening space could be maintained in which both retained their independent energies. After a while the bound electrons would cease to radiate and the wave lengths of the energy would continually be reduced to the smallest possible value within the capacity of the medium.

These concepts are very difficult both to grasp and to comprehend. Ideas developed early in the history of our race can usually be explained more simply than the later discoveries which are the culmination of a trend of thought and a series of experiments. It is easier to comprehend geometry developed by the Greeks than mathematical analysis of a correspondingly elementary character developed centuries later. The action of levers and the principles of hydrostatics do not require the penetration necessary to understand the law of fall-

---

[7] Über irreversible Strahlungsvorgänge, Ann. Phys., vol. 1 (1900), p. 69; Über das Gesetz der Energierverteilung im Normalspektrum, Ann. Phys., vol. 4 (1901), p. 553.

ing bodies.  As a general observation it may be said that one of the best ways to compare the difficulty of subjects is to compare the time of their introduction into the thought of the race.  This observation naturally is not to be interpreted with strict accuracy in all fields but it works very well with those branches of knowledge which have followed definite cumulative trends.  The subject of logarithms seems to be more easily acquired than a knowledge of the laws of exponents in algebra.  "It is one of the greatest curiosities of the history of science," says Florian Cajori, "that Napier constructed logarithms before exponents were used."[8]  This historical curiosity, however, can be used to decide which is the more profound theory, and scrutiny of the examination papers of college freshmen would probably bear witness to the correctness of the conclusion.

These general remarks are introduced merely as an apology for the difficulty inherent in an explanation of the foundations of the quantum theory and of wave mechanics.  Concepts which are at the basis of the most profound puzzle of the twentieth century are not to be compared with the concepts that puzzled those of earlier epochs except as one is generically related to the other.  The problem of the antipodes, profoundly troublesome to those who crossed themselves as they saw the caravels of Columbus sink below the sky, has yielded to the problem of action at a distance and the character of the ether.  As we probe deeper into the modern puzzle the paths grow darker instead of more luminous; we can but wonder what the great intellects of the twenty-first century will think about and whether new modes of thought and new positions of rational belief will make the road less obscure.

#### 4.  Recapitulation of Energy Concepts.

Let us pause a moment and recapitulate what has already been stated.  Our problem is to discover the nature of energy and we are using the new knowledge of the present century with respect to radiation as our probe.  The reality of the ether, or rather a rational set of postulates for this necessity of reason, eluded the profound researches of our predecessors of the last century.  We start with a handicap in that the old puzzle was not resolved before the new one presented itself, although in a fundamental way the two problems are but aspects of a single one.  When a biologist wishes to examine a bug he first isolates it and then turns the instruments at his command

---

[8]History of Mathematics, p. 149.

upon its activities and structure. A similar plan has been suggested in the scrutiny of a particle of space wholly enclosed within a shell of matter. To many this picture will seem very strange, for space devoid of matter is in the popular mind as nearly abstract as anything can be. That something could be captured which was not material by surrounding it with a wall of matter seems straining faith. But the evidence of temperature shows that the captive particle of space is not without content.

One thing, perhaps, that leads to the illusion of emptiness is the fact that a room is immediately dark once the electric light has been turned off. But suppose the walls of the room were heated to incandescence and a thermal covering used to envelope them. Would the room then darken? Could the light be extinguished? By no means, because the temperature in that case would be one for which the preferred wave length, containing the largest energy, is in the visible spectrum.

If, however, the energy of the medium postulated to fill our space resembled ordinary matter what should be expected to happen to the radiant energy contained in it? Slowly the electrons vibrating in the enveloping walls would cease their activities; their kinetic energy would be dissipated into the medium, and in the final state the total energy of the space would disappear from the higher wave lengths and be found in the smallest of which the medium is capable. If cosmic radiation be this ultimate wave length, the visible radiance in the enclosure with which we started would finally disappear in complete conversion into cosmic rays.

### 5.  Is Energy An Atomic Phenomenon?

We cannot linger over these interesting questions but must hasten on to the postulate of the quantum theory. Reflecting profoundly upon the difficulties which we have enumerated Planck finally had a brilliant inspiration. The difficulties in the picture which we have presented above could be overcome by a single postulate. Energy is not a continuous phenomenon; the vibrators in the walls of the cavity in equilibrium with radiant energy were not absorbing and radiating continuously.[9] *Energy as it relates to this mutual exchange between matter and the ether is an atomic phenomenon; quanta of this mysterious activity of the universe are given out by the vibrating*

---

[9]Planck's original theory assumed both discontinuous radiation and discontinuous absorption. In a later paper he modified his ideas to apply only to the radiation phenomenon.

*electrons; energy can never flow out of matter as though it were part of a continuous stream.*

Man in his bolder moments has postulated the atomic character of matter, but never from the distant past down to the opening of the twentieth century have his musings dared to give atomic structure to energy. That which surges into the falling ball; that which makes the wire from the battery glow must be regarded, as in classical physics, as a flow of something moving like a stream from the storehouse of the ether into matter along the mysterious lengths of Poynting's vector. But the words of Lorentz must be recalled. "The flow of energy can, in my opinion, never have quite the same distinct meaning as a flow of material particles, which, by our imagination at least, we can distinguish from each other and follow in their motion."

How can one refrain from appearing mystical who advances the theory that energy is an atomic concept? The great idea of Planck appeared in 1900, and soon the rumour spread that radiating electrons were ejecting energy in little packages which contained multiples of a quantity designated by the product $h \nu$, where $h$ is a universal constant, now known as Planck's constant, and $\nu$ is the frequency of vibrations of the oscillating source and of the emitted radiation.

The idea caught fire in the mind of Einstein and in 1905 he rushed boldly forward with one of those speculations which have been so characteristic of his genius.[10] Where Planck had confined his speculations to the interaction of matter and radiation within the confines of his cavities, Einstein postulated the quantum character of energy in its wanderings throughout space. The corpuscular theory of radiation was again to make its appearance less than a hundred years after the brilliant discoveries of Young and Fresnel had completely overwhelmed the followers of Newton. A beam of light falls upon a metal plate and the photo-electric stream of electrons commences to pour forth. The phenomenon is to be explained upon the assumption that each electron has swallowed an entire quantum of energy and flies off from the parent metal, once its meal has been completed. Conversely the radiating electrons that are left behind, whatever their activity may be before and after they have ejected a quantum, are merely waiting until they have accumulated one of these indivisible packages of energy before they can disgorge it into the ether.

---

[10] Ann. d. Physik, vol. 17 (1905), p. 145.

## 6. The Properties of Quanta.

How, then, are we to picture quanta? Are we to regard them as small quantities of energy, tiny electrons of activity, flying about in space, hither and thither, jostling one another, flying away from impacts, in a word, forming a statistical swarm to be regarded in the same way as we regard swarms of material atoms and amenable to the ordinary laws of statistics? Have quanta size? Can we assign a particle of space, defining its dimensions in terms of material units, within which a quantum of energy is to be found?

So far the answers to these questions have eluded those who have tried to find them. The problem is baffling. The ether in which the quantum may be thought of as residing has receded further and further from material concepts. The quantum appears to be similarly elusive. We shall briefly sketch a few of the experiments which show the puzzling nature of these packages of energy.

One of the most beautiful of these is a simple experiment in diffraction. If we regard light as consisting of swarms of quanta and picture diffraction as a statistical effect in which several quanta unite at a single point to cause interference, then a reduction of the intensity of the light used in making diffraction photographs should have an appreciable effect upon the sharpness of the dark and bright bands. This experiment was performed by G. I. Taylor in 1909 with light the intensity of which was so reduced that two thousand hours were required to obtain a photograph.[11] The pattern obtained by Taylor was as sharp as that formed by light of much greater intensity. This conclusion gives us material for reflection. If diffraction is to be attributed to the statistical distribution of quanta we must assume that our laws of chance apply to a swarm as tenuous as that consisting of one quantum in 10,000 cubic centimeters, a hopeless hypothesis.[12] In commenting upon this situation H. A. Lorentz states what must be the verdict of rational intuition:[13]

Now it must, I think, be taken for granted that the quanta can have no individual and permanent existence in the ether, that they cannot be regarded as accumulations of energy in certain minute spaces flying about with the speed of light. This would be in contradiction with many well-known phenomena of interference and diffraction. It is clear that, if a beam of light consisted of separate quanta,

---

[11]Proc. Cambridge Phil. Soc., vol. 15 (1909), p. 114.

[12]A different test by G. P. Thomson led to the same conclusion. Proc. Royal Soc., vol. 104 (A) (1923), pp. 115-120.

[13]Discussion on "Radiation" at the Birmingham Meeting of the British Association (1913). See Report on Radiation (loc. cit.), p. 381.

which, of course, ought to be considered as mutually independent and unconnected, the bright and dark fringes to which it gives rise could never be sharper than those that would be produced by a single quantum. Hence, if by the use of a source of approximately monochromatic light, we succeed in obtaining distinct interference bands with a difference of phase of a great many, say some millions, of wave lengths, we may conclude that each quantum contains a regular succession of as many waves, and that it extends therefore over a quite appreciable length in the direction of propagation. Similarly, the superiority of a telescope with wide aperture over a smaller instrument, in so far as it consists in a greater sharpness of the image, can only be understood if each individual quantum can fill the whole object-glass.

These considerations show that a quantum ought at all events to have a size that cannot be called very small. It may be added that, according to Maxwell's equations of the electro-magnetic field, an initial disturbance of equilibrium must always be propagated over a continually increasing space.

We turn to a second experiment which has been called by K. K. Darrow the *inverse photo-electric effect*.[14] It is, as a matter of fact, a phenomenon of X-ray radiation. If, when light is thrown upon a metal plate, electrons are emitted with velocities which never exceed a very definite limit determined by the frequency of the radiation, should there not be a corresponding effect when a stream of electrons in a cathode tube bombard a metal target and excite radiation? The technical difficulties which were overcome and the delicate arguments employed in investigating this problem can not be described here. *It is sufficient for our purposes to know that the inverse photo-electric effect is found in X-ray radiation in the existence of a maximum frequency of the rays.* The conclusion that we are to reach from this is precisely that derived from the consideration of Planck's oscillators and the photo-electric effect, namely that energy behaves as though it were concentrated in units of amount equal to $h \nu$. When an electron is stopped by impact against a metal it surrenders its unit of energy, which reappears in equivalent radiation.

Another question immediately presents itself. Radiation falling upon a metal plate generates a stream of electrons; electrons impinging upon a metal plate create radiation. What would be the effect if the electrons ejected from a target by bombardment of radiation were themselves allowed to fall upon another plate? This question was investigated during the earlier years of the present century and the answer discovered to be that the energy of the secondary stream

---

[14]Introduction to Contemporary Physics, New York (1926), p. 123.

of electrons depended wholly upon the energy of the primary ones and was independent of the metal targets and the distance over which the radiation traveled. This statement might at first sight appear to be a wholly reasonable one until one reflects that radiation may not be propagated as a stream of particles but as a wave. A wave spreads spherically through the ether and the intensity at any point on the wave front diminishes inversely as the square of the distance from its source. What a marvel is here discovered! Place a metal plate at such a distance from the source of the radiation that only the smallest portion of the wave front touches it. The amount of energy contained in the radiation at that point is an infinitesimal part of a single quantum; yet in an instant the first photo-electron will jump out with its load of energy. This marvelous fact has led to the celebrated analogy of Sir William Bragg, who stated that the situation, as far as material models are concerned, was as follows:[15]

It is as if one dropped a plank into the sea from a height of 100 feet, and found that the spreading ripple was able, after traveling 1,000 miles and becoming infinitesimal in comparison with its original amount, to act upon a wooden ship in such a way that a plank of that ship flew out of its place to a height of 100 feet.

### 7. Bohr's Picture of the Atom.

Before passing on to other more profound considerations of our problem let us pause a moment and see what can be saved out of the wreck of Newtonian mechanics and classical belief. Let us assume that energy is corpuscular and that there is an ether which in some mysterious way acts as a medium in which the periodic properties of the entity may exist. Can we, in any way, form a picture of the method in which the electrons of matter are behaving? Previously we have thought of them as analogous to knobs upon elastic rods, but this concept can be replaced by a far more satisfactory one. The atomic picture which we are about to describe is due to Niels Bohr, a Danish physicist, who devoted his attention to the problem of constructing a model of the atom which would accord with the revelations of Planck and Einstein. In this he was eminently successful and the Bohr theory has been in a large way one of the striking successes of this bewildering period.[16]

---

[15]Aether Waves and Electrons, Nature, vol. 107 (1921), p. 374.
[16]On the Constitution of Atoms and Molecules, Phil. Mag. (6), vol. 26 (1913), pp. 1-25; 476-502; 857-875.

The fundamental idea in the mind of the Danish physicist, apparently, was to save as much of the classical theory as possible while bringing his atomic model into line with the new quantum concept. In order to do this he first postulated that the principle of least action should be preserved. This mysterious principle, as we have indicated in the first chapter, for all its metaphysical origin and its remarkable resistance to rational interpretation, remains throughout all physics the one unchangeable law. Einstein in developing his theory of relativity postulated it as a cardinal principle; in the wave mechanics of Schrödinger we shall see that it is the main justification for his metaphysical theory; no man is bold enough to whisper that it should be discarded, for with its denial the structure of physics would totter. Hence the theory of Bohr begins with the assumption of the validity of this principle.

Starting with the concept of the simple hydrogen atom, Bohr postulated that it should be regarded as consisting of a single positive proton as nucleus with a single negative electron revolving about it under the influence of an attractive force varying inversely as the square of the distance. So far there is no violation of Newtonian mechanics. But the novel element of the new atom is found in the assumption that the electron, while moving in its orbit, neither radiates nor absorbs energy. There are so-called stationary states within which the electron moves without disturbance either from or to the ether. In these stationary orbits the electron is unmolested and unmolesting, which is, of course, a violation of the principle which asserts that periodic motion sets up vibrations in the surrounding medium.

But this cardinal postulate of Bohr was peculiarly adapted to the quantum hypothesis, which he introduced into the picture in the assumption that radiation takes place only when an electron moves from one stationary orbit to another, and that the loss or gain in energy in such a jump is exactly equal to $h v$ where $h$ is Planck's constant and $v$ is the frequency of the vibration. There is a good deal of mystery in this concept, however, for all of its success. How are we to reconcile with rational belief electrons which make their presence manifest only while in transit from one quantum orbit to another? What is the mechanism of such an atomic system and how is the energy transferred in these sudden erratic movements in which the radiating quantum is born? What is the condition of the electron when it is in transit? How long a time is required in these quantum jumps, or are they themselves definitive of time? Does time itself share the atomic structure of the universe and is its smallest unit the interval defined by the revolution of the electron in its nearest approach to the proton in the hydrogen atom?[17]   Truly this is the golden age of metaphysics!

The great success of the Bohr atom was in its explanation of spectrum lines, which for beauty of interpretation and accuracy of prediction is unexcelled by any contemporary theory.  Applying the simple postulates outlined above, first, that electrons move in systems derived from the assumption of the principle of least action and Newtonian force, second, that the radii of these orbits determine stationary states within which no radiation is possible, and third, that radiation occurs in discrete quanta generated by the electron in sudden, impulsive changes from one stationary orbit to another, Bohr derived his famous formula connecting wave lengths with a sequence of integers (n, m) :

$$1/\lambda = \nu = N\ (\ 1/n^2 - 1/m^2 ).$$

In this equation we shall note that, N ( = 109,677.69) is a number originally discovered empirically by J. R. Rydberg[18] (1854-1919) and named in his honor but theoretically derived by Bohr, and $\nu$ is the wave number, that is to say the reciprocal of the wave length, $\lambda$, of the radiation associated with the quantum integers n and m. This is a beautiful result from several points of view but most of all, perhaps, from the fact that spectral lines are reduced to an aspect of the theory of integers, one of the most abstract and apparently most useless (pragmatically speaking), branches of mathematics. In order to calculate the series of lines known as the Balmer series in the spectrum of hydrogen all we need to do is to set n = 2 in the Bohr formula and let m range over the integers 3, 4, 5, 6, . . . etc. The extreme accuracy of the formula is seen in the fact that the observed values of the wave length corresponding to the first three integers (m) are 6563.07, 4861.52, 4340.64 angstrom units, and the calculated values are less by .03 in the first two wave lengths and greater by .02 in the third.  What theory can hope for greater accuracy than this!

The fruitful concept of Bohr was added to in essential ways by A. Sommerfeld and others. Sommerfeld developed the subject in one of the most masterful of volumes on the new physics entitled "Atomic

---

[17]Norman Campbell has argued that time is a statistical phenomenon and that any temporal magnitude "represents a probability of transition characteristic of the individual elements." See Phil. Mag., vol. 1 (7th series) (1926), pp. 1106-1117. See also N. Bohr: Nature, vol. 121 (1928), p. 588.

[18]On the Structure of the Line-Spectra of the Chemical Elements, Phil. Mag. (5), vol. 29 (1890), pp. 331-337.

structure and Spectral Lines."[19] One of Sommerfeld's striking contributions to the Bohr picture was his formulization of the quantum conditions in terms of the periodic properties of the coördinates which describe the generalized momenta of the electrons. These conditions are mathematical in character and can not be described with any more ease or precision than the condition of material behaviour, in some ways similar, known as the principle of least action. By means of his beautiful postulates Sommerfeld was able to make some headway in describing the spectra of more complicated atoms than the simple hydrogen model and also predicted, by introducing the relativity procession of the perihelion of the electronic orbits, the fine structure of lines in the spectrum. This splendid prediction was amply verified when spectral lines were examined under the microscope and found to be resolvable into components of the predicted order of magnitude. Of other implications of this phenomenon we have spoken in an earlier chapter.

## 8. *Difficulties with Complex Atoms.*

The brilliant success of the hydrogen atom led at once to deeper exploration into the structure of those atoms in which more than one electron was involved. Here, however, difficulties multiply with incredible rapidity. The supreme efforts of astronomers and mathematicians have not been able completely to surmount the difficulties met with in the three body problem, that is to say the problem involving the motions of three material objects moving under their mutual gravitational attractions. The theory of the moon according to the analytic methods of Charles Delaunay (1816-1872) contains one equation exceeding 170 pages in length. One does not lift such a weapon with greater ease than he would bend the bow of Odysseus. The second attempt to explore the atomic depths was directed to the helium model, in which a central double protonic nucleus was surrounded by two electrons. The difficulties encountered here have not yet been completely surmounted. J. H. Van Vleck who has done fundamental work in this problem concludes that "as yet it appears possible to devise a satisfactory symmetrical model of the normal helium atom only with the aid of some such radical innovation as a reformulation of the quantum conditions or modification of the law of force between negative electrons."[20]

---

[19]English trans. of 3d ed. by H. L. Brose, London (1923).
[20]The normal Helium Atom and its relation to the Quantum Theory, Phil. Magazine (6), vol. 44 (1922), pp. 842-869.

But for all the inherent difficulties, the attempt at investigation of these more complicated atoms has been very far from fruitless. Let us assume that we progress in the periodic table of Mendeleéff by adding one electron to the structure of an atom in order to obtain the atom of the next element above it. A corresponding addition must also be assumed for the protonic nucleus, though this addition is somewhat more complicated than that postulated for the electron. In this way we can arrange the elements according to atomic numbers from the light hydrogen atom with its single electron to the heavy uranium atom with a planetary system of 92 electrons.

The intricacies of the picture are very greatly simplified by assuming that these electrons are effectively arranged in shells and that the chemical inertness of certain elements and the activity of others are due to the completeness with which the respective shells are filled. For example we may regard helium as having two electrons which compose the first shell; the second shell will include eight elements, which is completely filled in the atom of neon, a very inert element. The third shell, similarly, contains eight elements ending with argon, etc. It is not our purpose, nor could we hope within a single chapter, to elucidate all of the difficulties which this picture has produced nor the mental agilities of the host of theorists who have constructed and reconstructed the arrangement so as to make it more consonant with experimental evidence. The theory is enormously complex; there are many types of atoms and the vast amount of experimental data does not fit with suitable accuracy any model that has yet been constructed. In general it may be said that the picture of the shells with their full quota of electrons, accounting for the inertness of certain elements, and the presence of one or two valence electrons on the outside of completed shells in other atoms accounting for the chemical activity of these elements, is a rough approximation to the most generally accepted theory. The great probe into the mysteries of these minute quantities, from whose myriad swarms arise the massive edifices of the world, has been X-ray spectra and the swift particles from radium and other radio-active substances. The literature of these two subjects is large and technical and cannot be reviewed here. We return with regret from this alluring field to a further consideration of the quanta cast off by the sudden jumps of these electrons from one stable orbit to another.

We face again the problem of energy and the ether. While it fascinates us it also mystifies. It is, in this respect, like the strange story by A. von Chamisso, who related the adventures of "Peter Schlemihl, the Man Without a Shadow." With what apprehension and mystification, with what deadly fascination we watch the "man in gray" unhook the shadow from the wretched Schlemihl; how we race from incident to incident until at the climax we hear the unhappy man repeat his tragic soliloquy: "My horse was brought—I pressed my weeping friend to my bosom—threw myself into the saddle, and, under the friendly shades of night, quitted this sepulchre of my existence, indifferent which road my horse should take; for now, on this side the grave I had neither wishes, hopes nor fears." The problem of energy and the ether disturbs us. It is too bizarre to have reality but too real to be a dream. The ether is, indeed, the thing without a shadow and energy is its companion.

### 9. *The Philosophy of the Compton Effect.*

We have shown in previous paragraphs that energy is to be thought of as being ejected by matter in the form of packages or quanta. We have set forth in as simple terms as the subject will permit some of the reasons which have led almost inevitably to this conclusion. But we have also pointed out that we must never at any time be unmindful of the phenomenon of diffraction and the apparent lack of any evidence to show that quanta, once they have been ejected by the electrons, behave as swarms of spatial particles. The dilemma of modern physics is now before us. We have on the one hand, when we are regarding the relationship between matter and energy, a corpuscular theory of radiation, and on the other hand, when we consider light in the ether, the concept of a continuous medium propagating waves. We are like the shepherd of Aesop's fable, who would blow cold with his breath to cool his porridge, but would blow hot to warm his frozen hands.

Let us turn to another experiment, known as the Compton effect, in honor of the pioneer work of A. H. Compton both in the discovery of the phenomenon and in its elucidation.[21] We have seen that X-rays are produced if a stream of electrons be directed upon a metal target. What would happen if the radiation thus produced were allowed to fall upon another target? The answer is that secondary radiation, known as scattered X-rays, is produced, but curiously enough the new rays are of less penetrating power than the primary

---

[21]See Bulletin of the National Research Council, No. 20 (1922); also A. H. Compton: X-Rays and Electrons, New York (1926), chap. 9. A careful account is also to be found in K. K. Darrow: Introduction to Contemporary Physics.

rays because of their reduced frequency. The phenomenon of scattered X-rays suggests that the original quanta bombarding the metal plate have transferred only part of their energy to the electrons and have bounced off as smaller units.

In order to understand this statement let us consider what would happen if a quantum of energy should collide with a free electron, that is to say an electron detached from its atom. Some hypothesis will have to be made; hence we shall assume the simplest one consonant with Newtonian mechanics. Let this be the following: that both the energy and the momentum exchanged in the collision must be conserved. The quantum in the collision will confer part of its energy and part of its momentum upon the electron, subject to the laws of such impacts, and will then fly off as a reduced quantum, the losses of which will be measured in terms of its reduced power of penetration. The intricate nature both of the experiments and of the mathematical interpretation of the phenomenon can not be discussed here because of technical difficulties. It is sufficient to say that this quantum interpretation of scattered X-rays seems amply justified by the experimental facts. They lead again to the belief that energy actually goes about in packages, as earlier experiments indicated.

There is one feature of the theory that should be especially mentioned, however, because of its importance in the philosophical situation. When a quantum strikes an electron we can not predict the direction and velocity which each will take in its recoil. To be sure, if we know the direction in which one entity, say the electron, rebounds it is possible to predict the direction that the quantum will take; but even though we knew accurately beforehand the initial conditions governing the collision it appears impossible at the present time to predict the subsequent paths of both the objects. It is a weird billiard game that one would play in which the object ball was an electron and the cue ball a quantum. A novice would have an equal chance with the professional since the motions of the two balls would be wholly fortuitous.

A consideration of the implications of this remarkable fact has led P. W. Bridgman to the following melancholy conclusion about the nature of reality as it is revealed in the microcosm:[22]

The same situation confronts the physicist everywhere; when-

---

[22]Harper's Magazine, March, 1929. Heisenberg's principle assumes that the behaviour of nature can not always be described accurately, as in our inability to predict the mutual paths of the colliding electron and quantum. See section 15.

ever he penetrates to the atomic or electronic level in his analysis he finds things acting in a way for which he can never assign a cause, and for which the concept of cause has no meaning, if Heisenberg's principle is right. This means nothing more nor less than that the law of cause and effect must be given up. The precise reason that the law of cause and effect fails can be paradoxically stated; it is not that the future is not determined in terms of a complete description of the present, but that in the nature of things the present cannot be completely described.

## 10. *The Problem of the New Physics.*

Out of the new physics some facts are emerging which seem incontestable. We must modify our ideas about energy and the ether. We must have on the one hand a theory to explain diffraction and on the other a theory to account for the existence of quanta. We should be careful, however, not to apply the laws of statistics to these quantum swarms, because they are of a nature which defies such analysis. They may, to be sure, collide with quantities as tiny as an electron, but they may be regarded from certain aspects to be as large as balloons. To assume that quanta are long tenuous filaments of inconceivably small cross section is in contradiction with certain experimental evidence. To assume that they are huge, broad affairs, as some experiments indicate, must strain our belief in the evidence which says that they may collide with an electron. To try to give them any spatial reality whatsoever leads inevitably to one contradiction or another. The difficulty is deeper seated; it goes back to the original problem of the ether.

"A question intimately involved in any attempt to find a physical basis for the quantum theory, is that of the degree of reality or substantiality with which the ether must be supposed endowed," says Jeans in his report to the British Association in 1913.[23] "The modern school of British physicists have been inclined to regard the ether as a completely real substance—indeed to some of them the ether is the primary real substance. At the other extreme stand the relativity school, who almost deny that the ether has any reality at all. There are innumerable intermediate positions between these two extremes. . . .

"If the ether is regarded as too devoid of substantiality to be treated as part of the dynamical system, it is necessary to fall back on the changes of energy in the mechanism by which the radiation is

---

[23]Report on Radiation, 1st ed., pp. 87-88.

produced. Almost all the Continental physicists have regarded the quantum-theory from this point of view, which has the disadvantage that it is necessary to specify exactly the mechanism of radiation. Whatever this mechanism may be, and however many types of mechanism there may be, it is necessary that the energy of each should jump by quanta. So far no success has attended any explanation of why the energy of any type of mechanism should be incapable of changing except by quanta: assuming the fact, of course, the required results following, but the difficulty lies in making the assumption of the fact seem physically plausible."

From these conclusions one would believe that physics is the science of reconciling the irreconcilable, or in the words of the colored preacher, its problem is to "unscrew the inscrutable." How can matter be in motion with respect to the ether and the motion still be indetectable? How can waves be propagated with elements consisting of particles of energy? How can swarms of quanta exist and still defy analysis by the laws of chance? Why does all energy flow down toward a universal level and yet never arrive? How can quanta be at the same time both large and small? How can matter affect other matter across non-material space?

Faced by the dilemma of a quantum theory and a theory of diffraction based upon the assumption of disturbance in a continuous medium, the bolder theorists commenced to seek a mathematical way out of the difficulties. The success of Clerk Maxwell, who showed that the ether of James MacCullah, discarded because it could not be reconciled with rational physical models, was the mathematical picture of electro-magnetic waves, and the later triumph of Einstein, who replaced gravitation by the mathematics of non-Euclidean geometry, gave courage to those who would essay the bold attempt. If physical pictures of reality can not be made let us see what can be done by subjective principles.

## 11.   The Ether-Ring Theory of Quanta.

The first theory that we wish to describe is due to Sir J. J. Thomson and is not so wholly divorced from material models as is the later work of de Broglie and Schrödinger. The picture that the eminent English physicist suggested as a possible escape from the dilemma of the wave and quantum theories is that of the creation of rings in the ether by the stretching or contracting of tubes of force connecting positive protons with negative electrons. Let us, for example, think of such a tube joining the two opposite particles. If the mutual potential energy be diminished the two particles approach one another; the tube in which the energy resides is contracted and, in order to escape, is shaped into a ring and thrown off into space with the velocity of light. Conversely, when the system consisting of the proton and electron gains energy it absorbs one of these hoops into its connecting tube of force which is correspondingly lengthened. These hoops with their unitary character take the place of the quanta of the Planck-Bohr theory. When a sufficient number of such rings are absorbed into the atom the electron is torn loose from its atom and the energy represented by the length of the tube disappears into the kinetic energy of the escape.

In order to explain the diffraction of light Thomson makes the further assumption that these quantum loops are surrounded by a system of electrical waves of the ordinary type which vibrate with a frequency characteristic of the vibrations of the loops. This picture is summarized as follows:[24]

. . . light on this view is made up of units, each of which contains a core in which the energy is concentrated; this core is surrounded by a system of electric waves which, though they have but little energy, give rise in cases where diffraction or interference occurs to electric and magnetic forces which deflect the paths of the cores without altering their energy. The core is supposed to vibrate in a definite period, and this period coincides with that of the electrical waves which surround it.

### 12.  De Broglie and the Wave Mechanics.

We shall not comment upon the picture of Thomson which is suggestive of another that emerged from the speculation of this period and laid the foundation of the intriguing wave mechanics. This model, proposed the same year (1924) that saw the birth of the Thomson radiation, was suggested by Louis de Broglie, and if the metaphysical nature of its postulates can be surmounted it certainly achieves a remarkable success. The summary of de Broglie's paper exhibits the high ambitions of its author, who there says:[25]

"In the present paper it is assumed that the light is essentially made up of light quanta, all having the same extraordinarily small mass. It is shown mathematically that the Lorentz-Einstein transformation joined with the quantum relation leads us necessarily to

---

[24]Philosophical Magazine, vol. 48 (1924), pp. 737-746.
[25]Philosophical Magazine, vol. 47 (1924), pp. 446-457.

associate motion of body and propagation of waves, and that this idea gives a physical interpretation of Bohr's analytical stability conditions. Diffraction seems to be consistent with an extension of the Newtonian Dynamics. It is then possible to save both the corpuscular and the undulatory characters of light and, by means of hypotheses suggested by the electro-magnetic theory and the correspondence principle, to give a plausible explanation of coherence[26] and interference fringes. Finally it is shown that every quantum must take a part in the dynamical theory of gases and how Planck's law is the limiting form of Maxwell's law for a light quanta gas."

Surely the attainment of these results is sufficient to justify the existence of any paper. The theory of diffraction will be saved, the quantum theory will be maintained, and best of all, the laws of chance will be shown to apply to the statistical study of the swarming particles of energy. The only difficulty with this beautiful picture and the later extension of it by the methods of E. Schrödinger is that it is completely metaphysical in its final elements and wholly incomprehensible to rational intuition. It is based upon the assumption of oscillations of a quantity entirely mathematical in character and incomprehensible to ordinary intelligence, however much Schrödinger may try to connect it with physical entities.

In a previous chapter we have commented upon various types of atoms. Pearson would have us believe that the atom was a squirt from a mysterious fluid entering our perceptions from the fourth dimension of space; Lord Kelvin advanced the theory that the atom was a vortex ring in the metaphysical ether; Bohr, incorporating the new knowledge of electrons in his theory, molded an atom in the image of a planetary system with curious stationary orbits, within which the members were without effect upon the external ether. We come at last to the most metaphysical atom of all which replaces all material concepts by a train of waves. The quantity that undulates is mysterious and elusive; the thing in which it undulates is so wholly transcendental that one never hears a question raised about either its nature or its existence.

De Broglie's ideas arose out of a consideration of the two modern concepts of energy. According to Einstein the total amount of energy in a quantity of mass m is equal to $m c^2$, where c is the velocity of light; according to Planck and his successors the quantity of energy in a quantum is $h v$, where $h$ is the universal constant and

---

[26] The problem of coherence is that of explaining how several light quanta can be part of the same wave in order that diffraction and other optical phenomena may be accounted for.

$v$ is the frequency. Let us regard the equivalent energy in a particle of matter as being expressible in terms of these two concepts and let us equate them,

$$mc^2 = h \ v.$$

This simple appearing equation has bound up in it most of the mysterious features of modern physics. It is composed on the one side of the statement of a basic conclusion from the theory of relativity and on the other of the fundamental tenet of the quantum theory. Whatever mysteries are inherent in these two doctrines are inherited by the equation just written down.

Having made this beginning de Broglie reflected upon what would happen if the particle of mass m should start to move. According to the theory of relativity the mass would increase with growing velocity and the term on the left of the equation would thus be augmented. On the basis of the same theory, however, the frequency would diminish. Hence the equality which held for the material particle at rest would no longer be true after motion had set in. While reflecting upon these strange consequences, de Broglie, in a moment of brilliant inspiration, suddenly conceived the fundamental postulate of the theory which was to flower into the wave mechanics. Matter is not, as Kelvin thought, a vortex motion in the ether; it is a train of waves. *Associated with every particle there is an undulatory principle which spreads out continuously in all directions from it.* We dare not try to make the idea more concrete because all material analogies fail. The medium in which these waves exist is far less corporeal than the thinnest wraith left by the investigators of the nineteenth century; what this undulatory entity may be, wholly transcends our imagination to conceive.

Let us then regard matter as merely an aspect of an undulation which, when the particle is at rest, consists of a sphere of enveloping waves and when the particle is in motion, as a bodyguard of undulations which move with it, those in the rear disappearing as the matter progresses and new waves appearing in the direction of motion. It is possible, perhaps, to make a picture of the situation by thinking of a stone immersed in water and put in motion by some oscillatory device so as to set up a train of standing waves. If the stone then be given a rectilinear motion the train of waves will accompany it, those in the rear dying out and new waves appearing ahead.

And how can an atom be conceived in terms of this picture? Let us imagine the electrons in the Bohr atom. Around each of them is the train of waves, and as they move in their elliptical orbits these waves must arrange themselves in some kind of a stable configuration. It was the genius of de Broglie that saw how to account for the stationary states of the Bohr electrons by this method. If the waves accompanying the electron are to move around the orbit in any kind of a stable pattern it is necessary that their wave length be commensurate with the length of the orbit. In this way the beautiful discovery of Bohr, that the wave lengths of a spectrum can be calculated by means of a formula involving integers, may be apprehended. The total length of the orbits must contain whole multiples of the wave lengths of the constituent undulations.

### 13.  Schrödinger and His Creation of Psi.

Various other puzzling difficulties associated with the generation of radiation by matter were made plausible by de Broglie and his ideas rapidly gained adherents due both to the power of his point of view and to its exceptional novelty. They fell in particular under the scrutiny of E. Schrödinger, who in a series of brilliant papers in 1925-1926 seized upon the new concept of matter and rapidly moulded it into what is today known as the *wave mechanics.*[27]

The main point with Schrödinger is strangely like that of Einstein in the gravitation problem. To the latter, gravitational force appeared as a puzzling attribute of material things possessing properties impossible to reconcile with rational concepts. Hence he avoided further trouble by removing the difficulties from matter and placing them upon the framework of space-time. Gravitation then became a problem in the geometry of four-dimensions, which manifests the peculiarities of its manifold only in the presence of ponderable bodies. In a similar way Schrödinger studied the de Broglie picture and decided that the presence of the material particle was not essentially necessary to it. Why not let the train of waves entirely replace the substantive entity? Gravitational force is an aspect of geometry; material particles are aspects of a vibratory property of space. Is there not something stirring in this picture? Do we not feel that reality further and further eludes our attempts to find it? Of what was Chesterfield thinking when he said: "Every man seeks for truth; but God only knows who has found it"?

It is of immense interest to see where Schrödinger takes hold of the problem. He begins with that mysterious postulate, the founda-

[27]Quantisierung als Eigenwertproblem, Annalen der Physik (4), vol. 79 (1926), pp. 361-376; 489-527; vol. 80, pp. 437-490; vol. 81, pp. 109-139.

tion of the description of all physical law, which we have called the principle of least action. Here stretching over the centuries from its mystical derivation by Maupertuis, through his interpretation of the behaviour of the Deity toward the world of material things, this strange necessity of thought reaches into the very nature of matter itself. Nay more than that it assumes a dominating rôle in the structure of a new mechanics.

To explain the approach of Schrödinger in adequate terms would require considerable use of mathematical language. We can, however, state the matter descriptively as follows. The motion of material bodies, acting under impressed forces of any kind, may be accurately described by assuming that they follow paths determined by making the total action a minimum. Upon this assumption, as we have pointed out in the first chapter of the book, an adequate description of the behaviour of material bodies is always possible. But what is this mysterious action itself? It can not be visualized. We can not feel it, weigh it, or otherwise apprehend it in terms of our sensations. We can only calculate it. It appears, so to speak, to lack material handles. Through all the years since it was first stated by Maupertuis it has stood as a sort of spectre, always lurking in the background of every calculation, but disappearing once the desired motion has been obtained. It has moved the imagination of many men, but none has succeeded in explaining it. Schrödinger, fixing his attention upon this mysterious action, sought to find in it a revelation of the difficulties of the atom. His success exceeded his expectations, although the mystery of the entire situation can scarcely be said to have been dissipated by this penetration.

What Schrödinger found was that he could associate with each material particle a certain undulatory quantity involving a spatial rate of change of this mysterious action; he discovered that this vibrating quantity could be made to yield an accurate mathematical determination of many of the quantities involved in the quantum hypothesis, while at the same time it preserved the wave nature of light. Out of the equations of Newtonian mechanics which he derived in a straightforward manner from the principle of least action, Schrödinger was able to select a certain quantity involving action, or an equivalent expression in terms of kinetic and potential energy, which could be interpreted as the velocity of a family of wave fronts. This train of waves is the thing with which he replaced the corporeal particle.

Does the reader begin at last to think that modern physics is degenerating into the sophistry of the old schoolmen or does he believe that it is on the verge of revealing one of the most profound speculations yet made by the human race? Does it appear that modern dreamers are talking nonsense compared with which the metaphysics of the Middle Ages would be "as sensible as a dictionary"? Is there any impression of descending to a lower level of rationality when we review the reasons which led Duns Scotus to distinguish between three kinds of matter: "matter which is firstly first, secondly first, thirdly first," or the arguments advanced by Saint Thomas to settle the perplexing question: "whether a glorified body can occupy one and the same place at the same time as another glorified body"? We can only reply that those of the older age had no material experiments to control their imaginations; today the most searching gauntlet of physical fact must be run by those who would bring their dream into the tolerance of a skeptical age. "The wise man passes for a magician, the enlightened man for a heretic," says H. A. Taine of the mystics of that older metaphysics.[28] Today the dreamer is the sage, but his dreams must be built upon the solid rock of experience.

We return to the main theme, which is concerned, as far as simple language can tell the story, with an equation that defines the wave motion associated with matter. The unknown function whose undulations are the fundamental characteristic of material things has been designated by the Greek letter psi, $\Psi$, a wholly appropriate symbol under the dictum of Voltaire, previously quoted, that we should define that which we do not comprehend in a language which we do not understand. The quantity psi whose undulations are the essential characteristic of matter is a strictly mathematical symbol. As a matter of fact it is composed of two parts, one a real and the other an imaginary quantity in the mathematical sense of complex numbers. If the sign of the imaginary part of psi be changed and the new symbol multiplied by the old we obtain a real quantity which Schrödinger identifies with electric density. This is the only reality possessed by the mysterious function. It is just as elusive to physical definition as the concept of action which suggested it and in the same manner it fades out of the picture once the desired results of the quantum theory have been achieved. It resembles in this respect the catalytic agents with which chemists cause substances to unite and which they then remove unaffected from the reaction chambers. One is reminded of the story of the wise man who was called upon to

---

[28]History of English Literature, Book 1, chap. 3, sec. 6.

distribute a legacy of eleven cattle between three sons, the first of whom was to receive a half, the second a fourth and the third a sixth. The learned judge added one of his own cattle to the herd, gave six to the first son, three to the second, two to the third and then returned his own animal to the field. The mysterious psi is the addition from the wise man's herd; it retires from the scene once its labors have been performed.

We may be able perhaps to make the matter no less incomprehensible to the lay mind if we explain in somewhat technical language the main tenet of Schrödinger's picture of the hydrogen atom. Let us think of the electron as being endowed with a potential energy calculated from Newtonian assumptions. We are not to regard the electron in any sense as a small material object, as the Bohr concept leads us to believe, but merely as an entity possessing the customary potential energy of Newtonian mechanics. Let us substitute this value of the potential energy into the wave equation,—an equation which is partially, though not entirely, definitive of the undulatory entity psi. By this statement we mean that psi is incompletely defined because only its partial derivatives are involved in the equation. Schrödinger, in order to give precise values to the mysterious psi, then assumed that it was to remain finite both at its origin in the atom and at an infinite distance from it. This peculiar postulate, entirely mathematical, is at the very heart of the Schrödinger concept as is evident from the title of his series of papers: "Quantization as a Problem in Characteristic Values." These characteristic values, imperative necessities arising out of the method of defining psi, are found to be precisely the energies associated with the electron in its stationary state in the Bohr atom.

It is perhaps unnecessary and inadvisable to go further in popular exposition of this involved subject. The point is accomplished if the reader has perceived the metaphysical basis for the new physics. In this maze of speculation he must not lose sight of the fact that Maxwell's equations, defining the propagation of electro-magnetic disturbances through the ether of space, have essentially no greater reality than the equations of Schrödinger and of de Broglie. For all their plausible derivation from the picture of tubes of electric and magnetic forces Maxwell's equations must be regarded essentially as justifying the metaphysical belief of James MacCullah, whose choice among the elastic theories of the ether was regarded as the most untenable. The weird concepts at the basis of the wave mechanics can have justification only from their success in explaining in mathematical language what the laboratory technicians tell us they have seen. The keen-edged tools of mathematics must replace the desires of rational intuition and we must return to the melancholy belief that we can never completely understand the underlying structure of the universe. A new basis for epistemology is being forced upon us. Knowledge is not to be derived from material models; the light that comes to us from the petals of a rose is not the truth; the hard stone over which we stumble is only an illusion in our pathway and its reality exists in the mysterious undulations of the Schrödinger psi, the meaning of which is apprehended only through its behaviour in an equation.

## 14.  The Matrix Theory of the Atom.

Our story would not be complete without mentioning at least one other theory of the atom which has gained many adherents and has much success to justify its postulates. The principal founders of the socalled *matrix theory of the atom* are W. Heisenberg, Max Born, P. Jordan and P. Dirac.

The main postulate of this theory is contained in the following quotation from lectures given by Born during 1925-1926 at the Massachusetts Institute of Technology:[29]

In the case of atomic theory, we have certainly introduced as fundamental constituents, magnitudes of very doubtful observability, as, for instance, the position, velocity and period of the electron. What we really want to calculate by means of our theory and can be observed experimentally, are the energy levels and the emitted light of frequencies derivable from them. The mean radius of the atom (atomic volume) is also an observable quantity which can be determined by the methods of the kinetic theory of gases or other analogous methods. On the other hand, no one has been able to give a method for the determination of the period of an electron in its orbit or even the position of the electron at a given instant. There seems to be no hope that this will ever become possible, for in order to determine lengths or times, measuring rods and clocks are required. The latter, however, consist themselves of atoms and therefore break down in the realm of atomic dimensions. It is necessary to see clearly the following points: All measurements of magnitudes of atomic order depend on indirect conclusions; but the latter carry weight only when their train of thought is consistent with itself and corresponds to a certain region of our experience. But this is precisely not the case for atomic structures such as we have considered so far. . . .

---

[29]Problems of Atomic Dynamics, Cambridge (1926), pp. 68-69.

At this stage it appears justified to give up altogether the description of atoms by means of such quantities as "coordinates of the electrons" at a given time, and instead utilize such magnitudes as are really observable. To the latter belong, besides the energy levels which are directly measurable by electron impacts and the frequencies which are derivable from them and which are also measurable, the intensity and the polarization of the emitted waves. We therefore take from now on the point of view that the *elementary waves* are the primary data for the description of atomic processes; all other quantities are to be derived from them.

From this point on the theory is highly mathematical; the analysis of the vibratory motions, postulated as fundamental, is made through the manipulation of certain abstract entities of mathematics known as *matrices*. The theory is usually referred to in the quantum literature as the matrix theory which, from its very nature, precludes a popular description of its concepts. The classical theory of mechanics is modified to meet the conditions and the Bohr theory is made plausible by a beautiful though intricate mathematical analysis.

The theory of matrices has been extended in an important way by P. Dirac,[30] who introduced certain mathematical expressions called "Poisson brackets," which have properties similar to the matrices, but which are of a more general type. The exploration of these ideas belongs entirely to mathematical physics and we have made mention of them only to show how completely the physical picture has been submerged in subjective abstractions.

## 15. *The Principle of Indeterminacy.*

A principle of very deep philosophical significance was announced in 1927 by W. Heisenberg[31] and has been more fully developed in a monograph on "The Physical Principles of the Quantum Theory."[32] Its origin is in the observation that the conflict between the continuity view and the atomic view of nature is not one of words which may be cleared up by a re-definition of terms, or of contradictory experiments which further investigation will reconcile, but that it is a deep-seated struggle of fundamental principles.

In order to reconcile the quantum hypothesis with the views of the continuity postulate of wave motion, Heisenberg assumed that there exists in all physical actions a region of uncertainty which is

[30]Proc. Royal Soc. (A), vol. 109 (1925), p. 642.
[31]Zeits. Phys., vol. 43, p. 172.
[32]Eng. trans., Chicago (1930).

fundamentally associated with our measurements of space and velocity. If we attempt to specify the position of an elementary particle with greater exactness, then the determination of its velocity or momentum becomes more uncertain. The area of this region of uncertainty, that is to say, the elementary unit of space, by the elementary unit of momentum, is not smaller than Planck's constant, $h$.

"This uncertainty relation specifies the limits within which the particle picture can be applied," says Heisenberg. "Any use of the words 'position' and 'velocity' with an accuracy exceeding that given by the equation (stated in preceding paragraph) is just as meaningless as the use of words whose sense is not defined."[33]

The importance of this proposition cannot be over estimated, because it attacks the very foundations of causality and determinism upon which science rests its structure. As we shift from molecular to molar physics this basic postulate gains in validity, but the vital fact still remains that a complete indeterminacy is in the roots of nature. The situation is not unrelated to the statistical postulate that although a complete indeterminacy governs the toss of a single coin, the law of large numbers asserts itself when the tosses are increased without limit.

The following excerpt from a paper of Niels Bohr gives a penetrating appraisement of the philosophical importance of the indeterminacy principle :[34]

This postulate implies a renunciation as regards the causal space-time coördination of atomic processes. Indeed, our usual description of physical phenomena is based entirely on the idea that the phenomena concerned may be observed without disturbing them appreciably. This appears, for example, clearly in the theory of relativity, which has been so fruitful for the elucidation of the classical theories. As emphasized by Einstein, every observation or measurement ultimately rests on the coincidence of two independent events at the same space-time point. Just these coincidences will not be affected by any differences which the space-time coördination of different observers otherwise may exhibit. Now the quantum postulate implies that any observation of atomic phenomena will involve an interaction with the agency of observation not to be neglected. Accordingly, an independent reality in the ordinary physical sense can neither be ascribed to the phenomena nor to the agencies of observation. After all, the concept of observation is in so far arbitrary as it depends upon which objects are included in the system to be observed. Ultimately every observation can of course be reduced

[33]Physical Principles of the Quantum Theory, p. 15.
[34]The Quantum Postulate and the Recent Development of Atomic Theory, Nature, vol. 121 (1928), pp. 580-590; in particular p. 580.

to our sense perceptions. The circumstance, however, that in interpreting observations use has always to be made of theoretical notions, entails that for every particular case it is a question of convenience at what point the concept of observation involving the quantum postulate with its inherent "irrationality" is brought in.

## 16.  The Diffraction of Electrons.

We turn finally to a consideration of a great triumph for the wave mechanics and the general point of view that in these new concepts of matter and radiation we are actually discovering an unexplored territory for whose examination the ideas of the older physics, however seasoned by time and experience they may be, are unsuited. This victory was an experiment performed in 1927 by C. J. Davisson and L. H. Germer of the American Telephone and Telegraph Company.[35] The interpretation of these interesting discoveries indicates that the wave nature of the electrons as predicted by the theory of de Broglie and Schrödinger is factually revealed.

In order to appreciate the theoretical significance of this statement we might return to the wave equation and see what the character of the wave train associated with a beam of electrons would be. If proper sustitutions be made in the equation of the mystical psi we obtain a value of the wave length of the waves associated with the moving electron. This value is equal to $h/mv$, where h is Planck's constant, m the mass of the electron, and v the velocity of the particle. For velocities of the order of those ordinarily met with in experiment this value is easily computed to be of approximately the wave length of X-ray radiation. Hence a beam of electrons should exhibit characteristics similar to those found in X-ray phenomena.

It was not with the intention of checking the fundamental postulates of the wave mechanics that Davisson and Germer originally undertook their experiments, but rather to explore the structure of matter as revealed in the deflections caused in the path of bombarding electrons. If a stream of these tiny particles be directed against a metal target, electrons are scattered in all directions from the area under bombardment. The question first proposed by the investigators was this: What information could be discovered from these streams of electrons with regard to the arrangements of the atoms from which they were deflected?

---

[35]Diffraction of Electrons by a Nickel Crystal, Physical Review, vol. 30, 2nd ser. (1927), pp. 705-740.

Now it is a matter well known to technical workers that the wave character of X-rays is beautifully revealed through phenomena incident to their scattering by the surface of a crystal. This work, highly technical in character, is due essentially to M. von Laue and Bragg who have shown the existence of diffraction in the reflection of X-ray radiation.[36] If a beam of X-rays be directed toward a crystal such as zincblende the phenomenon of diffraction is revealed. The crystal has the surprising property of acting as a diffraction grating. A grating is a device made by tracing a number of very fine equidistant lines upon a plate by means of a fine diamond point. These lines are opaque to light so that the radiation which passes through the plate in the intervals between them will be reunited to form images. The discoveries of Laue showed that diffraction beams caused by the impinging of X-ray radiation upon a crystal were found both on the side of the transmitted beam and on the near or incident side of the target. The latter in particular are arranged in regular array about the point of incidence. The wave lengths of the diffraction beams are entirely characterized by the wave length of the incident beam. The exploration of these concepts involves highly technical considerations and for our purpose is unnecessary.

It is sufficient to say that when a crystal surface is bombarded by a beam of electrons of sensibly uniform velocity the same phenomenon exhibited in X-ray radiation is observed. For certain critical speeds the electron beam generates a scattered stream of particles which issue from the incident side of the crystal in sharply defined beams analogous to those found in the X-ray diffraction.

The actual arrangement of the diffraction rays are not identical with those of X-rays, but the assumption that we are observing a true diffraction phenomenon enables us to calculate the *wave length* of the incident beam. A remarkable fact emerges. The length of the wave conforms to the predictions of de Broglie and Schrödinger. It is inversely proportional to the velocity of the stream of electrons. This important result was anticipated by W. Elsasser in a suggestion made in 1925 that the wave character of electron beams might be discovered in a study of their interaction with crystals.[37] It is the great achievement of Davisson and Germer that they were the first to show the experimental fact.

The conclusions of the American physicists have also been verified by others. In particular George Thomson, son of J. J. Thomson,

---

[36] See Compton's: X-rays and Electrons (loc. cit.), pp. 16-25.
[37] Naturwiss, vol. 13 (1925), p. 711.

whose great achievement was to show the material character of electrons, has given clear evidence of this wave property of matter. He obtained diffraction patterns similar in appearance to the one shown in chapter four in connection with the undulatory theory of light.[38]

### 17. What Shall We Believe?

What are we to believe? In the last chapter we have reached the climax of that long period of investigation which started with the musings of Democritus and Lucretius and arrived at the suggestive tenets of the wave mechanics. We see in all this the battle between those who would look upon nature as a continuous phenomenon and those who would regard it as divisible into primary units. Those who hold to the belief that the substratum of phenomena is an ether stretching throughout all space and interpenetrating all matter are essentially of the former faith; those who see in the electron, indivisible and individual, the ultimate nature of the universe are clearly of the latter tenet. Inscrutable nature, forever holding out her promises and forever withdrawing them again, smiles sweetly at our efforts and says: "There is truth in the views of both." When we study light in the neighborhood of matter and view the interaction between it and radiating electrons, then the atomists are favored. But when we are dealing with light and other radiation remote from matter then the continuists have the better of the argument. Radiation is a wave; phenomena such as diffraction, in which light plus light may equal darkness, are supportable only on the assumption that periodic disturbances are occurring at the point in question. But the old thought forever intrudes: Disturbances in what? The lines in Alfred de Musset's "The Night of December" are brought to mind:

But all at once in depths of the sombre night,
    I've seen a form that glides with lightsome tread.
Across my shade I've seen the shadow pass;
    It comes to seat itself upon my bed.

There is no answer to the question and perhaps there never can be in terms acceptable to human intuition. We become the new agnostics who realize the presence of something in nature which can never be understood in terms of those things to which we wish to reduce comprehensible experience.

[38]Proc. of the Royal Soc. (A), vol. 117 (1928), p. 600; (A), vol. 119 (1928), p. 651.

The facts that seem to emerge from the investigations of these later years may be summarized as follows:

First: The interaction between matter and radiant energy is not explainable in terms of the ordinary concepts of Newtonian mechanics. Energy which does not disappear from vibrations of long wave length into vibrations of the smallest wave length capable of being set up in the medium is not in accord with the models of normal Newtonian intuition.

Second: The difficulties of the Newtonian ether may be resolved if we assume that energy is not a continuous phenomenon but is atomic. We may solve our problem by introducing quanta of energy which are characterized by the frequency of their periodic activity and a universal constant whose nature is still obscure.

Third: The material electron may be replaced by mathematical concepts derived from the study of the vibrations of a mysterious function associated with the quantity of action the minimizing of which describes the activity of natural objects. In other words electrons, in some of their behaviour, act as periodic vibrations similar to radiations; radiations, in some phenomena, assume atomic properties and may be regarded as possessing the attributes of matter.

Do not these concepts form a basis for a new metaphysical philosophy of nature? Do we not see emerging from these strange concepts, forced upon us by the most delicate and accurate technique of modern laboratories, a whole new foundation for knowledge? Shall we ever be able to integrate our experience into a system of belief which the future may take with assurance as the foundations of its new structure? Or are we to believe with Heraclitus that nature is naught but a ceaseless change; that nothing is secure; that the world of experience is but shifting sand upon which no permanent edifice of thought may be erected?

The present status of the electron is tremendously disturbing; that which was a solid has become a wraith and that which was a wraith has attained material attributes; we are faced by a strange dualism in nature which surprises us much as that excellent branch of geometry which assures us that for every theorem depending upon points and lines there is a dual theorem in which points take the rôle of lines and lines emerge as points. But the real difficulty is not so much in this as in our inability to make any headway with the mystery of the ether. Einstein throws the mystery of gravitation into conceptual experiences derived from an incomprehensible four-dimensional geometry; de Broglie and Schrödinger reduce the experience of light and electrons to a baffling activity of a Greek letter understandable, if it be understandable at all, in terms of mathematical analysis. Surely there is much truth in the chance remark of Hamlet:

There are more things in heaven and earth, Horatio,
Than are dreamt of in our philosophy.

# CHAPTER XI.

## THE DISCOVERY AND INTERPRETATION OF COSMIC RADIATION.

### 1. *Cosmological Speculations.*

MAN for his inspiration has always turned his face toward the stars; in them he has found the beginnings of his science; they have stirred his imagination and his reverence; his poetry and his religions would be sterile without their emotional appeal. There is something that moves us strangely in the following brief statement from a letter mailed by a young soldier just before he joined his last battle:

"I have been looking at the stars and thinking what an immense distance they are away. What an insignificant thing the loss of, say, 40 years of life is compared with them! It seems scarcely worth talking about. . . . This letter is going to be posted if. . . ."

Philosophical speculation began when man first raised his face out of the primordial slime and beheld the stars. One can scarcely controvert the observation that the scientific revolution emerged from the tables and data of the ancient astronomers. Our survey of the foundations of the new epistemology would scarcely be complete if we did not turn to a splendid modern speculation which finds its beginnings in an ancient problem of astronomy. What is the source of stellar energy?

One is reminded at the outset of the difficulty of sifting testimony, and arranging facts so that truth may be ascertained. The problem of stellar energy is a problem in fitting together the numerous parts of a jig-saw puzzle. Great quantities of data about the luminosity and size of the stars, their densities, their pulsations, their stabilities, their distributions, and their spectra are elements of the complex problem to which the attempt to probe the mystery of the source of their energy leads. That conclusions obtained by experts should differ greatly, that the theory of one year should be the folly of the next, that the foundation of any particular speculation is built upon shifting sands, are observations which appear unnecessary to anyone who even casually scans the content of recent treatises.

One is reminded of the difficulty met by the court in a trial of the Knave of Hearts when a certain anonymous poem composed of many intelligible phrases but no coherent thought was introduced as testimony:

"If any one of them can explain it," said Alice (she had grown so large in the last few minutes that she wasn't a bit afraid of interrupting him), "I'll give him a sixpence. I don't believe there's an atom of meaning in it."

The jury all wrote down on their slates, "She doesn't believe there's an atom of meaning in it," but none of them attempted to explain the paper.

"If there's no meaning in it," said the King, "that saves a world of trouble, you know, as we needn't try to find any. And yet I don't know," he went on, spreading out the verses on his knee and looking at them with one eye; "I seem to see some meaning in them after all. '. . . said I could not swim;' you can't swim, can you?" he added, turning to the Knave.

The Knave shook his head sadly. "Do I look like it?" he said. (Which he certainly did not, being made entirely of cardboard.)

"All right, so far," said the King; and he went on muttering the verses to himself: " 'We know it to be true'—that's the jury, of course—'If she should push the matter on'—that must be the Queen— 'What would become of you?' What indeed!—'I gave her one, they gave him two!'—why, that must be what he did with the tarts, you know——' "

"But it goes on, 'They all returned from him to you,' " said Alice.

"Why, there they are!" said the King triumphantly pointing to the tarts on the table. "Nothing can be clearer than that. Then again—'Before she had this fit'—you never had fits, my dear, I think?" he said to the Queen.

"Never!" said the Queen furiously. . . .

The present theorists who are trying to build a coherent picture out of the heterogeneous data of modern astrophysics eagerly seek each new revelation of physical science as another clew to the tangled skein. The difficulties are elusive. The solution of a puzzle in one place disturbs a factor in another. We elucidate the "mystery of the tarts" only to find that "the fits of the Queen" are in contradiction with the testimony.

The problem of stellar energy is twofold. We are interested not only in how this energy is generated and why it continues to pour out into space from the countless stars, but where its journey ends. You see in this another aspect of the problem proposed in the first chapter. Why does entropy never reach its fatal maximum? Why does the free energy of the world continually waste itself and yet the supply appear to be inexhaustible? Is the macrocosm a great thermodynamic engine working perpetually upon a Carnot cycle which winds itself up as it runs down? Is the universe self perpetuating? Is it meaningless to talk about its beginning and its end? Are these but terms which we may apply to the geometry of forms and not to their basic parts? Man's four-dimensional existence is bounded by the finite limits of the variables involved; the structure of all objects is wasted away by the "edacious tooth of duration," but the world-lines of the particles which compose the world-tube whose existence we contemplate are boundless.

Let us look first at the historical struggle and see what speculation is suggested by the attempts to probe the secret of stellar energy. At the outset we must admit that our real knowledge of the mysterious entity from which proceeds all the activity of the universe is sadly deficient. We do not know why a flying ball possesses that with which it flies; we say that the velocity within which its energy resides is only a manifestation of the reality of the principle of least action; but this statement in lieu of an explanation is sorry comfort. In order to examine the source of energy it would be well to have more adequate knowledge of the thing itself, but this information has so far been denied the human race. Thus, not knowing exactly what we seek, we launch upon the hazardous adventure of finding it.

### 2.  What Keeps the Sun Hot?

We pass over the speculations among the ancients which have little to contribute to modern investigation. Descartes in his "Principles" mentions the problem of stellar energy and points out the difference between the heat of the sun and the flame of the candle. The one, he observes, shines undiminishd for many centuries without appreciable need of anything to sustain its activity; the other consumes the material from which it emerges.

Perhaps the first attempt to give a rational explanation of the source of the sun's heat was made by Julius Robert Mayer (1814-1878), who advanced the theory that the heat of the sun was derived from a swarm of meteors continually falling upon its surface. This simple conjecture was easily shown to be untenable, however, because the meteoric swarm necessary to maintain heat for a century would have to be as massive as the earth and would double the mass of the sun in thirty million years. It is obvious that this source must be abandoned, and with it perish all attempts to find a cause exterior to the sun itself.

Another source of energy to be considered is that of combustion, or chemical transformation. A few figures, however, will make it readily apprehended that this suggestion is wholly inadequate. One must first remember the tremendous energy of the sun and the unthinkable ages during which this supply has been pouring into empty space. We who dwell on a tiny object nearly a hundred million miles from the source, presenting with our disk only an infinitesimal target for the rays, may well marvel at the magnitude of the emanating radiation. The radio-active content of the rocks on the surface of our earth makes it highly probable that geological time must be regarded as an epoch not less than 1,500 million years in duration. The age of the sun would probably be greater than this.[1] At the present rate of the sun's radiation this estimate would lead to the conclusion that each gram mass of its huge bulk has radiated into space an amount of energy estimated at $9 \times 10^{16}$ ergs, a total from 100,000 to a million times greater than could be accounted for by the chemical combination of any two atoms.

Herman L. V. von Helmholtz in 1854 advanced his famous contraction hypothesis. In this Helmholtz sought to show that the gravitational potential energy lost as the surface of the sun shrunk inward toward the center would be of sufficient magnitude to account for the radiation loss. This was a brilliant idea and has much interest for philosophical speculation. That the shriveling of the skin of an orange should create radiant energy is a novel idea to most people who think about it. What is the mysterious bond between the intangible concept of potential energy and the more readily apprehended energy of radiation? In their eager search for a source of energy sufficiently large to account for the continuous heat of the sun the astronomers saw in the suggestion of Helmholtz a probable explanation. But that was in a day before the discovery of radio-active elements in the crust of the earth and at a time when the demands of geologists were not so vast as they have recently become. When the modern estimate of the age of the earth is considered it is soon evident that the Helmholtz source is far too small to account for the energy demanded. Even though the sun's mass had been accumu-

[1] H. Jeffreys in "The Earth," New York, sec. ed. (1929), p. 80, says: "Collecting our results, we have found the following: 1. From the eccentricity of the orbit of Mercury, we saw that the whole time since the rupture is probably between $10^9$ and $10^{10}$ years. 2. The ages of the oldest known minerals, found from the lead/uranium ratio, are about $1.3 \times 10^9$ years, and since the geological evidence indicates that some sedimentary rocks are still older, the age of the ocean must exceed $1.3 \times 10^9$ years. 3. The amounts of uranium, thorium, and lead in the crust as a whole indicate a time less than $3 \times 10^9$ years since solidification. The second and third results are in good agreement with the first. The age of the earth is therefore probably between $1.3 \times 10^9$ and $3 \times 10^9$ years."

lated from infinite dispersion, the total energy available would be about two per cent. of the estimate which we have stated above.

### 3.  *Radio-Activity as a Source of Energy.*

With the discovery of radio-active substances new possibilities appeared.  The appearance of uranium in the rocks of the earth did two things.  The tiny atomic clocks extended the age of the earth far beyond the estimates of Lord Kelvin, based on the cooling of its surface, but at the same time they furnished another unsuspected source of energy to account for the greater age.  In a subject where so much is conjecture and where the extrapolation is so enormous compared with the extent of knowledge, one can not be too careful in safeguarding his statements.  Observations which may appear to the reader as having been made as elucidation of fact must be regarded merely as the most tentative estimates advanced for the sake of argument.  Science progresses in this way.  Some daring spirit makes a hypothesis ; others bring to bear upon his proposition their criticisms and data.  Out of the debate in which neither dogmatic assertion nor the weight of authority has the slightest force, a better approximation to the truth may be won.  It is in this spirit that we advance the estimates and arguments of our discussion.  Nothing is certain, although the probability seems higher for one proposition than for another.

There is quite enough energy in radio-active substances to account for any reasonable age of the sun.  If its mass were composed wholly of radium, for example, it could pour out its radiation at the present rate for approximately 5,000 million years ; if uranium were the active agent the life of the sun could be extended to 8,000 million years.  But the difficulty is of another sort.  The life of radium is only 2,800 years.  A sun composed of this magical substance would pour a tremendous flood of energy into space for a brief period and then would lapse into coldness and death.  On the other hand the life of uranium is too great ; its production of energy is slow and no known method can be adduced to change its rate of emission.  The two possibilities of atomic generation of energy are either, first, that it is spontaneous, or second, that it is caused by the stimulus of incident radiation.  Spontaneous generation is what we witness in the case of radium and uranium on the earth ; it is a phenomenon associated only with time ; there is neither acceleration nor retardation of its rate ; the processes that are at its root are automatic ; each second witnesses the liberation of a certain quantity of energy and never more nor less. Arguments may be advanced, however, to show that a certain increase of the disintegration of uranium and radium atoms may take place under tremendous temperatures; but this process is not operative except at temperatures estimated at 120 billion degrees. Hence the search for the source of energy in these disintegration phenomena, at least under present knowledge of radio-active substances, seems to reach a fatal impasse.

## 4. *The Theory of Celestial Alchemy.*

Another suggestion of intriguing possibility was made by J. Perrin in 1919[2] and elaborated by A. S. Eddington in 1920.[3] This involved the energy liberated when a helium atom is formed from atoms of hydrogen or more generally, when any atom is created by the uniting of the constituents of atoms of lower atomic weight. Thus in the case of helium we might regard its atomic weight 4.00126 to be derived from the uniting of the material elements of four hydrogen atoms each of weight 1.0078. But the difference between the mass of four hydrogen atoms and one helium atom is the appreciable amount .029. What happened to this material quantity in the transformation?

You will recall from a previous chapter that one of the consequences of Einstein's theory of relativity was the establishing of a close kinship between matter and energy. We do not have two laws, one that of the conservation of energy, and the other that of the conservation of mass, but the two are fused together into a new law in which mass-energy is together conserved. Hence the loss of mass experienced in the construction of an atom of helium out of four atoms of hydrogen, which in the old theory would be a violation of the law of conservation of mass, must be represented in terms of the new view by the creation of energy. An insignificant amount of mass, however, represents a very significant amount of energy since the energy which emerges from the destruction of mass is equal to the mass multiplied by the square of the velocity of light.

The theory of Perrin and Eddington assumed that the source of stellar energy is to be found in the construction of helium out of hydrogen and the heavier elements in turn out of helium which leads to an estimated source of energy equal to $6.5 \times 10^{18}$ ergs per gram mass. Assuming, then, that the sun was originally a great ball

---

[2]Annales de Physique, vol. 2 (1919), p. 89; also Revue de Mois, vol. 21 (1920), p. 113.

[3]British Association, Cardiff (1920), Address to Section A.

of hydrogen this estimate provides ample energy not only to account for the estimated duration of the epoch of geology, but for a vast future.

Objections of a significant character have been advanced against this theory on the basis that young stars should show a larger amount of hydrogen in their structure than older stars; but there is no evidence that this is actually the case, provided the present theory of the evolution of stars is correct. When one inquires into the mechanism by means of which the four hydrogen atoms are to be brought together for the creation of the new element certain difficulties arise which seem to imperil the stability of the star if they are to be surmounted. However there is much that is attractive in the idea, and one cannot help but agree with Eddington when he says: "But in the formation of helium we have a process which *must* have occurred at some time and place—and where more likely than in the stars where the atoms of primordial matter are for the first time kept in close proximity?"[4]

Do these figures and fancies leave you in a state of bewilderment and fatigue? Does the great majesty of view always experienced in cosmic considerations oppress you? Turn for a moment to the poet's fancy and marvel at the gulf that separates this picture of stellar energy from that which we have been developing above.

> And the sun had on a crown
> Wrought of gilded thistledown,
>     And a scarf of velvet vapor.
> And a raveled rainbow gown;
>     Tossed and lost upon the air
>     Was glossier and flossier
> Than any anywhere.[5]

It is one of the strange phenomena of life that man can turn from the superb views of scientific speculation to the gossamer structure of the poet's dream without rupture of that delicate thread of the aesthetic which runs through poetry and science. There is a common element in the meaningless music of Keat's "Endymion" and the useless artistry of the theorem on inscriptible polygons whose discovery turned the youthful Gauss from language to mathematics.

---

[4] The Internal Constitution of the Stars, Cambridge (1926), p. 296.
[5] James Whitcomb Riley: "The South Wind and the Sun.

## 5. *The Annihilation of Matter.*

Returning from our digression to the problem of cosmic radiation, let us examine a proposal first made by J. H. Jeans in 1904 and elaborated fourteen years later.[6] This hypothesis is in one way the direct opposite of that advocated by Perrin and Eddington, although in another way the two theories involve a similar assumption. Whereas Perrin and Eddington advanced the proposition that the heat of the stars comes from the construction of matter out of one primordial substance, the building of massive elements out of simpler ones, a sort of glorified celestial alchemy, so to speak, Jeans takes the darker view. The source of stellar energy in his hypothesis is the actual annihilation of matter. In some mysterious way a proton and an electron try to occupy the same space. Puff! The two material entities are blotted out. One minus one is zero. A negative charge and a positive charge of the elusive stuff of which lightning is composed must disappear together in that spot where they try to coalesce. What the nature of this union may be, how it can come about over the infinite resistance which would be met when two opposite charges approach one another against the repulsive force varying inversely as the square of the distance, what mechanism would be invoked in the cancellation of matter are problems to be solved by later generations. It would not be kind for one age to solve them all.

But who knows the interior of a star? The picture given below of the mad dance of the atoms would be regarded as better poetry than science, and yet the quotation graces the artistic pages of Eddington's profound treatise on the internal structure of the stars. Who says that there is not work for poets to perform in translating our new knowledge into aesthetic pictures?

The inside of a star is a hurly-burly of atoms, electrons, and ether waves. We have to call to aid the most recent discoveries of atomic physics to follow the intricacies of the dance. We start to explore the inside of a star; we soon find ourselves exploring the inside of an atom. Try to picture the tumult! Dishevelled atoms tear along at 50 miles a second with only a few tatters left of their elaborate cloaks of electrons torn from them in the scrimmage. The lost electrons are speeding a hundred times faster to find new resting-places. Look out! there is nearly a collision as an electron approaches an atomic nucleus; but putting on speed it sweeps round it in a sharp curve. A thousand narrow shaves happen to the electron in $10^{-10}$ of a second; sometimes there is a side-slip at the curve, but

[6]*Nature*, vol. 70 (1904), p. 101; Problems of Cosmology and Stellar Dynamics (1918), p. 287.

the electron still goes on with increased or decreased energy. Then comes a worse slip than usual; the electron is fairly caught and attached to the atom, and its career of freedom is at an end. But only for an instant. Barely has the atom arranged the new scalp on its girdle when a quantum of ether waves runs into it. With a great explosion the electron is off again for further adventures. Elsewhere two of the atoms are meeting in full tilt and rebounding, with further disaster to their scanty remains of vesture.[7]

In the compass of a single brief chapter one can not examine the numerous consequences which follow from one theory or another. There is much controversy over the problem of the source of cosmic energy; many phases must be considered. One may, however, start with the dance of the atoms with some assurance. The depths of every star must be a place of inconceivable activity. Energy from its mysterious source is pouring out through the various layers of the star. The mad rush of the released quanta is everywhere retarded by the envelope of electrons and protons. If Jeans be correct two of the primary particles comprising matter rush together. A quantity of energy is born and starts its journey toward the surface of the star. Perhaps its initial frequency is as great as that of cosmic radiation, which we shall later describe. But in the long journey to the boundary of its prison it must suffer innumerable collisions and reflections. According to the theory of the Compton effect the quantum will continually reduce as it proceeds, and when it emerges from the surface its frequency will be that of one of the beams that fall upon our telescope.

There are various questions to be answered about this birth of energy. Is it accelerated by pressure within the depth of the star? Does temperature affect it? What influence does ionization, that is to say the robbing of electrons from their constituent atoms, have upon the process?

If we follow the annihilation theory the answer seems to be that neither density nor temperature has anything to do with the process. The phenomenon is wholly an atomic one. Jeans estimates that the temperature necessary to affect the process of annihilation would be of the order of 7,500 billion degrees, reaching this figure from theoretical considerations based upon the necessary energy of quanta which might conceivably influence the process. He appeals to the evidence of stellar observation to show that no correlation exists between the absolute luminosity of stars and their internal density.

---

[7]The Internal Constitution of the Stars, Cambridge (1926), p. 19.

With the process of ionization however the matter is very different. A star from which most of the surface electrons have been stripped is going to be hard pressed to annihilate its matter if there are no negative particles to use in destroying the protons. The white dwarf companion of Sirius, for example, which we have previously employed as an example substantiating one consequence of Einstein's law of gravitation, is conceivably a star whose atoms are highly ionized. Its enormous density of 50,000 times that of water may be derived from the fact that its constituent nuclei are closely packed together. The electrons have largely disappeared and hence the process of material annihilation is nearing its end. Jeans points out that the white dwarf stars in general emit an abnormally small amount of radiation, which gives some substantial evidence of the correctness of the annihilation theory.

### 6. *The "Giant-Dwarf" Theory of the Evolution of the Stars.*

In the new astronomy there is a theory of the evolution of the stars which has important bearing upon our problem. A brief sketch of it will give some idea of the numerous elements that must be considered by those who evolve a hypothesis to account for the source of stellar energy.

The stars "numerous as glittering gems of morning dew in the meadows of the sky" are not all of the same size nor have they the same intrinsic brightness. On one hand we find the vast giants, great red gaseous globes of world stuff swinging their tremendous bulks in space; on the other hand we discover the tiny dwarfs, microscopic specks compared with the huge nebulous masses of their larger brethren. Both groups, however, have comparatively low surface luminosity, as is shown from the fact that they are both red and hence belong to the lowest spectral class, known technically as class M. From these two groups, stretching like two arms across the diagram of their luminosity-density distribution, emerge the other stars. To put the matter more intelligibly we mean that if the stars be arranged, first, according to their spectral class ranging from class M, i. e. these of lowest luminosity, to class B, i. e. those of highest luminosity, and second, according to absolute magnitudes, the giants and the dwarfs will be connected by a sequence of other stars. There is, however, a very definite trend of stars along what Eddington calls the "main sequence" (fig. 9), that is to say along the line which connects the tiny dwarfs with the brightest objects in the sky. A similar trend, though less clearly defined, connects the giants with the brighter stars of the main sequence. Between the great giants like Antares and Betelgeuse, the former perhaps 140 million miles in diameter, the latter 250 million miles, and the dwarfs, there are no M type stars for more than six magnitudes. This significant fact, first pointed out by E. Hertzsprung in 1905,[8] was confirmed and added to in 1914 by H. N. Russell,[9] and forms the basis for the "giant-dwarf theory" of stellar evolution.

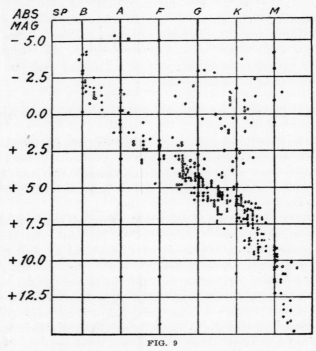

FIG. 9

The luminosity-density distribution of the stars. The line about which the stars seem to cluster is called the "main sequence."

Previous to the advancement of this theory it had been generally regarded by astronomers that the younger stars are the hottest and that evolution in cosmology is a process of decay where the young and luminous bodies gradually radiate their energies into the absorbing vacuum of space. Red stars in this view are at the end of their career and will in the course of time lapse into dark cold masses,

[8]Zeitshrift für Wissenshaftliche Photog., v. 3, p. 442; v. 5, p. 86. Astro. Nachrichten, No. 4296.
[9]Nature (1914). The conclusions of Hertzsprung and Russell were also confirmed by Adams and Joy in 1917, Astrophysical Journal, vol. 46 (1917), p. 313.

derelicts of heaven whose only chance for renewed life would be a cataclysmic encounter with some other astronomical mass.

But another line of argument shows that this may not be the true story at all. In 1870 J. H. Lane (1819-1880) published a paper entitled: "On the Theoretical Temperature of the Sun, under the Hypothesis of a Gaseous Mass maintaining its Volume by its Internal Heat, and depending on the Laws of Gases as Known to Terrestrial Experiment."[10] This fruitful adventure in reflection was further advanced by Lord Kelvin and others and reached its climax in the exhaustive treatise of R. Emden entitled: "Gas Spheres."[11] The essential feature of these investigations was the information derived as to the thermal behavior of a spherical cloud of gas acting under the mutual attraction of its molecules and subject to the well known laws of gases.

Lane reaches the interesting conclusion that a ball of gas as it contracts and radiates its heat will nevertheless grow hotter. The energy gained at the expense of the gravitational potential is not only sufficient to replace the loss due to radiation but will likewise add to the thermal content of the gas.

This striking result has immediate application in the problem of the evolution of stars. Let us assume that a star is assembled out of the molecules of a tenuous nebula of gas. In the course of time these primary particles are drawn closer together and the temperature of the whole mass increases to incandescence. We are witnessing the birth of a giant star. As time goes on the great bulk with its small density contracts still further and the temperature continues to rise. The star advances from its low intensity of radiation as a star of type M into the higher spectral classes of the main sequence. Finally, however, a limit is reached. Its surface luminosity becomes comparatively great; it enters the B class, but its early bulk has now become much reduced. The law of gases no longer holds and further shrinkage must be made at the expense of luminosity. The star is sinking to its death; its energy slowly ebbs and its mass wastes away. Finally it has reduced into a dwarf, and the redness of its light indicates that the vast supply of energy which it had in its former glory as a giant has at last almost wholly disappeared.

---

[10]American Journal of Science, vol. 50 (2) (1870), pp. 57-74.
[11]Gas Kugeln, Teubner, Leipzig (1907).

### 7.  The Mystery of the "White Dwarf" Stars.

There are, however, many difficulties with this picture; the new theory that the source of stellar energy is to be found in some mysterious sub-atomic transformation has set several puzzles for those who would fit it into the giant-dwarf hypothesis. In 1925 Russell offered the ingenious explanation that there is an interrelationship between the contraction hypothesis and the sub-atomic mechanism from which the stars receive their main supply of energy. He assumed a central temperature in the stars of the main sequence equal to thirty million degrees. When this temperature was attained the sub-atomic mechanism would operate, but if for any reason the temperature should fall below this figure then the generation of energy would automatically cease. The surface of the star, however, would continue to radiate energy, and as the supply gradually failed contraction would set in. When this shrinking had proceeded sufficiently far the temperature would rise until the central temperature was again at the critical value. In other words thermal equilibrium was maintained by a kind of celestial thermostat, which shut off the energy when it was too great and released it again when the surface radiation fell below its normal value. The theory is a very clever one but has certain features difficult to reconcile with the hypothesis that sub-atomic radiation can neither be accelerated nor retarded by temperature or density factors.

The theory which Jeans substitutes for the Russell picture has to do with the mechanism of ionization. In his belief the radiation of a star is retarded or accelerated by its degree of ionization. In the case of the white dwarfs where their atoms are conceivably stripped of most of their outer shell of electrons, the possibility of the generation of energy by the coalescing of proton and electron and the annihilation of matter is seriously impaired. Jeans' theory of the process by which the stars shrink from the great giants to the tiny dwarfs is descriptively summarized in the following quotation:

The contraction of the star is accompanied by an increase in its temperature and, by ionizing one ring after another of electrons, this causes the atoms to diminish in size. The star and its atoms contract together, but the star contracts steadily while the atoms, so to speak, contract by jerks. There will be times when the contraction of the star has rather outstripped that of the atoms, so that the atoms are jammed together. The ionization of a new ring of electrons may now relieve the congestion and set the whole structure free again.[12]

[12]Astronomy and Cosmogony, Cambridge (1928), p. 149.

If this be the true picture of the generation of energy within the stars then we are faced with a discontinuous evolution. Transformations from one luminosity to another are not necessarily continuous ones but abrupt changes, quantum jumps of cosmological magnitude, so to speak, by which the star slides from level to level of its existence. "The evolution of the stars must no longer be compared to the steady march of an army through a perfect flat featureless plain, but rather to the movements of an army scrambling down, and possibly at times up, a succession of terraces," says Jeans.[13]

In this suggestive speculation we must give some thought to the mode of creation of the white dwarf stars, whose spectacular feature is their enormous density. How can they fit into the scheme of stellar evolution? It is very evident that they do not conform to the theory outlined above because their abnormal density puts them below and to the left of the main sequence of stars upon the mass-luminosity diagram. They appear to be isolated phenomena, mysterious, inconceivable entities, whose existence seems easier to deny than to believe. How could such massive bodies ever come into being? What mechanism of the celestial cosmos could be brought into play to create matter fifty thousand times as dense as water?

In the picturesque language of Jeans the situation seems to be the following:[14] "the lowest terrace of all, the main sequence, does not lead to a further drop down. It is not bounded on its further side by a slippery unstable slope but by an impenetrable barrier formed by configurations in which the atoms lie as close together as they can be packed. In course of time most stars reach this barrier but cannot cross it, and sidle along it indefinitely. This explains the great concentration of stars along the left-hand edge of the main sequence, against which the stars seem to press like flies against a window-pane."

It is this last observation which leads to Jeans' theory of the creation of the white dwarfs. These stars on the extreme left of the main sequence are close to the edge of equilibrium. At any time factors which sustain their internal structure may give way and the star, falling through the window-pane, will slip down one of the terraces. This catastrophe in more scientific language is to be regarded as due to a stripping of one of the layers of electrons from the constituent atoms and hence to a greater ionizing of the material of the star. Of course the process by which this ionization takes

[13]*Ibid.*, p. 175.
[14]*Ibid.*, p. 175.

place is completely shrouded in mystery, if there actually be any mechanism by which it can be brought about. However the strange concentration of stars along the line representing the main sequence and the peculiar absence of those below it, excepting the mysterious white dwarfs with their abnormal concentrations, give some support to the picture of the English astrophysicist.

At any rate there is poetry in the idea and man, with his feeble tools and his limited insight, can sometimes have high satisfaction in replacing actual knowledge by flights of imagination into the unknown. The same element of melancholy beauty that we find in the lines of the Rubáiyát of Omár Khayyám:

> One moment in Annihilation's Waste,
> One moment, of the Well of Life to taste—
> The stars are setting and the Caravan
> Starts for the Dawn of Nothing—Oh, make haste!

is found again in the following suggestion of Jeans as to the possible fate of man.[15] "It is slightly disconcerting to find that our sun's position in the temperature-luminosity diagram suggests that it is pressing with perilous force against the dangerous edge of the main sequence, so that its collapse into a feebly luminous white dwarf may commence at any moment."

## 8.   *The Cepheid Variables.*

In probing the source of stellar energy we can not wholly omit mention of one of the most mysterious puzzles in the sky. This puzzle is presented by the variation in luminosity of a group of objects known as the Cepheid variables, stars which are at one time much brighter than at a subsequent period. These stars, which occur frequently in the globular clusters and such objects as the Megallanic clouds, appear like breathing spheres, pouring forth great volumes of radiation at one epoch and lesser amounts at another, giant cosmic engines of variable production.

Various theories have been proposed to account for these phenomenal stars, but the one in most general acceptance was proposed by H. Shapley[16] and developed mathematically by Eddington.[17]

[15]Astronomy and Cosmogony, p. 177.

[16]On the Nature and Cause of Cepheid Variation, Astrophys. Journal, vol. 40 (1914), pp. 448-465.   H. C. Plummer had as early as 1913 hinted that the cause of Cepheid variation was to be found in the radial movements of the atmosphere of the star.   See, Monthly Notices, vol. 73 (1912-13), p. 665.

[17]On the Pulsation of a Gaseous Star and the Problem of the Cepheid Variables, Monthly Notices, vol. 79 (1918-19), pp. 2-22; 177-188. See also, The Internal Constitution of the Stars, Cambridge (1926), chap. 8.

This theory assumes that the variable stars, or at least a class of them, are ocular examples of energy in a state of stable oscillation. This *pulsation theory* attributes the phenomenon to a contraction and expansion of the material of the stars under the mutual action of gravitation and thermal forces.

For example suppose that a star like the sun were for some reason compressed. This change would augment internal forces due to gravitational attraction and elastic stress. A considerable amount of energy would be stored in ensuing changes of potential, oh mysterious word! But this disturbance in equilibrium of the various elements of the star would then result in an increase in temperature; the gases would expand and the surface of the star, aided by the pressure of radiation, would be pushed out beyond its normal position of equilibrium. But this expansion could not be indefinitely continued. At some place it would slow down and stop. The gaseous sphere would again come under the control of its gravitational forces. Contraction would set in and hence the great pendulum of energy would swing back and forth as the star oscillates between points of high and low density. There is a great deal of mystery in the vibration of a simple pendulum. How, for example, does the potential energy at the top of the swing, transform into the kinetic energy at the bottom? How much greater then is the difficulty experienced in a contemplation of these great stellar transformations where the exchange takes place between potential and thermal energies!

The impression must not be left, however, that the only alternative in explanation of the Cepheid variables is to be found in energy transformations, although this seems to give a very good account of most of the characteristics of these curious stars. Jeans has advanced the hypothesis that the phenomenon is due to a star in the process of dividing into two components.[18] The elongated ellipsoidal mass that would result in this process of evolution would cause both by its oscillation and by its rotation a very complex type of light curve whose possibilities seem sufficiently numerous to account for a majority if not all of the observed facts. In this brief survey of a large question we can not linger to review the arguments for either theory.

### 9. *The Puzzling Novae or New Stars.*

There are many mysteries in the sky which have to do with processes in which the nature of energy contains the kernel of the

[18]Monthly Notices, vol. 85 (1925), p. 797. See also, Astronomy and Cosmogony, pp. 380-383.

explanation.   In none of these, however, is there more mystery than in the novae, or new stars, which occasionally blaze up in the heavens, burn brilliantly for a short time, and then fade rapidly into oblivion. One of the most interesting of these was the new star of Tycho Brahe, which appeared in November 1572.   The account of its discovery follows from Tycho's own description:[19]

On the preceding year on the eleventh day of the month of November, just after sun set, when according to my custom I was contemplating the stars in the serene heavens, I observed almost overhead that a new and unknown star shone forth, more conspicuously than the others about it.   Since it was almost evident to me, who from boyhood have known all the stars of the sky perfectly (for there is no great difficulty in acquiring this knowledge), that none had ever existed in this part of the sky before, or at least no star of such conspicuous brightness, I was overcome with astonishment at this thing and was not ashamed to doubt the evidence of my eyes. But when the place had been pointed out to others and I observed that they too saw it, then doubt no longer assailed me.

This magnificent spectacle is not an infrequent one in the annals of astronomy, and in our search for the source of stellar energy the truth that may lie in these cosmic cataclysms must not be overlooked. Apparently there exists beneath the surface of stars a tremendous quantity of energy which can be quickly touched.   The expansion of Nova Aquilae, for example, proceeded at the rate of approximately one astronomical unit per day, and the star grew from one of eleventh magnitude to one only a single magnitude less brilliant than Sirius. What strange mechanism could create so suddenly this tremendous burst of energy?   As in everything connected with the ultimate about energy the answer is still in doubt.   The phenomenon might be due to the collision between two stars, but this possibility is ruled out by the fact that more Novae occur than would be accounted for by statistical probability derived from a consideration of the relative distances between stars.   The *detonator theory* advanced by W. H. Pickering[20] assumes that a small object of size not greater than the earth might collide with the star and, sinking below the surface, vastly accelerate its hidden source of energy.   But this is only a guess at best, and the explanation must remain hidden until we learn more about the nature of the elusive activity of the universe.[21]

---

[19]See Tychonis Brahe Opera Omnia, edited by J. L. E. Dreyer (1913), vol. 1, p. 16. De nova et nullius aevi memoria, a mundi exordio prius conspecta stella, quae in fine anni superioris omnium primo apparuit.
[20]A suggested explanation of the phenomena presented by a nova, Popular Astronomy, vol. 26 (1918), pp. 599-607.
[21]For a discussion of these and other theories see A. C. Gifford: The Physical and Chemical Principles that underlie the Interpretation of Novae, Scientia, vol. 49 (1931), pp. 169-182.

### 10. *What Happens to Radiant Energy?*

In summarizing the results of preceding paragraphs we must be impressed with the mystery that envelops the concept of energy. In other chapters we have found that its relationship with the ether is strangely perplexing and that every approach leads to metaphysical concepts. In the present discussion we have found the source of energy in the stars to be similarly difficult. Our present choice lies between two hypotheses: The first affirms that the source of energy is in the manufacture of higher forms of matter from lower forms, in the transmutation of the elements, in the creation of helium out of hydrogen by some process whose nature is entirely obscure. The second hypothesis presents the possibility of the annihilation of matter. Instead of being a creative process the generator of stellar heat is found in the destruction of material things. The interiors of stars are great annihilating engines, where conditions exist favorable to the coalescing of positive protons and negative electrons. Each theory, however, rests upon the assumption that matter, which disappears either in the creative or destructive processes is transformed into energy according to Einstein's law.

We turn next to a consideration of the second problem set by the present chapter, which may throw some light upon the mystery of solar radiation. This second question has to do with the destiny of radiation. Where do these vast stores of energy go which pour so steadily from the surfaces of the stars? If the universe be finite in the dictum of Einstein and de Sitter what becomes of the energy of radiation? Is it building up a new universe at some remote distance from the boundary of the stars? Does it transform again into matter by a process as mysterious as the mechanism by which it is generated in the sun? Are the vast cold regions of interstellar space which seem the very antithesis of the interior of stars the laboratory within which radiant energy is recondensed into the atoms from the annihilation of which it emerged?

Curiously enough our problem starts with a very simple question and one which at first sight seems inconceivably remote from cosmic speculation. What is the thief that steals the charge from an electroscope? An electroscope is an elementary instrument consisting of a metal rod supported on a cork or other insulating material and carrying two leaves of gold foil suspended from its lower end, the leaves being enclosed in a glass vessel. If a charge of electricity be placed upon the foil the leaves will immediately diverge, due to the repulsive action of the charge.

Now it had been observed for a long time that if a charged electroscope be sealed and set aside the leaves of the device would gradually draw together again. Some thief was abroad in the land. The long search to find this thief is one of the romances of modern scientific research.

### 11.   *The Discovery of Cosmic Radiation.*

Study of the problem of cosmic radiation began in 1903, when it was observed by several British physicists[22] that the leakage from an electroscope was reduced by as much as thirty per cent. by enclosing the instrument within an air-tight metal box several centimeters in thickness. This was interpreted to mean that the loss of charge experienced by the metal foil of the instrument was due to the ionizing of the air by some unknown radiation which was sufficiently *hard,* that is to say, penetrating, so that it could pass through the metal covering surrounding the electroscope. The question then was asked : What is the nature of this mysterious radiation and whence does it come ?

The first speculation turned to the possibility that the rays were emanating from radio-active elements in the earth and were perhaps identical with the gamma rays of radium. In order to test this hypothesis A. Gockel, a Swiss physicist,[23] took an enclosed electroscope up with him in a balloon to a height of 13,000 feet and found that the rate of discharge at this elevation was not significantly different from that found at the surface of the earth. The source of the mysterious ray thus appeared to be located in the upper atmosphere or beyond it.

The intriguing possibilities awakened by this report struck fire in the imaginations of the physicists, and from 1911 to 1914 the balloon measurements of Gockel were repeated by V. F. Hess,[24] a Swiss physicist, and W. Kolhörster,[25] a German. The latter attained a height of 5.6 miles and reported that the radiation affecting the electroscope first decreased slightly and then increased in a marked

[22]J. C. McLennan and E. F. Burton: Some Experiments on the Electrical Conductivity of Atmospheric Air, Physical Review, vol. 16 (1903), pp. 184-192. E. Rutherford and H. L. Cooke: A Penetrating Radiation from the Earth's Surface, vol. 16 (1903), p. 183.

[23]Observation of Atmospheric Electricity from a Balloon, Phys. Zeitschrift, vol. 11 (1910), pp. 280-282.

[24]Measurement of the Earth's Penetrating Radiation on a Balloon, Akad. Wiss., Wien, Berichte, 120, 2a, pp. 1575-1585; also Phys. Zeitschrift, vol. 12 (1911), p. 998; vol. 13 (1912), p. 1084.

[25]Penetrating Atmospheric Radiation, Phys. Zeitschrift, vol. 14 (1913), pp. 1066-1069; 1153-1155.

manner, attaining, at the flight's highest point, a value eight times that at the surface of the earth.[26]

The war then put an end to the experimental work on this problem, but the investigation was resumed by R. A. Millikan and I. S. Bowen in the spring of 1922.[27] These men sent up sounding balloons equipped with specially constructed electroscopes to altitudes as great as ten miles. To their surprise they found that the rate of discharge, while it increased with altitude, as had been reported by the European investigators, was very much less than that expected. Although at the great altitudes attained by their apparatus only twelve per cent. of the atmosphere was above the electroscopes to serve as a screen for the bombarding radiation, the acceleration of discharge of the instruments was only slightly greater than that at lower elevations. The conclusion derived from this was that the rays under investigation were of tremendous penetrating power, much greater probably than that of any heretofore known radiation.

In the meantime Kolhörster[28] had continued his researches carrying them on this time in holes and crevasses in Alpine glaciers. From the results thus obtained he had very materially reduced his estimate of the alteration of the rate of discharge with altitude. This coincided with further discoveries made by Millikan and R. Otis,[29] who experimented with the phenomenon at the top of Pikes Peak and decided that the cosmic rays, if they existed at all, must be of very different character from any previously known to science.

The next move in the adventure was to find some critical method by means of which the nature and reality of the rays could be unequivocally determined. Millikan, in collaboration with Harvey Cameron, decided to seek this proof in the waters of some deep snowfed lake whose waters would be free from any radio-active constituent which might interfere with the experiment.[30] Such a body of water was found in beautiful Muir Lake (11,800 feet high) just under the brow of Mount Whitney in the Sierra Nevada range of Southern California.

Here in the heart of the mountains the great truth was revealed. During the last ten days of August, 1925, the two experimenters

[26]See also for an account complete to 1915, A. Gockel: The Penetrating Radiation Present in the Atmosphere, Phys. Zeitschrift, vol. 16 (1915), pp. 345-352.
[27]High Frequency Rays of Cosmic Origin, I. Sounding Balloon Observations at Extreme Altitudes, Phys. Review, vol. 27 (2) (1926), pp. 353-361.
[28]Intensity and direction Measurements of Penetrating Radiation, Preuss. Akad. Wisss., Berlin, Sitzungsberichte, vol. 34 (1923), pp. 366-377.
[29]High Frequency Rays of Cosmic Origin, II. Mountain Peak and Airplane Observation, Phys. Review, vol. 27 (1926), pp. 645-658.
[30]High Frequency Rays of Cosmic Origin, III. Measurements in Snowfed lakes at high Altitudes, Phys. Review, vol. 28 (1926), pp. 851-868.

lowered their electroscopes into the waters of the lake to varying depths down to 67 feet. Is there not poetry in the adventure? "I have stolen the golden vases of the Egyptians," cried Kepler in the exultation of his discovery; is there less thrill for us in the simple language of the report of the American experimenters:

*"Our experiments brought to light altogether unambiguously a radiation of such extraordinary penetrating power that the electroscope-readings kept decreasing down to a depth of 50 feet below the surface."*[31]

The results of the experiment showed that a radiation of sufficient penetrating power to pass through the depths of our atmosphere and through fifty feet of water besides, is bombarding the surface of our earth from some source within the mysterious region known as interstellar space. This penetration is equivalent to a depth of 73 feet of water, the atmosphere being estimated as equivalent to 23 feet of water. This statement translated into other terms means that these rays would exhibit their activity through six feet of lead. When one reflects that the most penetrating X-rays used in our hospitals will not pass through a half-inch of lead the marvelous character of the new radiation is strikingly revealed. Where do these strange cosmic rays come from? What activity of nature is capable of creating them? Are they the ultimate in penetrating power? Do we find ourselves with them at the lower limit of radiation frequencies, just as at 273 degrees below zero centigrade we attain the lowest temperature and at 186,000 miles per second we consider the ultimate velocity? Have we surprised from nature another limiting value for her activities?

In order to check their beautiful conclusion the experimenters next moved to Lake Arrowhead, an expanse of water in the San Bernardino mountains, 300 miles south of Muir Lake and 6,700 feet lower in altitude. The experiments were again repeated and identical results obtained when the corrections were made for the absorbing power of the blanket of air represented by the difference between the two altitudes. The report says:

*"Within the limits of observational error, every reading in Arrowhead Lake corresponded to a reading 6 feet farther down in Muir Lake, thus showing that the rays do come in definitely from above, and that their origin is entirely outside the layer of atmosphere between the levels of the two lakes."*[32]

---

[31]Loc. cit., p. 855; see also, Proceedings of the National Academy of Sciences, vol. 12 (1926), p. 51.

[32]Loc. cit., p. 856; see also, Proceedings of the National Academy, loc. cit., p. 52.

But there were still several questions to be answered. From what part of the sky do these penetrating rays come in the greatest abundance? Is it from the concentration of stars which we call the Milky Way? Are the rays manifestations of energy transformations on the surface or within the depth of the stars or have they, perhaps, a more mysterious origin in the dark cold recesses of space itself?

These interesting questions were next explored.[33] The scientists whose adventures we are describing decided to go to the lakes of the high Andes in South America. Readings similar to those taken at Muir and Arrowhead Lakes in the northern hemisphere were made in Lake Miguilla, near Caracoles, Bolivia, and in Lake Titicaca. The former is a snow-fed lake 125 feet deep at an altitude of 15,000 feet and is entirely surrounded by mountains. This was a particularly favorable situation for the investigation of the source of cosmic rays because the mountains formed a perfect screen against radiations which might be generated by the lightning in thunder storms, a possible cause of the rays.

The results obtained in South America agree substantially with those found in California and point unquestionably to the cosmic origin of the radiation. The rays enter the atmosphere of the earth with undiminished intensity both night and day from all directions.

Criticism of these conclusions, particularly the arguments of Bothe and Kolhörster (Zeitschrift für Physik, vol. 56 (1929), p. 751) advanced to show that the phenomena attributed to cosmic radiation may be due to high speed electrons, led Millikan to essay a trip to the polar regions to investigate the matter further. His conclusions substantiate his original findings and he states: "Since the portion of the sky from which the rays come at Churchill (730 miles due south of the North pole on the west side of Hudson Bay) is quite different from that at Pasadena, the indications of these experiments are, then, First, *that the cosmic rays enter the earth uniformly from all portions of the sky;* Second, *that they consist as they enter the earth's atmosphere of ether waves, not of electrons.*"[34]

Speculations as to the place of their origin naturally directed attention to the question whether or not the position of the Milky Way had any influence upon the electroscope discharge. This question had previously been investigated by Kolhörster,[35] who reported that at an altitude of 11,650 feet the presence of the Milky Way overhead

[33]High Altitude Tests on the Geographical, Directional, and Spectral Distribution of Cosmic Rays, Phys. Review, vol. 31 (1928), pp. 163-173.
[34]On the Question of the Constancy of the Cosmic Radiation and the Relation of these Rays to Meteorology, Physical Review, vol. 36 (1930), pp. 1595-1603.
[35]Sitzungsberichte der Preus. Akad., vol. 34 (1923), p. 366.

caused an increase of approximately fifteen per cent. in the intensity of the radiation, although he failed to detect such variation at sea level. The experiment was repeated by Millikan and Cameron in a pocket in the mountains at a height of 15,400 feet, where the Milky Way was practically out of sight for four hours and a half. These experimenters reached the conclusion that the influence either of acceleration or diminution of the intensity to be traced to the Milky Way is at most very slight.

### 12.  *The Origin of Cosmic Radiation*

Here then is an intriguing fact. Somewhere in interstellar space there originates the most intense radiation known to man. The penetrating power of these rays is far greater than that which leaves the surface of the sun or any of the stars. It exceeds in hardness the gamma rays of radium. It stands at the bottom of the great spectrum of radiation which man has won for himself both ways from the infinitesimal band of visible light through which he apprehends the universe. It is well worth our while to meditate for a few moments occasionally upon the tiny band of vibration which limits our experience and to reflect upon the wonders that might be revealed to us if we could survey the world from different points on the spectrum. Is there not much to captivate our imagination in the following brief table of the conquest of man in these recent years of science?

| *Character of the Radiation* | *Its Wave Length* |
| --- | --- |
| Long electromagnetic waves | Hundreds of miles to 25,600 meters. |
| Waves used in wireless telegraphy | 25,600 to 400 meters. |
| Waves in wireless telephony | 1,000 to 40 meters. |
| Short electromagnetic waves | 40 meters to .03 centimeter. |
| Heat waves | .03 cm. to 70 millionths of a centimeter. |
| Visible light | 70 to 35 millionths cm. |
| Ultra-violet light | 35 to 1.3 millionths cm. |
| X-rays | 450 to 1 thousand millionths cm. |
| Gamma rays of radium | 1 thousand millionth cm. to 560 million millionths cm. |
| Cosmic radiation | 6.7 to 4.0 million millionths cm. |

What a marvelous picture of the activity of nature is this! And what mystifying properties must a medium have which can transmit radiations from the infinitesimal lengths of cosmic radiation to the tremendous lengths at the other end of the spectrum! What strange accident in the evolution of the eye of man picked out that tiny band between the ultra-violet and the infra-red in order to interpret the world of nature to the chemistry of the human mind? These are questions about which we may perpetually marvel, but the solution of which we are agnostic enough to believe may never be discovered.

After the reality of cosmic radiation had been determined and the remarkable penetrating powers exhibited as fact, speculation centered around the question of its cause. W. D. MacMillan, who previous to the discovery of the rays had wondered about the strange fact that the free energy of the universe does not appear to exhaust itself according to the second law of thermodynamics, saw in the new radiation an explanation.[36] Here was evidence that matter was being re-created from the energy radiated by the stars. The intense cold of interstellar space was the laboratory within which electrons and protons could be produced from the radiation into which they had been transformed by the intense heat of the stars.

This fruitful idea was explored by Millikan and Cameron in October, 1929,[37] and the conclusion reached that the phenomenon of cosmic radiation can be accounted for theoretically by the assumption of an atom building process going on in interstellar space. Even more than that it seems impossible, in the present state of physical science, to conceive of any other process than that of atom building which would lead to the creation of radiation of the kind discovered. Here in the intense cold of space where the temperature is conceivably at the absolute zero, a situation impossible to attain in earthly laboratories, the process of condensing radiant energy into ponderable matter is taking place. The theory that the source of stellar energy is an annihilation process in which proton cancels electron is here found to have its converse. There exist in nature two unknown cosmic mechanisms by means of which radiant energy can be converted into matter and matter can be reconverted into energy. One requires the intense heat and tremendous activity of the atoms; the other takes place in the unimaginable conditions found where energy is at its lowest value.

One must realize that in all of this we indulge in reckless speculation. Nothing is certain save the fact of the existence of the cosmic rays. In this beautiful synthesis we are assuming that Ein-

[36]The New Cosmology, Scientific American, vol. 134 (1926), pp. 310-311; see also: Stellar Evolution, Astrophys. Journal, vol. 48 (1918), pp. 35-49.
[37]The Origin of the Cosmic Rays, Phys. Review, vol. 32 (1928), pp. 533-557.

stein's law of the equivalence of matter and energy is true; we are assuming the validity of laws about the loss of mass in the construction of helium out of hydrogen and of the higher elements out of the lower, laws which have been derived empirically as the most probable explanation of processes observed in the laboratory. There are incontestible facts, however, which await explanation. There is some source of unimaginable power within the interior of stars; else why can they continue to burn for countless centuries? And if this source of energy be derived from the destruction of matter why has not all material substance long since wasted away?

Here then is a partial answer to the question proposed in the first chapter. The universe is not necessarily running down. In the macrocosm the second law of thermodynamics is not necessarily true. The universe may be a vast perpetual motion machine, and what it loses in one place as energy it may regain as matter; what recondenses in the cold regions of space as matter may be collected again into the stars by means of the mysterious action of space-time which we call, in our ignorance, the force of gravitation. Has the mind of man ever achieved a more stimulating or hopeful theory than this?

# CHAPTER XII.

## WHAT SHALL WE BELIEVE?

### 1. *Man and the Key-Hole.*

IN THE preceding chapters of the book we have traced the origin of man's philosophical speculations where they turned to the world of matter, space, time, and the activity known as energy. We have explored the methods that man has used to probe the mysteries; we have reviewed the things that he has discovered, the instruments that he has used, the speculations that have arisen in his attempts to synthesize his new knowledge.

But we must turn at last to that phase of the philosophical problem which is after all the most important. What is man's relation to the universe of matter, energy, and their geometrical framework of four dimensions? What part has the human mechanism in the cosmic scheme? What is man to believe about the mysteries which have been set forth in earlier chapters?

Man's experience is vastly limited. He peers into the unknown reality about him through a tiny key-hole. We have exhibited the size of this key-hole in comparison with the great gate in the case of radiation. There the infinitesimal slit is less than a span of fifty millionths of a centimeter, wholly insignificant in comparison with the total range stretching from the inconceivably small wave length of cosmic radiation to electromagnetic waves hundreds of miles in extent. We feel like poor Alice after she had found the golden key that unlocked the door into fairyland:

Alice opened the door and found that it led into a small passage, not much larger than a rat-hole; she knelt down and looked along the passage into the loveliest garden you ever saw. How she longed to get out of that dark hall, and wander about among those beds of bright flowers and those cool fountains, but she could not even get her head through the doorway; "and even if my head *would* go through," thought poor Alice, "it would be of very little use without my shoulders. Oh, how I wish I could shut up like a telescope! I think I could, if I only knew how to begin.

How is man to attain knowledge of reality through such a tiny crack in the wall of nature? It perpetually amazes us to think that he has been able to see so far and to probe so deep.

In one sense the question what is the nature of reality, is but the phrasing of another. What is the nature of man who asks the question? It will be amusing if not instructive to look at a few of the estimates of ourselves.

"Man is a two legged animal without feathers,"[1] said Plato; which so aroused the disgust of Pascal that he himself essayed a definition.[2] "What a chimera, then, is man! what a novelty, what a monster, what a chaos, what a subject of contradiction; what a prodigy! A judge of all things, feeble worm of the earth, depositary of the truth, cloaca of uncertainty and error, the glory and shame of the universe." Does this satisfy any more than the words of Plato? Turn then to the anthropologists. They, in the words of A. R. Wallace, place man apart, "as not only the head and culminating point of the grand series of organic nature, but as in some degree a new and distinct order of being."

Can the psychologists and philosophers tell us more? They are evasive; they will not give a definition: they will only cite characteristic attributes and behaviours of the assemblage of atoms that constitute the being. In the words of William James we find:[3] *In its widest possible sense, however, a man's Self is the sum total of all that he can call his,* not only his body and his psychic powers, but his clothes, and his house, his wife and children, his ancestors and friends, his reputation and works, his lands and horses, and yacht and bank account." The behavourist school would have us think in the summary of J. B. Watson: "Our personality is thus the result of what we start with and what we have lived through. It is the 'reaction mass' as a whole."[4]

In our despair we turn to the literary appraisal. "What a piece of work is a man!" mused Hamlet, "how noble in reason! how infinite in faculty! in form and moving how express and admirable! in action how like an angel! in apprehension how like a god! the beauty of the world! the paragon of animals! And yet, to me, what is this quintessence of dust?"[5]

Alexander Pope in his celebrated "Essay on Man" would have us regard the problem thus:[6]

---

[1]Man is the plumeless genus of bipeds, birds are the plumed. Politicus, 266. See also Diogenes Laertius: Life of Diogenes, vi.

[2]Thoughts, chap. 10.

[3]Principles of Psychology, vol. 1 (1890), p. 291.

[4]Psychology from the Standpoint of a Behaviorist, Philadelphia (1919), p. 420.

[5]Act 2, scene 2, l. 316.

[6]Epistle 2, l. 3.

Plac'd on this isthmus of a middle state,
A being darkly wise, and rudely great:
With too much knowledge for the skeptic side,
With too much weakness for the Stoic's pride,
He hangs between; in doubt to act, or rest;
In doubt to deem himself a God, or beast;
In doubt his mind or body to prefer;
Born but to die, and reas'ning but to err:
Alike in ignorance, his reason such,
Whether he thinks too little or too much:
Chaos of thought and passion, all confus'd;
Still by himself abus'd or disabus'd;
Created half to rise, and half to fall;
Great lord of all things, yet a prey to all;
Sole judge of truth, in endless error hurl'd:
The glory, jest, and riddle of the world!

Perhaps we can not go beyond these estimates and perhaps it is impossible for man to explain his nature to himself. At bottom the mystery of mind may be akin to the mystery of the ether. The energy which actuates the one may be the same elusive stuff which led us from rational concepts into the metaphysical behaviour of Schrödinger's psi.

Avoiding these esoteric thoughts, however, we prefer to regard man as a mechanism, mysterious though the mind-stuff which moves it may be, that peers into the unknown through five tiny cracks in the wall dividing sensuous perception from the thing perceived. That which is designated under the psychologist's term of behaviour means to us only the power to assemble world-points into world-lines and world-lines into the world-tubes along which our knowledge moves. This is the mechanism that wants to explore the meaning of reality. This is the thing that would look into the unknown and the unknowable,—an entity which receives stimuli from five insignificant sources and which has the mysterious power of classification and arrangement. Man is characterized by his ability to distinguish between cause and effect, to recognize curious recurrences in inanimate things and to codify them into the system of science. Is it any wonder that a being so circumscribed by ignorance, with vision so narrow and with entrances to truth so restricted, should be puzzled at what he finds? The wonder would be many times multiplied were it found that all stimuli which came through the narrow crevices of perception could be joined into world-tubes that would everywhere accord with rational expectation.

In the final summary we must review the great speculative material through which we have passed. We must see what it means in terms understandable to this mysterious creature who has been able to feel so marvelously along the great spectrum of radiation. We are like the three blind men who, according to the tale, fell to examining an elephant that they had met on their travels. The first, who felt of its leg exclaimed: "Why the thing is like a tree"; the second, whose examination began with the trunk, cried out: "No, you are wrong; the thing resembles a serpent"; the third who had grasped the elephant's tail, said: "Both of you err; this thing is like a rope." Any problem of epistemology approached from a different point of view must lead to similar divergent opinions. We are examining the elephant in the dark.

## 2.  Is Nature Continuous or Atomic?

In our proposed summary let us first turn to man as the subjective philosopher. This was his earliest rôle and one in which he has perhaps been the most successful. It reaches its highest point with that great race of men who began their thought near the bright waters of the Aegean, where,

> Again his waves in milder tints unfold,
> Their long array of sapphire and of gold,
> Mixed with the shades of many a distant isle,
> That frown—where gentler ocean seems to smile."[7]

The struggle in subjective thought has been waged around the question: Is nature continuous or is nature atomic? We find among the geometers a curious blending of the two concepts, and this attempt to mingle two fundamentally different modes of thinking has reached fruition in the bewildering postulates of the mathematical theory of point-sets.

Euclid with a subtlety that has few counterparts in the history of thought began with a point. "Three cheers," cried the atomists. But a point, Euclid went on to say, has neither breadth, width, nor thickness. Shouts of delight from the adherents of continuity! What better quantity would one wish for if he desired to picture a continuous substratum for reality.

---

[7]Byron's The Corsair, Canto 3, ll. 1219-1222.

The material ether of the nineteenth century was on the contrary very far from furnishing a continuous medium. As soon as the concepts of elasticity or of density were invoked an atomistic philosophy of nature was necessarily postulated. However the wraith of the ether that remains in the twentieth century, if it may be thought of in terms of reality at all, is fully as continuous as the psi-function of the wave mechanics. And less metaphysically than this, a medium, material or otherwise, which is capable of supporting undulations as small as those forced upon us by the discovery of cosmic radiation has aspects of continuity.

The modern theory of the quanta of energy and of the electrons and protons of matter again modifies the answer. The full atomistic philosophy emerges. Even time itself may share the concept, and the psychologist's picture of "the flow of duration" is a statistical illusion occasioned merely by insufficient refinement of sensuous experience.

But the behaviour of light in space, the sharp diffraction patterns of the laboratory, are arguments which the atomist must yield to his opponents.

The atomist deals in integers; his theories must ultimately be reduced to whole numbers; he must be able to count the points on a line and enumerate the atoms in a piece of matter. His universe is bounded in fundamental ways; it is broken up into units; his spatial measure must have a lower limit be it the electron or be it something smaller; his time must be ticked off in multiples of the vibrations of atomic clocks, in terms of the rate of disintegration of heavy atoms such as uranium and radium. Quantities can be sorted and arranged. There is a first thing and a last thing in every sequence. The paradoxes of Zeno have no place in the philosophy of the atomist. Achilles passes over a finite number of electrons and his rate of passing must be measured in terms of the atomic units of time. There are no points without breadth, thickness, and width. These are but fairies of the intellect, from whose activities beautiful subjective theories may be evolved. No deduction which depends wholly upon the assumption of "absence of dimension" will have meaning in his world of physics.

On the contrary, the continuist affirms that the picture of reality is a flow, that the substratum of the universe can not be divided into unitary particles, that there is no categorical imperative to define the first and last of any sequence. The succession of points in a straight line is non-denumerable; the integers are insufficient to count the quantities in the universe. The continuists may well have admitted a shaken faith when the discovery of cathode rays pointed unmistakably to the atomic nature of matter and of electricity; but the more recent argument is on their side. The mystery of radiation, once it has emerged from matter as a quantum, is again defined by a continuous function. The medium in which the undulation takes place has, to be sure, lost precise meaning, but the continuous function and the evidence of diffraction remain as powerful arguments as before.

It is instructive to debate these matters with others. The arguments seem to pile up on both sides. One almost believes that both points of view may be true. Energy is an undulation in a continuous ether and yet possesses atomic properties. Matter is a group of indivisible electrons and protons and yet behaves as a train of waves. There is much upon which to reflect in the following argument which Alice had with a certain wise man of antiquity. The author has not been able to find this adventure in the treatises of Lewis Carroll. Hence one must regard the account as apocryphal:

Alice had just come to an opening in the forest when she saw a man standing silently by the side of a stile.

"What a homely face he has," thought Alice to herself.

The man regarded her thoughtfully for a few moments and then asked: "Are you going far, Alice?"

This was puzzling. "How do you know my name?" she inquired politely.

The man smiled kindly. "To be regarded as having wisdom, my dear, one always asks questions but never answers any."

"How wise my teacher must be, then," thought Allce to herself.

The stranger leaned against the side of the stile and for some time seemed to be in deep thought.

"I wonder whether you know anything?" he suddenly asked regarding her closely.

Alice found herself growing angry. What disagreeable people one sometimes met. "Of course I do," she said rather more sharply than she had intended to, "everybody knows something."

"Then perhaps you can tell me how much two and two are?"

"Why four, of course."

"And perhaps you also know what a point is?"

"How silly," thought Alice, but not wishing to appear impolite she replied: "A point is a place which has no dimension."

"Very good," said the stranger approvingly. "And what would you say two points and two points are?"

"Dear me," thought Alice, "what a disagreeable person!"

"Do you get along well in your lessons, my dear?" the stranger went on in the friendliest tones without seeming to notice her embarrassment.

"I don't do very well in geography," admitted Alice slowly. "I missed half the questions in my last test."

"That was too bad," said the man sympathetically, but went on in a more hopeful voice; "however, that is better than nothing."

"Nothing is better than perfect," said Alice.

"And so to miss half the questions is better than to get them all?" suggested the stranger.

"Oh dear me," said Alice in dismay. "I should have said zero."

"Then zero is not nothing?" asked the man in an eager voice.

"Of course not," replied Alice doubtfully.

"Then zero must be something?"

Before Alice could reply to this unpleasant question there was a sudden noise behind them. The stranger looked up quickly and a painful expression appeared on his face.

"I have enjoyed our conversation very much, my dear," he said hastily, "but I have suddenly recalled an engagement with the Queen on the croquet grounds. Shall I see you there?"

Without waiting for a reply he started off swiftly into the forest. Alice looked around to find the cause of his dismay and saw a woman hastening in her direction.

"Have you seen Socrates, my dear?" she asked between breaths; "I must see that he gets into his new clothes for the Queen's tournament. He is so absent minded."

"I wonder why?" thought Alice to herself.

The question between the two schools of thought is in the existence of a smallest unit. Shall we believe with MacMillan that "the sequence of physical units is infinite both ways. That is to say, there is no largest physical unit and there is no smallest one," or shall we share with Eddington the belief that "we can more readily admit that the laws of the actual world are specialized by the accidental circumstances of a particular number of particles occurring in it, than that they are specialized by the same number occurring as a mysterious ratio in the fine-grained structure of the continuum."

Shall we essay an answer? It would be folly. The delight in the new physics is not to be found in the ability which it gives us to answer questions, nor in its machines, nor in its ameliorating inventions; but rather the charm is derived from the questions which it presents and the new experiments that it finds with which to bewilder us. Modern philosophy differs from the old in this fact: it makes us more cautious in arriving at conclusions. We dare not set up absolute systems of thought; we dare not answer yea or nay to the question of the atomism of nature; we must move with circumspection in framing postulates of normal intuition. The genius of Einstein was able to show us how to avoid the dilemma which required us to believe that the earth had an absolute motion in space and yet that the motion could not be detected. But the question whether nature is continuous or atomic can scarcely be answered at the present stage of philosophy and experimental science. Perhaps the question will ultimately prove to have no meaning at all.

### 3.  Geometry and Nature.

The second rationalistic concept with which the Greeks struggled and which they passed on to their successors is the concept of space and time. That is to say, the Greeks studied the subject of geometry. We commonly regard geometry as a painful discipline of the school room, with a disagreeable maze of intersecting lines and bothersome angles from which unimportant truths are to be discovered. Nothing is further from the truth. Geometry is a way of surveying the substratum of nature. "Geometry, no doubt, is the knowledge of what externally exists," said Plato; "Then, my noble friend, geometry will draw the soul towards truth, and create the mind of philosophy, and raise up that which is now unhappily allowed to fall down."[8]

In this noble subject one finds the pure rationalistic powers of man at their highest. In it he has learned to postulate. From a contemplation of its history he has learned the one great truth: that there is probably no absolute truth. All knowledge is deduction from a set of beliefs. You and I belong to the same intellectual faith because there is accord between our systems of postulates. Or if we differ, I may be able to point out that your postulate that the earth was created by a miraculous event ten thousand years ago is controverted by the evidences of geology. You, however, may counter by demanding that I show proof that the world existed prior to yesterday, or that it has ever had objective existence. These matters of belief are derived from a certain instinctive weighing of probabilities and the assumption that there is a continuity in the acts of nature.

"Geometry in every proposition speaks a language which experience never dares to utter; and indeed of which she but half comprehends the meaning," said William Whewell. "Experience sees that the assertions are true, but she sees not how profound and absolute is their truth."[9]  The subjective model which geometry constructs is

---

[8]The Republic, book 7.
[9]The Philosophy of the Inductive Sciences, London (1858), pt. 1, bk. 1, chap. 6, sec. 1.

the best example that man has found to exhibit the nature of postulates. The mind, unaided by laboratory experiment, may probe a long way into the nature of itself, but finally there is a limit. A time comes when a choice must be made and this choice can not be made fortuitously. This is exhibited in man's three geometries.

A line is drawn and a point is given exterior to it. What shall we assume with regard to the number of lines that can be constructed through the point so as to be parallel to the given line? The mind, exploring itself, can find no answer. Ingenious though the proofs have been to show that the answer is "one," they are all fallacious. Pure logic is circumvented. There is no rationalistic imperative that says we must choose none, one, or many. We explore the matter in its intricate windings and we arrive at the mystical and mysterious concept of infinity. We invent a symbol for it as though it were a reality. But the enigma is not solved by any exploration of infinity. Finally we are led in our subjective puzzle to affirm that all the answers are equally logical. If we feel that it is satisfactory to postulate one as the answer, we follow Euclid; if "none" be better suited to our needs, we are disciples of Riemann; otherwise we belong to the faith of Lobachevski and Bolyai. There is great beauty in this knowledge, and one can see why the mathematicians of the early nineteenth century were greatly stirred by the discovery. The rationalistic intellect is free. It can postulate its points without dimensions, its continuous universe, its infinity, its three geometries. There is no necessity to force one doctrine rather than another. One is guided by his own free will in making the original assumptions. It is only thereafter that he must become obedient to a higher discipline.

The intellectual excitement of the twentieth century has centered around another discovery which has a curious relationship with these ideals. "Plato said that God geometrizes continually" affirmed Plutarch.[10] This idea has reached fruition in the modern period. One way of paraphrasing Einstein's theories would be to say that: "Nature is the great geometer." We can look at the world of reality in terms of this subjective edifice which the Greeks founded and which modern minds have explored. We need merely add the fourth dimension of time. With this addition the metric of geometry, the distance between two points, is sufficient to tell us the story of the activity of nature. Subjective intuition was not enough to give us a choice in the basic postulates; but a casual survey of some experi-

---

[10]Convivialium dispectationum, book 8, l. 2.

mental facts unlocks the mystery. We can make an objective choice if we are willing to throw the difficulties back, not upon the mystery of infinity, but upon physical assumption. Light, for example, is the ultimate velocity.

The law of gravitation is in one sense merely an agent to aid us in geometrizing. It helps us to decide which of the three logical edifices to occupy. The law of gravitation is an aspect of space-time; its reality is in the subjective creation; it resides in a set of equations.

These observations receive interesting confirmation in the recent paper of Einstein entitled: "Regarding a Unified Field Theory," which has created so much excitement among laymen. It is one of the curiosities of this strange race of men that they will pass over, without the evidence of any interest, important theories and discoveries comparatively easy to comprehend and yet will struggle in vain to understand an abstract question which requires the keenest penetration of the expert. It is small wonder that Einstein was amazed at the American reception of his abstract paper, which could never in a thousand years be made comprehensible to the average lay mind. Perhaps the explanation is to be found in the fact that all of us have a latent awareness of the great mystery of existence and we eagerly grasp at the thoughts of one who can see into the darkness further than we shall ever be able to see.

The paper of Einstein derives its interest for us here in its geometrical point of view. What is the mystery of gravitation? What is the meaning of electro-magnetism? The answer stirs us. Both mysteries can be traced to an aspect of Riemannian geometry. Their equations can be derived from a manner of regarding parallelism. There is a certain sense of awe aroused in us when we look at the two equations, simple in appearance, which Einstein assures us govern respectively the electromagnetic and the gravitational fields. But the statement is more impressive when we realize that these equations are derived from the modern development of the subjective thoughts of the ancient Greeks. The activity of reality and the logical exploration of human intellect are seen to be, in one sense, equivalents.

So what shall we believe? Is the activity of nature but an illusion and is the reality, after all, the subjective geometry which we have discovered in ourselves? Which is the shadow and which the substance? Or is this statement but a manner of speech? Are we after all indulging in arguments which would put to shame the metaphysics of the schoolmen?

We should be willing to admit our folly were it not that experimental evidence of a remarkable kind confirms the subjective theories of Einstein. The light bends as it passes through the space-time framework of the sun; the spectrum lines on the massive white dwarf companion of Sirius are shifted toward the red in the geometry of that remarkable region of the sky. Perhaps we may escape the dilemma in the same way Alice and the unicorn resolved their difficulties of belief:

"I have always thought they (children) were fabulous monsters!" said the Unicorn. "Is it alive?"

"It can talk," said Haigha solemnly.

The Unicorn looked dreamily at Alice, and said, "Talk, child."

Alice could not help her lips curling up into a smile as she began: "Do you know, I always thought Unicorns were fabulous monsters, too? I never saw one alive before!"

"Well, now that we *have* seen each other," said the Unicorn, "if you'll believe in me, I'll believe in you. Is that a bargain?"

Let those who believe in an external reality, which can be investigated only through the precision of measurement, believe also in a geometry of space-time which will accord with what they find. Let those who dwell in a more subjective philosophy give as much reality to their geometry as they choose; let them make their predictions and expect nature to show them correct; let them substitute a metric of space-time for the activities of nature; let them reduce experience to the behaviour of sixteen coefficients obedient to a subjective law. But let them not forget in all of this that something external to their system has forced the choice upon them of one of three logical geometries.

## 4. *The Problem of Determinism.*

We turn to another problem which has long been a battleground for the philosopher. What is the nature of cause and effect? Is there a determinism in the physical universe? If we were infinitely wise could we tell the events of the future? Is the destiny of the human race already written in the stars?

The mathematician boasts: Tell me the initial conditions of a planet, the coordinates of its position, its velocity at a given instant, the forces under which it is to move, and I shall tell you for all time to come its history. With what feeling of satisfaction Leverrier, the French astronomer, must have looked at the planet

Jupiter and reflected: "Here in my tables, embodied in these rows of figures, is the future of your course. For a thousand years my speculative eye is upon your path. Your movements are known to me. Nothing that happens to your course will surprise me. The problem is solved. No younger astronomer will come along and do more than alter figures a few places removed from my decimal points." Is it any wonder that the assembly rose when a mortal so god-like entered to issue his decrees?

Science has been pursuing its course on the assumption that nature follows laws; that one event predetermines another; that a determinism is at work in the natural world. There are intimations among the philosophers that determinism is not limited to inanimate nature, but that man, as a complex of atoms, must also share this universal law. Mark Twain in the cynicism which marked his last philosophy has explained the matter through the words of "The Mysterious Stranger":[11]

Among you boys you have a game: you stand a row of bricks on end a few inches apart; you push a brick, it knocks its neighbor over, the neighbor knocks over the next brick—and so on till all the row is prostrate. That is human life. A child's first act knocks over the initial brick, and the rest will follow inexorably. If you could see into the future, as I can, you would see everything that was going to happen to that creature; for nothing can change the order of its life after the first event has determined it. That is, nothing will change it, because each act unfailingly begets an act, that act begets another, and so on to the end, and the seer can look forward down the line and see just when each act is to have birth, from cradle to grave.

In the complicated acts of life we are not able to trace the effects of all the events. Many things are in unstable equilibrium, and the smallest cause may produce a conflagration. A mutilated telegram may create a war devastating a nation. A careless match may destroy a city. The merest breath from a random breeze will upset a top balanced upon its peg.

But the complexities of many situations are solved for us in the doctrines of the theory of chance. We cannot trace the adventures which befall every life, but we can tell with high accuracy the future of a group. The path of Jupiter is not more certainly known than the span of life of the average mortal. No business is more solvent than that of life insurance. Is it, perhaps, due to the statistical

---

[11]New York (1916), p. 87.

model that we are determinists? Is it from our observation of the
infallibility of the law of averages that we believe all things can be
determined? Perhaps we have lost sight of the adventures of the
individual in the behaviour of the mob.

It is of immense speculative interest, therefore, that we see the
first failure of statistical law. The equipartition of energy lapses
when we try to apply a normal scheme to the mysterious radiations
of the ether. We are greatly perplexed at this unkind revelation
that nature is not all she seems to be.

The Compton effect is another mystery in kind and has led to the
formulization by Heisenberg of a "principle of indeterminacy." This
startling principle found in the pages of the new physics, that subject
devoted to the exploration of the realities, the foe to mysticism and
excoriator of magic, is nothing but a denial of the philosophy of
determinism.

According to the new principle it is impossible, as was explained
in chapter ten, to define the position and velocity of an electron at the
same time. The consequences of this revolutionary postulate are
of the highest philosophical interest. If we define the position of a
thing, but by so doing have destroyed our ability to predict its
velocity, then our most cherished belief in the determinacy of natural
phenomena falls to the ground. Practically this belief may have no
effect upon the ordinary affairs of life, since the principle of indeterminacy is confined to the activities of nature's smallest unit, but its
implications are important in the foundation of our philosophy.

P. W. Bridgman, reflecting upon the consequences of this
principle takes the following melancholy position:

The physicist thus finds himself in a world from which the bottom has dropped clean out; as he penetrates deeper and deeper it
eludes him and fades away by the highly unsportsmanlike device of
just becoming meaningless. No refinement of measurement will avail
to carry him beyond the portals of this shadowy domain which he
cannot even mention without logical inconsistency. A bound is thus
forever set to the curiosity of the physicist. What is more, the mere
existence of this bound means that he must give up his most cherished convictions and faith. The world is not a world of reason,
understandable by the intellect of man, but as we penetrate ever
deeper, the very law of cause and effect, which we had thought to be
a formula to which we could force God Himself to subscribe, ceases
to have meaning. The world is not intrinsically reasonable or understandable; it acquires these properties in ever-increasing degree as we
ascend from the realm of the very little to the realm of everyday

things; here we may eventually hope for an understanding sufficiently good for all practical purposes, but no more.[12]

Is this denial of determinism in the microcosmic universe the end of exploration? Does it impose a fundamental bound to physical insight? It may be. We may, perhaps, have proceeded as far as we can into the mysteries of the infinitely little. That realm far beyond the direct reach of our senses may be an undiscoverable country to which the intelligence of man has been denied a passport. We have reached an impasse in the case of the luminiferous ether. This new situation is as disturbing as the problem of the medium filling space. As we have advanced to meet it it has forever retreated from our grasp. It has had all the aspects of a mirage. The electron may be a similar illusion and its activities may be forever beyond the comprehension and the reach of man.

However, the human spirit always hopes. These gloomy speculations on the ultimate futility of knowledge may be without foundation.

> So, when dark thoughts my boding spirit shroud,
> Sweet Hope! celestial influence round me shed
> Waving thy silver pinions o'er my head.[13]

It seems strange when one thinks about it that the discovery of a lack of determinism in nature, a free will of individual electrons, so to speak, should evoke such gloomy speculation. Those who have adhered to the freedom of the human will as one of the individual glories of man, will now decry a similar aspect in primary nature. On the one hand we demand our own freedom, but on the other this very freedom demands an absolute determinism in nature which, while it gives us the power of absolute prediction, sets no bound upon the accuracy with which we shall know nature.

### 5. *The Wisdom of Prospero.*

Has there been mysticism in this picture which we have traced in the earlier chapters of the book? Have we shown that the universe is irrational? Does it appear that man, peering through his tiny keyhole, will ultimately be unable to explain to himself all that he has seen?

---

[12]The New Vision of Science, Harper's Magazine, vol. 158 (1929), pp. 443-451; in particular p. 450.
[13]Keats: To Hope.

We have traced the concept of the ether from the substantial postulates with which it started down to this modern period in which only the most tenuous wraith remains. We have explained gravitation in terms of a geometry difficult to comprehend. The mystery of least action we have shown is as perplexing as it was when first formulated by Maupertius. The only modern clue is in the fact that we find it occupying a prominent rôle in the wave theory of the electron.

The most hopeful concept emerging from these mysterious adventures of modern science is that which negates the gloomy law of Clausius. The universe does not appear to be running down. There will never be a time when all the cosmic energy will have attained a universal level and all activity will have ceased. By some mysterious methods, which we do not comprehend but which are implied in the discovery of cosmic radiation, there is a mutual conversion of energy into matter and matter into energy, which assures the eternity of cosmic activity.

Much, however, remains mysterious in nature. We have set many problems and have resolved but few. Wherever we probe we find that new difficulties beset our pathway. But all this is gain. The puzzle that has been solved always lacks savor. The brief satisfaction which is felt when one finds that the answer to his problem is correct is not to be compared with the zest of the conquest. The object of the present book will have been attained if it has set forth the problems of modern science as living things; if it has shown that the nature of man is intimately bound up with his test tubes, his formulas, his galvonometers, and his telescopes. It will be a sorry day for man when he has once definitely answered the questions: Is space-time limited? Does determinism rule the activities of nature? The quest of modern science is not a material one. It's motto could well be the dictum of Keats:[14]

> "Beauty is truth, truth beauty,"—that is all
> Ye know on earth, and all ye need to know.

Have we appeared too mystical in all of this? Do the struggles of man with the mysterious ether, the elusive energy, the subjective concepts of space and time, have the appearance of battles waged in the mists of unreality. Or is there a place in the nature of man for these unscientific musings? Is it this sense of the strangeness of the

[14] Ode on a Grecian Urn.

physical facts, of the data of the laboratory itself, that accounts for man's yearning for the beauty best expressed in the language of poetry and music? Can we conclude better than with the summary of Prospero, whose reflections are typical of the mystery of man and man's relationship to nature?[15]

> These our actors,
> As I foretold you, were all spirits, and
> Are melted into air, into thin air:
> And, like the baseless fabric of this vision,
> The cloud-capp'd towers, the gorgeous palaces,
> The solemn temples, the great globe itself,
> Yea, all which it inherit, shall dissolve,
> And, like this unsubstantial pageant faded,
> Leave not a rack behind. We are such stuff
> As dreams are made on; and our little life
> Is rounded with a sleep.

---

[15]The Tempest, act 4, sc. 1, l. 148.

### THE END

# INDEX